'Unfair discrimination against patients or colleagues on the grounds of race or for any other reason is unacceptable but the potential to offend, often unconsciously, exists in most if not all of us. This book explains why and provides the evidence that more must be done to ensure that racism is eradicated from the practice of medicine. Importantly, it provides guidance for individuals and organisations on good practice both in behaviour and in audit. It deserves to be read carefully by practitioners and especially by those with management responsibilities in the NHS and in universities.'

Sir Cyril Chantler, Chairman, Great Ormond Street Hospital for Children NHS Trust

'This is an excellent publication. It presents to the discerning reader the reality of racism as it is today within the NHS. The book traces racism encountered in the career pathway of doctors from medical school through to the senior posts within the National Health Service. This is a book that is a must for both staff and managers. They will gain an understanding of the problems that could be encountered by others whilst working within the NHS.'

Lord Dholakia, OBE, DL, President of the Liberal Democrats

'I am pleased to support this initiative. It is a really important and most timely contribution to an issue which is a fundamental aspect of human rights. We all have a responsibility to work to make racial equality a reality, and to tackle racism wherever it is found. Discrimination has no place in the culture and practice of medicine. This book helps us to meet this challenge.'

Sir Donald Irvine, CBE, President of the General Medical Council

'This book attempts to illustrate how discrimination manifests itself, sets out an agenda for change and provides practical advice. It is an essential read for all those committed to improving both the morale and the delivery of service in the NHS.'

Baroness Prashar of Runnymede, CBE, First Civil Service Commissioner

'I have for a long time recognised that racism in the health service is pervasive. This book eloquently documents this sad state of affairs. However, as well as giving a comprehensive background to the innumerable manifestations of racism, the real virtue of this book is the practical help it offers to all those who are determined to free our health service of racial discrimination. I commend the book as essential reading to all who are working toward this goal.'

Robin Stott, FRCP, Consultant Physician and Lewisham Site Dean for GKT Medical School and Chairman of Medact

'Across the health service, institutions now have a duty to actively promote racial equality. This book shows very clearly why the introduction of such a duty was necessary, and gives a clear and direct account of some of the effects and consequences of institutional racism. The second part of the book offers practical advice on how to deliver the fundamental changes that are required. I welcome the valuable and timely contribution that it makes, and have no hesitation in recommending it to anyone involved in medicine and health care.'

Gurbux Singh, Chair of the Commission for Racial Equality

Racism in Medicine

An agenda for change

THE UNIVERSITY
OF BIRMINGHAM

INFORMATION SERVICES

Racism in Medicine

An agenda for change

Naaz Coker

Published by
King's Fund Publishing
11–13 Cavendish Square
London W1G 0AN

© King's Fund 2001

First published 2001

214-10674

ISBN 1 85717 407 0

A CIP catalogue record for this book is available from the British Library

Available from:
King's Fund Bookshop
11–13 Cavendish Square
London
W1G 0AN

Tel: 020 7307 2591
Fax: 020 7307 2801

Printed and bound in Great Britain

Cover design: Vertigo Design Consultants

Contents

Part 1 Racism: the evidence

Part 2 Agenda for action

Acknowledgements

This book owes so much to so many people. I am indebted to all the doctors and health professionals with whom I have had long conversations and who have shared their stories, their pain and their frustrations with me. I would like to thank: the authors for their contributions and adherence to tight deadlines; Michael Mansfield, QC, for writing the foreword; Rabbi Julia Neuberger for her contribution, advice and support; Ian Wylie, CEO of the British Dental Association and previously Director of Corporate Affairs at the King's Fund for his backing and encouragement; Michelle Dixon, the Fund's Director of Public Affairs for her comments and invaluable support. The following people helped me enormously with their critical comments and useful conversations: Ray Coker, Andy Bell, John McClenahan, Cyril Chantler and Robin Stott. I owe sincere thanks to Lyndsey Unwin, Head of Publishing and Marketing at the King's Fund, for her personal enthusiasm, commitment and backing for this whole initiative. Thanks also to the Fund's publishing and marketing team, particularly the managing editor, Trevor Anderson, for their hard work. Finally, Carolyn Bann, my assistant, deserves a special word of thanks for her superb secretarial support and organisational skills; she liaised with the authors and publication staff with calmness and charm.

Naaz Coker

Contributors

Dr Shona Arora	London GP and former Visiting Fellow, King's Fund
Dr Aneez Esmail	Senior Lecturer, General Practice, University of Manchester
Naaz Coker	Director, Race and Diversity, King's Fund
Mike Collins	Equality and Diversity Consultant and former Programme Director, Tackling Racial Harassment in the NHS, NHS Executive
Dr Shahid Dadabhoy	London GP
Dr Karola Decker	Organisational Consultant, Liverpool
Dr Paramjit S Gill	Clinical Senior Lecturer, Department of Primary Care and General Practice, University of Birmingham
Dr Stephen Gillam	Director, Primary Care, King's Fund
Michael Mansfield, QC	Barrister and Head of Tooks Court Chambers, and Visiting Professor of Law, University of Westminster
John McClenahan	Fellow, Leadership Development, King's Fund
Rabbi Julia Neuberger	Chief Executive, King's Fund
Dr Lena Robinson	Senior Lecturer in Psychology and Social Work, University of Birmingham
Lyndsey Unwin	Head of Publishing and Marketing, King's Fund
Dr Anne Yardumian	Consultant in Haematology, North Middlesex Hospital NHS Trust

Foreword

I regard it as a privilege to be afforded the opportunity to provide a few words to this timely and necessary book. Having represented black members of our community over many years, they have given me an understanding and insight into the need for constant reappraisal and awareness – not just in relation to overt prejudice, but also its insidious and innate forms. Doubtless those of us who have the temerity to engage in this exercise will be castigated as suffering from the disease of political correctness, or still worse, we will be diagnosed as the cause of the problem. Note how the Macpherson Report into police handling of the murder of Stephen Lawrence has been used by senior politicians to explain flagging police morale and an alleged increase in crime! Simplistic clap-trap of this kind does no more for the provision of an effective and constructive system of social welfare than Dr Liam Fox's observations mentioned in Naaz Coker's Introduction.

Whether the arena is policing, the law or medicine, there is a paramount and imperative need to recognise the ailment before any progress can be made towards a society in which the distribution and application of resources and services are, and are seen to be, justly made. This concept lay at the root of the Truth and Reconciliation Commission in South Africa and the several other similar Truth Commissions held in other parts of the world, most notably Chile. The process not only seeks truth; it also demands integrity and dignity for those who can bring themselves to confront it. It involves, unquestionably, conscientious pain and anguish. Until such boils are lanced they will fester forever within the body politic.

Such was the function of Macpherson, as is, in a sense, the role of these collected thoughts and essays. Given the magnitude of the threat posed to our environment by the many theatres of war, famine and pollution, our priority has to be a collective and global response that combines the efforts of all those endeavouring to provide practical care and security. Rarely are they politicians; more often they are people in organisations on the front line with their feet firmly on the ground. They must be accorded support and, above all, respect.

In order to achieve this objective, the following fundamental and unanimous conclusions of the four-man panel (a well-known High Court judge, a senior medical practitioner, a respected bishop and a high-ranking police officer) in the Lawrence Inquiry deserve close attention:

'Racism' in general terms consists of conduct or words or practices which advantage or disadvantage people because of their colour, culture or ethnic origin. In its more subtle form it is as damaging as in its overt form.

'Institutional Racism' consists of the collective failure of an organisation to provide an appropriate and professional service to people because of their colour, culture or ethnic origin. It can be seen and detected in processes, attitudes and behaviour which amount to discrimination through unwitting prejudice, ignorance, thoughtlessness, and racist stereotyping which disadvantage minority ethnic people.

Michael Mansfield, QC
6 April 2001

Introduction

'Racism' is one of the most difficult and painful words in the English language. It is a word that inspires fear, anger and revulsion in equal measure from all manner of people. It both describes and creates barriers between people. It is a word associated with conflict, with power and with ideology. Not surprisingly, then, it is a word that gets a great deal of use but which is rarely discussed openly, dispassionately and with neither malice nor dismissiveness.

This volume is an attempt to begin that discussion in the field of medicine. For many years, the King's Fund has been aware that the NHS, the medical profession and many other areas of the UK health system are no less affected by racism than any other part of our society. From a wide range of anecdotal accounts and research work, we know that racism, however defined, exists in the health system and weakens its ability to perform the tasks with which it is charged. We know that it affects the careers of individuals working within the system and that it can damage the health of people using, or wishing to use it. But we do not know exactly how it all fits together, what it all adds up to, and what can be done to tackle the problem in the round.

Racism is at once a set of beliefs (though not a coherent one) and a form of behaviour (or rather a set of behaviours). It can exist as overt hostility or passive neglect. For the person at the receiving end, it can take the form of exclusion, of isolation, of injustice, of harassment or of violent attack. In the field of medicine and health care, it can have one or more of these effects across all of the different kinds of relationship that exist within those fields. This includes relationships between professionals and patients, those between individual workers, and those concerned with education, training and the planning of services.

In the following chapters, the effects of racism on a number of these relationships are investigated in some detail. Dr Aneez Esmail, for example, draws together persuasive evidence which indicates that admissions to medical school do not simply reflect people's abilities and qualifications – that discrimination on the basis of 'race', nationality and class continues to prevent true equality of opportunity in entrance to the medical profession (Chapter 4). In particular, he argues that assumptions that Asian applicants to medical school are of a lower calibre than their white counterparts because of parental pressure remain strong, despite clear evidence this is not the case. Nor does discrimination stop there. Lyndsey Unwin (Chapter 6) shows that doctors who began their training overseas face discrimination throughout their working lives, often being forced into career paths that deny them the same opportunities as their European Union-trained peers. Mike Collins, meanwhile, compiles evidence to show that racial harassment takes on many different forms in the NHS, both among colleagues and (in both directions) between health workers and patients (Chapter 8). He shows that patterns of racist behaviour match closely patterns of more general workplace bullying and harassment, with verbal abuse, deliberate exclusion, malicious complaints and unfair treatment among the most common problems reported in the NHS.

The book goes on to examine what can be done about racism in medicine. In this, at least, there is finally cause for hope. Throughout the NHS, there are examples of good practice in tackling racist behaviour and getting to the root of institutional racism. There are some excellent examples of health services making significant efforts to reach out to disadvantaged ethnic groups to reduce the burden of avoidable illness they carry. What is missing, though, is a sense of purpose across all of these diverse activities – a clear direction of travel and a commitment from the whole of the health service to make change significant and sustainable.

Many medical schools are now monitoring their performance on recruiting people from black and minority ethnic groups. Where they uncover evidence of discrimination, positive action is taken to improve the situation (Chapter 4). In the NHS, many primary care groups and trusts are examining how the services they provide and commission meet the needs of different sections of their populations. Some have then gone a stage further by developing innovative approaches to improving communication with 'hard to reach' groups, in particular through the use of advocacy services (Chapter 7).

Above all, what this book shows is that racist behaviour is keeping both medical practice and the NHS from achieving their avowed aims and objectives. Medicine aims to give people – whoever they are – the best possible chance of having a healthy life. Its ethical codes emphasise the importance of care for the individual, always putting their best interest first and doing as much as possible for their health. The NHS, meanwhile, is a system by which citizens of Britain pool their risk of ill health through taxation. It is a national agreement, that by paying according to means we can receive support for our health when we need it, without regard to ability to pay. It assumes, therefore, that the services our taxes fund will be accessible equally to all citizens and that no group should be excluded.

Moreover, as a public service the NHS has a moral obligation to employ people in a fair way. The NHS's social function is not merely that of a provider of health care – it is a major employer and a member of the communities in which it works. In an unequal society, public services can help to redress inequalities by taking positive action to employ people on merit and to ensure that the education and training they provide are accessible to people from all walks of life. In some cases, this will mean taking affirmative action to include groups that are under-represented in existing public sector workforces.

There is, then, a clear rationale for a root-and-branch approach to tackling racism in health care. The employment practices of the NHS, the training practices of the professions, and the services provided to patients, are all tied up in the same equation. Racism in any one of these arenas will have a serious effect on both of the other two. If there are insufficient young people coming forward for medical training from a particular ethnic group, the NHS cannot recruit enough new doctors from that group. If NHS organisations are providing insufficient training and support to its black workers, those people will continue to occupy the lower echelons of the service and be unable to tackle any weaknesses in health care provision for black communities. And if the NHS is still failing to provide responsive and culturally competent services for minority groups, it may be less likely to recruit people from those groups – particularly if those people who do work in the service experience bullying and abuse and then discourage others from working there.

The business case is clear. Ideas about good practice are already floating around in the service and the professions. We now even have a high level of political support for the eradication of racist practice from the NHS. Under the current Labour Government, both Secretaries of State for Health have given NHS managers and professional bodies clear messages that they should take concerted action to stamp out both discrimination and harassment. Many have already responded with energy and enthusiasm. But they are only too aware that racist practices are deeply rooted, both in society as a whole and in the organisations they manage. It is enormously difficult to make significant changes to long-held assumptions and age-old ways of working. It takes up time that hard-pressed people working in health care can ill afford to commit. Without that time and effort, though, our health system will always be failing to meet its core values and ambitions.

Rabbi Julia Neuberger

Editor's Introduction

This is a book I never expected to write or edit. Having worked as a health professional in the NHS, I believed that Britain had become a multicultural nation where diversity was valued, especially amongst the educated and professional groups, and that racist and intolerant language and practices were confined to a very small minority of the uneducated and the politically extreme. But then came the publication of Sir William Macpherson's report of the Stephen Lawrence Inquiry, which has been the subject of lengthy debate and discussion in the media and in public sector organisations generally. This was followed by more public discourse generated by the carnage caused by the nail bombs that targeted the black, Asian and gay communities in London, and more recently the debate over the asylum and immigration issues. It became quite evident that the domain of intolerance and prejudice was not just the province of the ignorant but was widespread in many levels of British society.

In 1991, I gatecrashed a meeting of largely white, male senior and junior doctors, where I heard comments and opinions that were so overtly racist in both tone and language that it made me embark on a journey of exploration and research. Over the last ten years, this journey has taken me to unexpected places and resulted in amazing conversations. I heard stories of struggle, inner pain and anger. I heard about a world of injustice, cynicism, mistrust and intolerance. I read about discriminatory recruitment practices in the medical schools and in the NHS, about exclusion, power struggles and discrimination in the medical profession. This book is a result of those meetings, conversations and research.

Many of the doctors I have met frequently raised the complex question of identity and belonging. People acknowledged that belonging takes time. Yet for diversity to be respected and valued, the feeling of belonging is critical and will only be achieved through discussion and negotiation. Victimhood only results in the further disabling of oneself, so everyone has a responsibility for creating a sense of belonging whilst respecting difference. Michael Ignatieff, the Canadian philosopher, in his book *The needs of strangers*, discusses the idea of natural human identity based on all human beings feeling a common and shared identity in 'the basic fraternity of hunger, thirst, cold, exhaustion, loneliness or sexual passion'. He goes on to say that 'a society in which strangers feel common belonging and mutual responsibility to each other depends on trust, and trust reposes in turn on the idea that beneath difference there is identity.'

There is no doubt that we live in a vibrant, multicultural society, and that we shop together, we pray together, we have fun together and that large numbers of people, both white and black, have a stake in creating a successful multicultural Britain. But there is also no doubt that there is discrimination against people from minority ethnic communities, against women, against older people, against gay people. The statistics make depressive reading. The recent negative and positively vitriolic language used in the media about asylum seekers and immigrants, especially in the tabloid press, has made me realise how difficult it is to deal with the emotive and very personal response people have when talking about the impact of racism in our society – and what a long way we still have to go.

It became evident that tackling racism required one to think beyond the traditional boundaries of equal opportunities to the domain of ideology – the ideology of the superiority of certain 'races'. It is this ideology that perpetuates the set of beliefs and perspective about 'us' and 'them'; 'us' being superior and therefore more powerful, and 'them' being inferior and less powerful. These perceptions seem, then, to be held as self-evident truths, which become rooted in societal and organisational norms and cultures.

There is clearly no scientific basis for our classification of 'races'. Our beliefs about the existence of 'races' are flawed and misleading. Our social, physical and cultural environments have a greater role in shaping our identities than our genetic differences. Racism and oppression are about the abuse of power that denies people dignity and choice. Responding merely to requirements of race relations legislation is not going to be enough. What has to change is the mind-set that labels people who are different as 'deviant' and 'inferior'. Our own mental models of equality, feminism, ethnicity, religious differences and class must be recognised and challenged. If one believes that all human beings deserve the power to make dignified choices, then it is clear that fighting racism is not enough; all oppression, be it based on social class, culture, sexuality, gender or skin colour, has to be a part of the struggle.

If we look at public discourse and public policy, as well as private conversations, one gets a sense that we do not collectively have a vision of what a Britain committed to equality might look like. Those who influence, inform and make public policy have failed to appreciate and indeed understand the integral relationship between issues of equity, justice, exclusion and human rights.

Diversity is about difference and yet as a society we are so afraid of difference. *What are we afraid of? Why can we not learn to appreciate our differences and capitalise on the advantages that differences offer?*

Freud referred to 'the narcissism of minor differences' – we celebrate difference by killing 'the other', as demonstrated by the numerous awful examples of so-called 'ethnic cleansing' both in Africa and Europe. Successful communities are ones where differences are celebrated and there is interdependence between groups. Yet this is a hugely complex issue, and so difficult to achieve, as illustrated by a refugee who recently reminded me that 'interdependence is a choice that only independent people can make; we need to have independence and feel empowered and valued before we can even think of interdependence!'

During my conversations, with doctors and others, two names that kept recurring were those of the British doctors Aneez Esmail and Sam Everington. These two were described as 'a pair who were brave enough to raise their heads above the parapet', who set out to expose the racist practices and attitudes that permeated the medical system. In 1993, when they first published their findings, the medical establishment, instead of learning from their work, condemned it and had them arrested and charged. Aneez Esmail is one of the contributors to this book.

As recently as August 2000, a senior politician, who is also a GP, Dr Liam Fox, claimed that many of the doctors who came from abroad do not have the requisite English language skills to work in Britain. This view was widely reported in the media. As *The Times* of 28 August reported, Dr Fox claimed that 'their English language skills are not up to scratch and patients are suffering as a result'. Many of us working in the field of race relations, including many doctors, groaned in despair when this was published. Polly Toynbee asserted in her column in *The Guardian* of August 30, 'with no evidence, no research and apparently zero knowledge of how the system works, his cavalier assault on the quarter of the doctors now working in the NHS who trained elsewhere was insulting and unpleasant.'

Whilst discriminatory attitudes continue to exist, many professionals I encountered during my journey, black and white, recognised the injustice of racism. They confirmed that it will require our collective imagination in dealing with our 'humanness', and that principle alone will not resolve the situation; behaviours and practices have to change too.

In 1996, the Commission for Racial Equality (CRE) published a report of their investigation of the recruitment processes of NHS consultants and senior registrars. The CRE said that there was 'great cause for concern' in the way these senior doctors were appointed. The report stated that 'the disparities in success rates for different ethnic groups were so marked and consistent, and the omission of procedural safeguards so routine, that the possibility of discrimination cannot be ignored.'

This was a clear challenge to the NHS and especially to the medical leadership to take determined action to ensure that good equal opportunity practice standards were embedded in selection procedures and practices.

So, the theme of this book has important implications for one of the biggest social issues affecting our society today. The authors, who come from culturally diverse backgrounds and experiences, provide a commentary on the nature and evidence of racist practices and experiences through stories, personal testimonies, historical perspectives and research. The book attempts to set out an agenda for change by drawing together areas where changes in policy and practice are needed to embark on an anti-racism agenda that will improve the experiences and health of doctors and patients from Britain's minority ethnic communities.

One of the key skills for the next century will be the ability to interact and communicate effectively across ethnicity, cultures, class and gender. Capitalising on workplace diversity is a challenge for all organisations and institutions.

The medical profession, with a strong ethic that requires equal treatment for all, is highly valued by society. Now is the time for the profession to show leadership and demonstrate that it has put unfair prejudice behind it and that it respects and values difference.

Naaz Coker

Part I

Racism: the evidence

Chapter 1

Understanding race and racism

Naaz Coker

*Isn't it strange that for one person to feel great
another has to be demeaned!*
Mahatma Gandhi

Introduction

This chapter provides background information on the terminology of race, ethnicity, cultural identity and racism. It explains the meaning and complexity associated with these terms and how they are often used inaccurately and in misleading ways. The impact of racism and institutional racism on individuals and groups is also discussed.

The terminology in this area is a source of on-going debate. The fact that ethnicity, culture and identity are dynamic entities subject to contextual factors means that there is no simple way of describing individuals and groups that is either consistent or stable. A continuing puzzle is why human differences are still perceived to be so threatening. People have been seeking answers in anthropology and evolutionary genetics. Analogy with animal behaviour is sometimes used to justify racism. Will anthropology provide the answer? How does it explain cultural racism, which is so widespread? The anthropological concept of culture, which suggests an inherited framework of shared notions of knowledge, beliefs, customs, morals and habits, only partly explains a person's identity and behaviour. These are highly contextual. People's specific behaviours may be more driven by their social circumstances, such as economic status or education, rather than their inherited cultural beliefs. Perhaps the fear of difference is something human beings have to unlearn actively and consciously.

Advances in human genetics have largely eroded the commonly held hypothesis and beliefs that 'race' is a biological fact. A growing body of evidence shows that the concept of different races has its roots in socio-political discourse and that the social consequences of the way racial differences have been used has led to social injustice perpetuated by flawed ideology and prejudice.

There is overwhelming evidence that skin colour is a major influence on the way people are treated. Understanding the language, philosophy and practice of discrimination and racism, coupled with its relationship to the underlying ideology of white superiority and power, is key to developing anti-racist strategies, policies and practices for the future.

Throughout the book, the term 'black', a term indicating political unity to represent a shared experience of discrimination, has been used to describe all people whose skin colour is not white. The terms 'minority ethnic communities' and 'minority ethnic groups' are used to describe those groups who differ from the majority 'white' ethnic population. The term 'white' is used to describe the majority ethnic group that generally does not experience racism. It is acknowledged that both the minority ethnic groups and the white group are not homogeneous, and that some white minorities – such as the Irish and some Jewish and Greek communities – have experienced racism.

What is race?

The Oxford English Dictionary defines 'race' as 'a large group of people with common ancestry and inherited physical characteristics'. In other words, race describes a group of individuals that are recognised as being biologically different to others.

The subject of race has a long history of debate, claim and counter-claim in anthropological, biological and social science studies, the key controversy being whether race is a biologically valid fact or a social concept that serves social purposes. There are undoubtedly obvious differences between people from different countries and nations. People vary in skin colour, eye colour and shape, food tastes, communication styles, etc. Some of these differences are clearly biological in nature and depend on genetic make-up; others are cultural and rely on learned behaviours, which are socially determined. Many of the so-called genetic differences are a consequence of climatic and environmental adaptation, which are subsequently inherited among people who live in the different climatic conditions over a long period of time.

These visible differences have led people to believe that population groups are pure and homogeneous. But recent advances in human genetic studies have confirmed that homogeneous races do not exist and that racial purity is unachievable except through cloning. Studies conducted by Cavalli-Sforza,[1] a geneticist who has been working in the field of human evolution genetics for several decades, have confirmed that racial purity cannot be achieved. To achieve even partial purity, he says, would require 'at least twenty generations of inbreeding'. As such, the term 'racial groups' does not provide an accurate or a useful way of classifying people and population groups. Numerous studies lead us to conclude that biological variation between 'races', defined by their country of origin or any other criteria, is statistically small. The variation within population groups is much greater than between them. Thus, modern genetics has undermined the biological explanation for race by showing that there are no clearly definable subspecies in the human race.

Classification based on continental origin becomes meaningless too, when the heterogeneity of the different population groups is considered. If you take the example of the term 'South Asian', it is often used to describe people who were born in the Indian subcontinent (India, Pakistan, Bangladesh and Sri Lanka) or people who descended from those who were born there. And yet many of these people have different religions, languages, diets, dress and customs. Furthermore, this term only applies to 'brown-skinned people'. It does not apply to white people who were born there or born of parents who were born there.

Racial categories are largely socially created. In the USA, there was widespread prejudice against black Americans and theories were proposed about them having low IQ scores as a result of genetic traits. These theories were soon disproved by studies in the early eighties, which clearly established that only 30 per cent of variation in IQ scores among individuals was due to heredity; the rest being due to socio-cultural factors. In spite of evidence to the contrary, there is a lot of intellectual sloppiness in this field and eminent professors still write books such as *The bell curve*,[2] which seeks to promote the obviously racist message that the low IQ scores of black Americans were due to a real genetic difference. However, the suggestion that the average Japanese IQ was greater than that of the average white American, by the same factor ascribed to the difference between black and white Americans, was met with blame being placed on the poor educational standards of American high schools.[1]

It has to be acknowledged that the race concept is deeply rooted in human societies and has been abused historically to justify inequalities that existed in the context of slavery and colonialism, and more recently in access to education, employment and health care. In fact, in many parts of the world, the dominant cultural grouping usually sees itself as 'raceless', race being an attribute of others. So, in the West, white people frequently see themselves as 'raceless'. However, people do not necessarily differentiate between biological and cultural differences. Prejudice and intolerance are shown towards the most superficial of differences, such as noisy eating habits, tastes in music, dress and diet, accents and pronunciation. Skin colour still remains one of the most influential factors governing societies' attitudes to members of minority ethnic groups.

In order to move away from the biological determinism that is inherent in the concept of race, in Britain, the term 'race' is being replaced by 'ethnicity', without any great attempt to explain or shape public understanding of the meaning underlying the idea of race.

Ethnicity

Ethnicity, from the Greek word 'ethnos', meaning a people or a tribe, has been defined as:

> *Shared origins or social background; shared culture and traditions that are distinctive, maintained between generations, and lead to a sense of identity and group; and a common language or religious tradition.*[3]

The term ethnic group refers to groups or communities who feel a common sense of identity, often based on shared cultural traditions, language, religion or geographic origins. Ethnicity is only one dimension of personal identity and at one level it is a way people identify themselves as a part of a group with shared cultural traditions. They may draw strength and meaning from these traditions and maintain a sense of solidarity within the group. Whilst these differences may be of importance to the individuals and groups as far as their social relationships are concerned, they have tended to become ethnic markers whose usage has resulted in social exclusion and isolation.

Ethnicity is frequently imposed by others, based on physical or national characteristics with which individuals themselves may not necessarily identify. For example, the term 'white', which is now used to describe the white majority population, does not differentiate, for example, between Scottish and Welsh communities, although some Irish groups have been identified as an ethnic minority population in the UK.

The problem is that, as in the case of racial difference, ethnicity also focuses on difference as 'fixed' and separate, i.e. 'not one of us'. Therefore, to be ethnic is to be different, definitely foreign, sometimes exotic. It does not take into account the dynamic and shifting nature of people's cultures and behaviours. 'I am British, I was born here and I live here,' vehemently stressed a young black man I met recently. 'I am not African Caribbean and I am not black British, I am just British!' Conversely, when discussing the concept of ethnicity and identity, an irritated white doctor exclaimed: 'Why do I have to say I am white in the UK?; I never saw my identity as white, I am English.' It is interesting to note that in medical research, the significance (and the advantage) of being white is rarely considered.

Ethnicity is clearly not the only defining feature of an individual. People do not go through each day focusing upon the fact that they are Bengali or African Caribbean. Many people have multiple ethnic identities and may choose to define themselves in a number of ways: British Muslim, Indian, European, or simply Londoner. Ethnicity, however, should not be confused with nationality or migrant status.

This raises the issue of first generation immigrants and their children and grandchildren who are born in Britain, and whose notions of ethnicity and identity are different from their parents. Furthermore, the identities of children of mixed marriages, which will inevitably increase with increasing globalisation and as societies become more culturally diverse, will add further complexity and controversy to the discourse on ethnicity and identity.

Is ethnicity an identity or a category? Should it be self-selected or imposed? These are some of the problems that arise in health studies and health services research. As described earlier, ethnicity is contextual and people describe their ethnicity in different ways; so, for example, as an African Asian living in Britain, I describe myself as 'black' in certain circumstances, when I am discussing experiences of racism, or a 'Muslim' to identify my beliefs about health and death, or 'Indian' to describe my family origin. As Smaje[4] suggests, depending on what is being studied, it may be appropriate to think of 'black' as a category if discrimination is the common factor underpinning the health experience, whereas, at other times, the different ethnic identities may be more relevant if the different beliefs and cultural traditions influence how health services are accessed and utilised.

Grandparents' national origin and name analysis have also been used to ascribe ethnicity.[3] While the former ignores the fact that grandparents may come from more than one country, the latter leads to confusion when Indians or Africans who are Christians have similar names as the Christians from white communities. A black doctor described his experience of going for an interview and being told by the reception manager that his name was not on the list. 'But I have not told you my name yet,' said the doctor. Suffice it to say that his name was very similar to a white Christian person's name.

The way ethnicity is operationalised in the health service continues to translate ethnic differences in genetic terms, so, for example, when considering specific diseases or disease patterns across ethnic groups, the emphasis is on cultural or biological characteristics of individuals rather than any associated social factors. This frequently leads to ethnicity being pathologised: inappropriate conclusions are drawn about ethnic factors being the cause of ill health rather than ill health being caused by the individual's experience of the health system. As Cochrane and Sashidharan reported:

> *It is also a common assumption that the behaviours (and problems) of the white population are normative and that deviation from the white pattern shown by another ethnic group in either direction reveals some cultural or racial pathology: higher rates of schizophrenia among blacks than whites must be produced by genetic factors or cultural disintegration or abnormal family structures.*[5]

In ethnicity monitoring, the current preference is to allow self-identification of ethnicity. However, in order to make meaningful assessments about needs and service design, it is necessary to collect information about multiple factors, such as culture, religion, beliefs and languages.

Culture

Culture is a difficult term to define, as it is a dynamic entity. It describes a shared set of values, perceptions and assumptions based on shared history, language, or learned beliefs and experiences. These act as a conceptual map, which guides the way people see the world and shape their behaviours, thoughts and responses. Culture is a social construct, characterised by the behaviour and attitudes of a social group. It has a profound impact on every aspect of an individual's life but affects each one of us differently. There are both visible (clothes and language) and invisible (norms, values, behaviours) aspects of culture. Culture is not something we are born with but rather something we are socialised into. Whilst the culture of the group we grew up within predominantly comes to shape and influence our behaviours and views, members of one ethnic group can, and do, adopt aspects of other cultures. Determined by upbringing and choice, culture is constantly changing and notoriously difficult to measure. In today's global environment, many people are exposed to and can identify with several cultural influences. However, defining identity and ethnicity according to any one of them will lead to inaccurate conclusions.

Within a cultural group there are also micro-cultures, influenced by other variables like class, gender and age. Families, as well as social, religious, occupational/professional groups, have micro-cultures within them. In itself, the occurrence of such diversity within the human species is not necessarily harmful, and in fact is likely to be beneficial. However, in Europe, there is often a tendency to assume (sometimes unwittingly) that the 'majority white' or European/British culture is the acceptable norm. This sometimes results in labels of 'bad', 'mad' or 'sick' being applied to behaviours that are culturally different and which embarrass the middle classes.

Identity and belonging

Is a label an identity? Is identity about who I think I am or what others think I am?

Identity, similar to ethnicity, is a fluid concept, which changes with context and time. One's identity is a combination of both self-selected identity and an imposed one. However, many people from black communities feel that the labels or identities associated with labels such as 'ethnic minority', 'people of colour', 'overseas doctors', 'black GPs' are designed to frustrate belonging. And until there is belonging, people will always remain marginalised in British society. A young black doctor described a conversation he had with his tutor about Equal Opportunities training. When he questioned the apparently slow and timid approach towards the equality agenda, he was told: 'Be patient, young man, we are doing this for your future.' The doctor retorted: 'People like me need a present before we can have a future!'

Dr Phil Hammond and Michael Mosley, in their book *Trust me (I'm a doctor)*[6], describe how in 1986 the influx of very bright Asian students caused grief to some senior medical staff. One consultant was quoted as saying: 'I've got nothing against them *per se*, but most of them don't drink or play rugby, and even if they did they wouldn't be much good. You can't push in the scrum if you're fasting for Ramadhan.'

Does belonging translate into conforming to the cultural norms of the dominant cultural group? Many overseas doctors learned to 'play the games' for the sake of professional endurance and according to some, 'for the sake of our children'. It seems that there is still a hankering for the assimilationist theories of the sixties and seventies. There is an underlying value that suggests cultural unease with cultural differences. A German doctor recently commented, when referring to immigrant doctors: 'If only they dressed like us and sounded like us and behaved like us, it would be so much easier to not think of them as foreigners.'

This poses an interesting dilemma – how far does a person need to emulate the dominant culture in order to belong? The perception is that to truly belong, the excluded or the marginalised have to give up so much of their cultural beliefs and behaviours that they lose their unique differences, and yet if they remain totally unchanged by the dominant cultural practices they may always remain marginalised. This is a tension for all black doctors. As one black doctor said: 'Remaining at the margin and being critical of the system, may be attractive, but it will paralyse the process of change.'

Understanding racism

Racism, in general terms, consists of conduct or words or practices which disadvantage or advantage people because of their colour, culture or ethnic origin. In its more subtle form it is as damaging as in its overt form.[7]

Racism is generally interpreted as the doctrine or dogma that drives the belief that some races are superior to others. The problematic nature of defining exactly what race means has already been discussed, but in the context of racism it usually refers to distinctions made on the basis of physical characteristics such as skin colour. Racial discrimination occurs when someone is treated less favourably because of his or her racial characteristics. Cavalli-Sforza[1] suggests that racism arises out of the belief that 'one race, usually, though not always one's own, is biologically superior and that superior genes puts that race at an advantage over all others'. He further goes on to say that 'it is not necessary to *be* superior to be convinced that one is'.

Personal racism occurs when individuals, either consciously or unconsciously, denigrate or demean those of different colour or ethnic origin. The impact of this may be overt or covert. Racial discrimination in Britain is largely based on colour and directed overwhelmingly against the visible ethnic communities. Table 1.1 shows the results of a 1997 study carried out by the Policy Studies Institute; 25 per cent of white people said they were prejudiced against minority ethnic groups.

Table 1.1 Percentage of white people who said they were prejudiced against ethnic minorities

	White men	*White women*	*All whites*
Asian	28	24	26
Caribbean	23	18	20
Muslim	28	23	25
Chinese	9	8	8

Adapted from: Modood T *et al. Ethnic minorities in Britain: diversity and disadvantage.* London: Policy Studies Institute, 1997

A Mori survey of 2118 adults carried out in July 2000 for the *Reader's Digest*, which was widely reported in the press, found that 63 per cent of the respondents thought that the Government did too much to help immigrants and asylum seekers. They also thought that 26 per cent of the British population were from an ethnic minority when the true figure is around 7 per cent, and they thought that 20 per cent of the population are immigrants; the true figure is around 4 per cent. Eight out of ten respondents believed that refugees came to Britain because they regarded it as a soft touch and two-thirds thought there were too many immigrants. *Reader Digest's* editor-in-chief, who commissioned the survey, said at the time:

> *This widespread resentment of immigrants and asylum seekers has worrying implications in a society that has traditionally prided itself on racial tolerance.*

Even more worrying is the fact that many health professionals, who are in a position to act on their prejudices, also hold such views.

Many people from minority communities are worried about racial attacks, as the chart below illustrates. The Metropolitan Police figures showed that the number of reported racist incidents in London increased from 11,050 in the year ending March 1999 to 23,345 in the year to March 2000.

Figure 1.1 Percentage of people who worry about being racially harassed

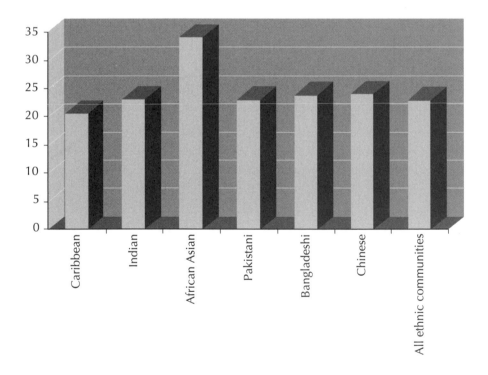

Adapted from: Modood T *et al. Ethnic minorities in Britain: diversity and disadvantage.* London: Policy Studies Institute, 1997

The Race Relations Act 1976 was a turning point in combating racial discrimination in Britain. Under the Act, it became illegal to discriminate in employment, education and in the provision of services and goods. The Act defines two types of discrimination: direct and indirect (See Box 1.1).

BOX 1.1 THE RACE RELATIONS ACT 1976

The Race Relations Act makes it unlawful in Great Britain to discriminate on racial grounds in employment, training, education, the provision of goods, facilities and services and other activities.

'Racial grounds' includes colour, race, nationality (including citizenship) or ethnic or national origins.

The Act distinguishes two main types of racial discrimination:
  direct discrimination – treating a person, on racial grounds, less favourably than others are or would be in similar circumstances
  indirect discrimination – applying a requirement or condition which puts people from a particular racial group at a disadvantage compared to others

It is unlawful to instruct or put pressure on others to commit racial discrimination. It is also unlawful to victimise anyone who makes a complaint of race discrimination or supports another's complaints.

Source: Kirsch B. *Ethnic diversity in Britain.* London: Foreign and Commonwealth Office, 1999

Direct discrimination occurs when a person is treated less favourably than others on grounds of their race or sex. It includes racial abuse and harassment, as well as attempts to exclude or segregate people on the grounds of their nationality or ethnicity.

Indirect discrimination occurs when a rule or condition that applies equally to everyone has a disproportionately adverse effect on people from a particular racial group, or either sex, and there is no objective justification for the rule.

The prevailing view in some parts of the health service portrays overt or direct racism as more unacceptable than the unwitting or unconscious sort. However, there is clear evidence that while the unwitting racism is more difficult to prove and challenge, its impact is more damaging and longer term. In fact, institutional racism is frequently the result of the unwitting and unthinking prejudice of a collective.

The Race Relations Act does not allow positive discrimination: an employer cannot try to change the balance of the workforce by selecting someone mainly because he or she is from a particular racial background. However, it does allow *positive action* to prevent discrimination or as redress for past discrimination. This might include providing training for people from a particular racial group, or by encouraging people from that group to apply for certain kinds of work. The aim of positive action is to ensure equality of opportunity. Selection itself must be based on merit and all applicants should be treated equally.

Anti-racism requires an understanding and recognition of the processes and expression of racism, including the power relationships between black and white people. It seeks to challenge the assumptions and cultural stereotypes in favour of policies, structures and practices that are sensitive to, and value, the cultural differences.

Many organisations have embraced anti-racism for reasons ranging from the ethical to the expedient, and their human resources departments have been busy putting together race equality strategies. When it comes to implementing these strategies, the results have been disappointing. Even more disappointing is the fact that when health professionals are required to take a public position on race issues, many of them sit on the fence or look away in order to avoid any personal responsibility for action.

The Race Relations (Amendment) Act received royal assent in November 2000; this new Act, which strengthens and extends the scope of the 1976 Act, is targeted specifically at the public sector – the NHS, schools, police, local councils and government ministers. Instead of the previous duty simply not to behave in discriminatory ways, all public services now have a positive duty to promote equality in every area of their work. This duty is now enforceable by law. There are several initiatives at the European level too. The UK is a signatory to the EU Joint Action on Racism and Xenophobia and to the Treaty of Amsterdam 1997, both of which provide a legal base for Community action to combat discrimination based on race.

Institutional racism

This phrase 'institutional racism' was first coined in the USA in 1967 to represent the systematic and more covert forms of racism perpetuated by dominant groups, social systems and institutions. Jones[8] defined it as, 'those established laws, customs and practices which systematically reflect and produce racial inequalities in American Society'. It is not an indictment of individuals working within institutions, who themselves may not be racially prejudiced, but more of the systematic operation of an institution.

In the UK, institutional racism was raised in the Macpherson Report,[7] published after the Stephen Lawrence Inquiry, which in itself was a brave and courageous campaign for justice following the police handling of the murder of a black south London teenager. It raised fundamental questions about how society addressed discrimination, racism and racially motivated violence.

The report had considerable impact largely because:

- it generated publicity and raised much wider awareness of racial discrimination and prejudice that exist in Britain today
- it provided a working definition of institutional racism
- it prompted government departments to take practical steps and new initiatives towards building an anti-racist society.

Institutional racism is defined in the Macpherson Report as:

> *The collective failure of an organisation to provide an appropriate and professional service to people because of their colour, culture or ethnic origin. It can be seen or detected in processes, attitudes and behaviour which amount to discrimination through unwitting prejudice, ignorance, thoughtlessness and racist stereotyping which disadvantage minority ethnic people.*

There has been much debate about the definitions of the terms in the Report. There are people who say that the term institutional racism has let individuals off the hook: they can now blame racism on the institution. Conversely, when others are challenged with following practices that are institutionally racist, they feel personally affronted. What is quite clear is that racism is an issue affecting individuals, institutions and society.

Although the Macpherson Report focused on the police service, it noted that:

> *It could be said that institutional racism is in fact pervasive throughout the culture and institutions of the whole of British society, and is in no way specific to the police service.*

The Report asserts that institutional racism is the reason why the public sector has significantly failed to provide an adequate, professional and appropriate service to black and minority ethnic people. The Report also stresses the need for every institution to examine its policies and practices to guard against disadvantaging sections of the community. It suggested 'a colour-blind approach fails to take account of the nature and needs of the person or people involved'. Treating everyone the same will not provide equal opportunities for people who are substantially disadvantaged and discriminated against and whose culture may not be understood.

Tackling institutional racism is a critical challenge for the NHS, and despite overwhelming evidence to the contrary, many parts of the institution have been in denial that racism and especially institutional racism exists. Without this acknowledgement, it becomes extremely difficult to address this agenda.

Discrimination, racism and ideology

Discrimination results when an individual or group is able to act on their assumptions and prejudices in a way that discriminates (negatively or positively) against another individual or group; implicit in this is the individual's power over another to act in a discriminatory way. The outcome of negative discrimination is a denial of dignity and self-respect, denial of access to employment or development opportunities, and denial of access to resources or services.

Racial discrimination occurs when individuals or groups have the power to discriminate on the basis of visible physical or cultural characteristics such as skin colour, dress or religion. The power differential between the groups is therefore critical, and it is inevitable that the more powerful will use processes and mechanisms to maintain their advantage.

Farhad Dalal[9] introduces the concept of ideology to understanding the power differentials between groups; he describes ideology as 'a particular way of viewing the world – a way that is defined by the more powerful'. Ideology seems to be informed by a particular set of beliefs, values and thought processes that become embedded in cultural norms and practices. These then become institutionalised through societal, political and social frameworks that are sustained through language, media, professional values, education and legislation.

How does ideology work?

> *Ideologies are the ruling ideas of a particular society at a particular time. They are ideas that express the naturalness of any existing social order and help maintain it. The ideas of the ruling class are in every epoch the ruling ideas; i.e. the class which is the ruling material force of society is at the same time its ruling intellectual force.*[10]

A fundamental premise of ideology is that whilst it is rarely learned consciously – i.e. it is absorbed subconsciously – it nevertheless serves to preserve the *status quo* by making it seem natural and unquestionable. It also enters the culture of all the groups involved. So, in the case of the power differential between white and black groups, the ideology of white superiority – fed by colonialism, economic and military power – enters the psyche of both groups and thus reinforces the 'us – superior/them – inferior' dynamic. The inferior group develops a self image of its own inferiority, which is then reinforced by societal factors such as economic position, employment conditions and status within mainstream society. Meanwhile, the established group (which considers itself superior) feels threatened by the presence of outsiders, who do not share its common memories and norms of respectability developed over a period of time. So it creates ways of excluding the outsiders in lots of different ways to prevent them from sharing its power base. Whilst the initial power differential may exist through the possession of technology and economic resources, this gets translated by the more powerful into the belief that they possess human superiority.[11]

Figure 1.2 (overleaf) illustrates the relationship between discrimination, ideology and racism. The history of race relations in Britain and in Europe has amply demonstrated that the impact of ideology is powerful and persistent; we have not found ways of challenging or shifting it. Yet, it is imperative that we do if we are to make any significant inroads into the removal of racial discrimination in all its forms and move towards an agenda of integration and social justice.

Figure 1.2 The nature of racism

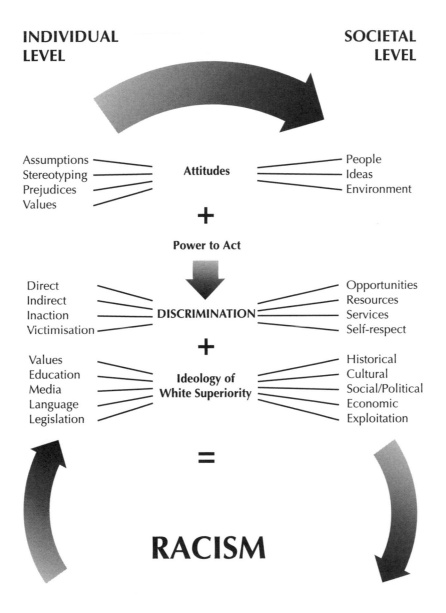

INDIVIDUAL
LEVEL

SOCIETAL
LEVEL

Assumptions
Stereotyping   **Attitudes**
Prejudices
Values

People
Ideas
Environment

+

Power to Act

Direct
Indirect
Inaction   **DISCRIMINATION**
Victimisation

Opportunities
Resources
Services
Self-respect

+

Values
Education
Media   **Ideology of**
Language   **White Superiority**
Legislation

Historical
Cultural
Social/Political
Economic
Exploitation

=

RACISM

Adapted from: Davies W, Ashok O. *Developing anti-racist practice for home carers and home care organisers.* OSDC Ltd, 1992

Multiculturalism

The term 'multiculturalism' has been used to celebrate and legitimise the existence of different cultural traditions and belief systems that characterise British society today. The recent debate in the press about the nature of multicultural Britain, the concept of British identity, immigration, refugees and institutional racism is characterised by emotion, conflict, misunderstandings, misinformation and misrepresentations. Inflammatory language used by some politicians and journalists has been most unhelpful in taking this agenda forward.

The continuing debate between multiculturalism and anti-racism has been highlighted by Smaje.[5] Multiculturalism puts emphasis on promoting understanding and tolerance of the different cultural traditions that exist in Britain today, whereas anti-racism places a more specific emphasis on challenging and changing the structural instruments that determine access to influence and power.

Social exclusion

'Social exclusion' is a term for describing groups or communities of people who suffer from a combination of linked problems such as unemployment, low skills base, low income, poor housing, high crime environments, poor health, family breakdown and social marginalisation. All these factors lead to social isolation of individuals or groups. Social exclusion is also based upon a severe lack of community capacity, where the assets and strengths of a community are not fully recognised or utilised; for example, refugee or recently migrant communities. Institutional and cultural discrimination and lack of access to public services can further increase social exclusion.

People from some black and minority ethnic communities are excluded due to multiple factors. They are exceptionally concentrated in many of the deprived areas around towns and cities, and experience all the problems that affect other people in these areas. In addition, they experience the consequences of racial discrimination and racial harassment. Services that do not meet their immediate and long-term needs, combined with language and cultural barriers, and a lack of general information about ways of accessing support services, increase this isolation further.

The British government and some EU governments have recently started actively to address the problem of social exclusion. The British Cabinet Office established a Social Exclusion Unit, which recently produced a report called *Minority ethnic issues in social exclusion and neighbourhood renewal*.[12] The report provides a broad analysis of many aspects of social exclusion in black and minority ethnic communities.

Cultural diversity in Britain

The latest estimates, based on the 1997 Labour Force Survey, suggest that there are about 3.4 million people living in Britain who consider themselves to be from an ethnic minority. This represents 6.4 per cent of the population. Figure 1.3 shows the breakdown of this by ethnic group category. This is likely to be an underestimate of the true minority ethnic population because the Labour Force Survey takes place in private households only. Therefore, groups such as travellers, refugees and asylum seekers are likely to have been excluded.

Figure 1.3 Ethnic minorities by category – 1997 Labour Force Survey data

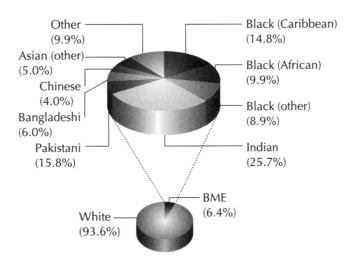

Total percentage of UK population = 6.4%

Adapted from: Arora S *et al. Improving the health of black and minority ethnic groups: a guide for PCGs.* London: King's Fund, 2000

As the diagram shows, these communities comprise a diverse group representing many different ethnic groups, cultural traditions and religions. The largest group originates from the Indian subcontinent – Indians, Pakistanis, Bangladeshis and Sri Lankans – followed by the Caribbeans, Africans and Chinese. The other communities are: Mauritians, Arabs, Filipinos and Vietnamese, who are not identified separately but form significant communities in certain areas. In London, nearly one person in four is from a minority ethnic community, and in some London boroughs almost half the residents are from a minority group. It is estimated that there are 250,000 refugees living in the UK, 85 per cent of whom reside in London.

Most ethnic minority populations are concentrated in urbanised parts of the country. Nearly three-quarters of the ethnic minority population are located in Greater London, Greater Manchester, West Yorkshire and the West Midlands. This distribution of black and ethnic minority populations does not, however, mean that the health of these groups should be the sole concern of the big cities. The myth of 'there aren't any/we're not London or Bradford or Birmingham' has been described as 'needs-denying'. Failure to recognise that small black and minority ethnic populations have specific needs can mean that they are further marginalised and remain invisible to the health and other services, thus perpetuating the perception that 'there aren't any'.

The age profile of black and minority ethnic groups suggests that they are younger than the white population. This means that current service provision for these groups needs to focus on children, young mothers and preventative health measures. Of equal importance, however, is the need to plan future services for an emerging 'ethnic elder' population, projected to rise by 100–200 per cent over the next 15 years in London.

Religious and language diversity

The main faiths practised in the UK are Christianity, Islam, Sikhism, Hinduism, Judaism, Buddhism, Zoroastrianism and Baha'i. Religious practice cuts across ethnic communities, and one geographic ethnic community can have several religious groups within it; for example, Indians may be Hindus, Muslims, Sikhs, Christians, Buddhists or Jains. There is evidence of discrimination for some groups as a result of religious beliefs. For example, many Muslims have articulated the notion of 'Islamophobia' that exists in some parts of UK society. Religious beliefs and practices have a significant impact on health beliefs, and it is intended that religion will feature as a category in the next national Census.

Other than English, there are almost 200 languages spoken in the UK. Among the more widely spoken are Punjabi, Urdu, Hindi, Gujerati, Bengali, Sylheti, Turkish and Greek. Most of the people from the minority ethnic groups who are born in the UK speak English, however there is a sizeable population of the older and recently arrived groups who do not speak English and for whom language barriers pose a considerable problem.

Implications for the health system

Diversity comprises visible and non-visible differences, which include gender, sexuality, ethnicity, age, cultural background, religion and disability. Thus, managing diversity means that the health system has to accept that the society and its workforce will consist of diverse population groups and learn to harness the richness and talents that these differences offer. A demoralised and de-motivated workforce will ultimately affect the effectiveness of the whole system. A 1984 King's Fund report highlighted the fact that:

> *Feelings of inadequacy, powerlessness and hopelessness culminate in the alienation of the black labour workforce. This alienation manifests itself in increased sickness and absence, apathy, anger, indifference and diminished output. These symptoms are often sited as the cause rather than the effect of racist employment practices.*[14]

In practical terms, it means examining institutional practices such as employment, promotion, reward systems, training and development practices. These should be monitored for inadvertent bias, racial discrimination and harassment, and ways must be found to eradicate them. A tougher line must be taken on those who abuse staff and patients.

In service provision, it means looking at what services are provided and the degree to which they meet the needs of all the different communities served. Specific services may need to be developed for communities with particular needs or changing the way mainstream services are provided in order to reach out to groups who cannot access them, do not use them or do not benefit from them. The use of health services and treatments is influenced by people's health beliefs, which in turn are shaped by cultural influences. Although some health beliefs may be at odds with those held by health professionals, within every culture there are norms and values that promote good health. Health professionals need to learn to work with the positive aspects of different cultures and not just focus on the cultural barriers.

In spite of its complex and dynamic nature, ethnicity monitoring is necessary and useful both in describing a population's health and health outcomes and in exposing discrimination and bias in employment and training opportunities. Senior and Bhopal[3] warn against 'ethnocentricity': the tendency to assume that one's own culture is the norm against which others are judged. In Britain, this translates into the white majority culture being the standard against which other cultures are compared. This will clearly influence the analyses and conclusions about causes of disease and ill health, as well as individuals' abilities to perform tasks and work.

McKenzie and Crowcroft[15] suggest that in medical research, researchers should describe the ethnic markers they have used and why and how they were assigned to groups or individuals being researched. A more useful and meaningful range of information could be based on factors that not only describe the individuals but which will also have an impact on how they use or receive services. These could include migration history, religious beliefs, cultural beliefs, dietary habits, beliefs about health and ill health, as well as language. Imposing identities and making assumptions only result in stereotyping, and inappropriate conclusions about the 'problem' being the consequence of a person's ethnicity rather than their experience – the so-called 'victim blaming' as described by Smaje.[4]

Conclusion

As a society, we see people through a mind-set that categorises them into a 'race' or ethnic group defined largely by physical traits such as skin colour, facial shape, hair texture, etc. Although most geneticists and biologists have abandoned racial taxonomies, we persist in using race as an explanation for our differences. I would suggest that this has more to do with social and political factors than any biological reality.

Whilst genes contribute to our physical make-up, social, cultural and environmental factors play a greater role in shaping us. Genetics research continues to assert that genes make proteins, they do not make human beings. The genetic variation between individuals is greater than that between population groups, the so-called races. Ethnicity, which has largely replaced 'race', is an equally complex concept. Ethnicity, as way of thinking about differences in the human race, has also unfortunately been translated into the 'us/them' dichotomy, which conveys value judgements about 'us' being 'normal' and 'them' being 'deviant', resulting in the usual social consequences of who gets included and who gets excluded.

As Sheldon and Parker articulate:

> If public health workers continue to use the term 'race' because people act as though race exists, they are guilty of conferring analytical status on what is nothing more than an ideological construction.[16]

Ethnicity and culture are fluid concepts that shift with time and context, nevertheless to be ethnic is to be foreign and a minority. The category of 'white' as an identity generates much anger and conflict. Given that ethnicity is now largely self-reported, the emerging view is that one's identity is shaped by many factors beyond ethnicity and culture, and these should all be considered in shaping health services research and delivery systems.

Discrimination can be built into organisational life at many levels: personal and social levels, employment processes, promotion and development processes, as well as access to power and decision-making levels. Equal opportunities policies have not succeeded in eliminating discrimination and disadvantage. True equality of opportunity will require active and sustained anti-racism and anti-discriminatory strategies.

Undergraduate and postgraduate establishments must ensure that anti-racism and cultural diversity training are incorporated as an integral component within their educational and training programmes. For doctors and other health professionals, this is critical. Caution must be exercised in ensuring that the emphasis *is not on the problems caused by ethnicity and difference*, but on the way the mainstream can marginalise individuals and groups who have different cultural traditions. This means going beyond cultural awareness training. Exploring individual attitudes, prejudice, stereotypical views and ideology is an important part of the educational process, as is learning the skill to communicate effectively in an intercultural therapeutic setting.

The challenge for medicine and medical institutions is to begin to explore and understand the mechanisms that perpetuate the ideology of superiority among the medical profession, where it resides and how it is transmitted. Then perhaps the process of developing a different world-view can begin, a world-view that promotes equality and values diversity.

References

1.   Cavalli-Sforza L L. *Genes, peoples and languages*. London: The Penguin Press, 2000.

2.   Herrnstein R J, Murray C A. *The bell curve: intelligence and class structure in American life*. New York: Free Press, 1994.

3.   Senior P A, Bhopal R. Ethnicity as a variable in epidemiological research. *BMJ* 1994; 309: 327–30.

4.   Smaje C. *Health, 'race' and ethnicity: making sense of the evidence*. London: King's Fund, 1995.

5.   Cochrane R, Shashidaran S P. Mental health and ethnic minorities. In: *Ethnicity and health*. York: NHS Centre for reviews and dissemination, 1996.

6.   Hammond P, Mosley M. *Trust me (I'm a doctor)*. London: Metro Books, 1999.

7.   Macpherson Sir W. *The Stephen Lawrence inquiry report*. London: The Stationery Office Ltd, 1999.

8.   Jones T. *Britain's ethnic minorities*. London: Policy Studies Institute, 1993.

9.   Dalal F. *Taking the group seriously*. London: Jessica Kingsley Publishers Ltd, 1998.

10. Rose S, Lewontin R C, Kamin L S. *Not in our genes*. London: Pelican, 1984.

11. Elias N, Scotson J. *The established and the outsiders*. London: Sage 1994.

12. Social Exclusion Unit. *Minority ethnic issues in social exclusion and neighbourhood renewal*. London: The Stationery Office, 2000.

13. Arora S, Coker N, Gillam S, Ismail H. *Improving the health of black and minority ethnic groups: a guide for PCGs*. London: King's Fund, 2000.

14. Agbolegbe G. The experience of black nurses in the UK. In: *Race and employment in the NHS*. London: King's Fund, 1984.

15. McKenzie K. Crowcroft N S. Describing race, ethnicity, and culture in medical research *BMJ* 1996; 312: 1054.

16. Sheldon T A. Parker H. Race and ethnicity in health research. *Journal of Public Health Medicine* 1992; 14 (2): 104–10.

Chapter 2

Overseas doctors: past and present

Karola Decker

British and Asian doctors are agreed that an Asian doctor with a basic degree from a recognised overseas medical school and with postgraduate qualifications is likely to be rejected when in competition with a white applicant with similar or identical qualifications and experience.

Brian McAvoy, Liam Donaldson*

Introduction

Approximately one-third of hospital doctors are from 'ethnic minorities', an unsatisfactory term lumping together a very diverse group of British and foreign non-white doctors. The majority of them are referred to as 'overseas doctors', having gained their primary qualifications outside the countries of the European Economic Area (EEA).† In 1999, 50 per cent of overseas doctors were of Asian origin, 41 per cent of these were from India.[1] Most have come for the purpose of postgraduate training. The yearly influx and outflow of overseas doctors is not monitored. In the early 1980s, it was estimated that around one-third of the yearly influx did not return,[2] but the situation may have changed after the introduction of a work permit scheme for overseas doctors in 1985.

The number of European doctors in Britain has increased considerably, especially in the pre-registration house officer grade. Most of them are 'white' and thus not affected by racial prejudice and discrimination, which is also true for the relatively small group of white Anglophone doctors qualified outside the EEA. Since 1977, Europeans are protected under EC directives (e.g. 93/16/EC) that ensure equivalent recognition of qualifications and free movement throughout the European Union.[3,4]

---

* *Health care for Asians.* Oxford: Oxford University Press, 1990.
† The EEA currently comprises all countries of the EU, plus Norway and Iceland.

'Racism' in the given context is rarely a matter of overt abuse. As the high proportion of non-white doctors indicates, it does not imply exclusion in a simplistic sense. Rather, an 'ethnic penalty'[5] is added to a system that is often experienced as punitive by white doctors as well, especially by junior doctors in the lower training grades. The problem is in fact highly complex and requires a historical perspective.

This chapter explores the linkages of non-white doctors' grievances with the established organisational, professional structure and culture of the hospital service and certain fundamental issues in the NHS, in particular consultant expansion and the changing role of consultants. It implies an emphasis on junior doctors, especially the senior house officer grade (SHO) and the conflicting requirements of service provision, teaching and training that has characterised the NHS from its inception.[6]

Other relevant aspects, for example racial harassment and violence by patients, or alleged racial bias of the disciplinary actions of the GMC and the debate on consultants' distinction awards,[7,8,9,10] are not addressed. The motives of overseas doctors for coming to Britain other than for postgraduate training are also not discussed. This would require a separate study and a thorough analysis of the health systems in their home countries, especially in South Asia.[11,12,13]

Two social surveys on overseas doctors have informed this chapter. The first was commissioned by the Department of Health,[14] and the second by the Commission for Racial Equality.[15] Although out of date in some respects, both still provide a valid basis for information on this subject. The official NHS statistics for England have also been used to measure the contribution of non-white hospital medical staff in all grades and to highlight the extent of their promotion to the consultant grade in selected specialties.[*]

Medical migration

Recruiting overseas has ethical implications, which are increasingly debated internationally. This debate is reflected in the *Lancet* of 15 July 2000, especially in Bundred and Levitt's contribution 'Medical migration: who are the real losers?'[16] The debate concerns the phenomena of 'brain drain' as well as 'brain push'. Brain drain is largely driven by imbalances caused through the insufficient output from medical schools in the UK, USA and Canada. Political oppression in some of the less

---

[*] If not stated otherwise, data are taken from the Department of Health *Statistical Bulletins* for England 1994 to 1999, in which selected data of the annual medical and dental workforce census on NHS hospital staff are presented and analysed. Detailed results on selected specialties by ethnic origin and country of qualification for England in 1999, which are not published in the respective *Statistical Bulletin*, were made available by the statistical workforce of the Department of Health.

developed countries is a vicious kind of 'brain push', although not necessarily caused by direct personal persecution.[17] Lack of opportunities for postgraduate education and research in developing countries is a significant factor for medical migration.

It has been proposed that the gaining country should reimburse the cost of medical education, and the World Organisation of Family Doctors (WONCA) Durban Declaration 1997 called for action to review policies in developed countries on doctors' recruitment from less developed countries.[16] The World Health Organisation will have to take a lead in establishing international co-operation in this regard, and there may be some form of regulation in the future. Most recently the UK has developed guidance for international recruitment of nurses – but none for doctors so far. However, the ultimate objective should not be 'limitation of mobility but equity of health'.[18]

Immigration to Britain

Medical immigration has been part of the general immigration to Britain from the late 1940s onwards. Until the first Commonwealth Immigration Act 1962, labour was encouraged into Britain without any restrictions. In the late 1970s, 31 per cent of all doctors in the NHS in England were overseas-qualified.[14]

A work permit scheme to regulate the employment of foreigners in Britain had been introduced as early as 1919, but it did not apply to post-war immigrants from the New Commonwealth until 1971. Instead, from 1962 a voucher system had been established that curbed and controlled immigration, especially after 1965 when it was largely restricted to qualified workers and professionals. With respect to immigration rules, doctors enjoyed a privileged position for a long time. Only in 1985 was the work permit scheme eventually extended to them.[19,20] In clear contrast, debates about the employment of overseas doctors reach back to the early 1960s.

Overseas doctors have been employed in the hospital service in significant numbers, presumably from 1953 onwards when junior posts increased considerably.[21] By 1958 it was estimated that up to 2500 overseas doctors were working in hospitals in England and Wales.[22] The need to employ them was partly a consequence of an embarrassing error in manpower planning, anticipating a surplus of doctors when there was actually a critical shortage. In the Willink Report (1957) a 10 per cent cut in the yearly intake of medical students had been recommended,* a decision that was reversed in 1960.[23] A yearly increase of 10 per cent became adopted policy – without settling the problem for the future.

---

* Exactly the same error occurred in Canada in 1999 (see Bundred P, Levitt C. Medical migration: who are the real losers? *Lancet* 2000; 356: 245–46).

In this context, the high number of 3628 junior overseas doctors, between 30 and 40 per cent of all juniors at the time, was 'discovered' through the Platt Report (1961) and immediately hotly debated by the medical profession following an initiative of Lord Taylor in Parliament on 29 November 1961.[24] Arguably, all the increase in junior doctors in the years 1957–60 was due to recruitment from overseas.[21]

The NHS was set to expand further, and towards the end of the decade a new crisis point was reached, as documented in the Todd Report (1968). The answer was a marked increase in the employment of overseas doctors, at a time when xenophobia had been ignited by Enoch Powell, the Tory politician. The overwhelming majority of overseas doctors came from the South Asian subcontinent, especially India. They were qualified doctors, and most of them had several years' experience in their home country. They entered Britain as visitors and tourists without much prior information, and made their arrangements only on arrival.

It was a largely unplanned process that had started as a 'family affair' in the Commonwealth under the quasi-official concept of 'mutual benefit', which has survived as the underlying ideology to the present day. The Empire Commonwealth Medical Advisory Bureau, later renamed Commonwealth Medical Advisory Bureau, now the International Department of the British Medical Association, had been set up in 1948.[25] The phrase 'family affair' can be taken literally for this early period, as the Bureau helped to establish personal contacts and provide hospitality for new arrivals.[26] Albeit rooted in colonial-patrimonial concepts, at that point in time overseas doctors were made to feel welcome.

The 1960s and 1970s

From the late 1960s, the climate changed profoundly. An editorial in the *British Medical Journal* (BMJ) of 22 March 1969 highlights that only one year after the publication of the Todd Report, the situation was perceived as increasingly competitive.[27] Factors inducing the change were a stricter immigration policy of the US, a rising output from British medical schools, and an overall increase in medical immigration.

Doctors of Asian origin came under particular scrutiny. In the Merrison Report[28] on the government inquiry into the regulations in the medical profession, the clinical competence and language skills of overseas doctors were questioned. This 'discourse' had already taken shape in the early 1960s. In a letter to the *BMJ*, published on 24 February 1962, a young Indian doctor from Calcutta, S K Agarwal, wrote:

Every issue of the B.M.J. in the last few months contains an article or letter which directly or indirectly attacks the knowledge and efficiency of foreign graduates, especially Asians. The main points raised are: [1] Low standard academically and skill, [2] inability to speak or understand English.[29]

However, the Merrison Report made such generalisations quasi-official. At the same time, it accused the General Medical Council (GMC) of allowing 'its duty as the protector of medical standards to be compromised by the manpower requirements of the NHS'.[28]

The recognition of Indian medical schools was immediately withdrawn. In 1980, as a consequence of the Medical Act 1978, reciprocity in the Commonwealth was generally revoked. In a tit-for-tat reaction, India, Pakistan and other developing countries, Chile for example, de-recognised British medical qualifications, creating serious problems for doctors returning to these countries.[30]

A lasting impact of the Merrison Report has been the introduction of a two-tier system of 'full' and 'limited' registration, which has made the procedure of medical registration for overseas doctors very complex.

The 1980s and 1990s

Since 1980, overseas qualifications are recognised at the discretion of the GMC, and registration is linked *either* with the passing of, *or* the exemption from, a test of the Professional and Linguistic Assessment Board (the PLAB test) of language and clinical skills.

The extension of the work permit scheme to doctors in 1985 did not reduce the numbers of overseas doctors to the extent it was initially feared.[2] Since then, work permits are granted only to holders of career posts (grades after completion of training), not for training posts. But an official 'loop hole' was immediately created to secure the long-standing tradition of postgraduate training of foreign doctors in the UK. A permit-free period of four years for postgraduate training, extendable for a further year if approved by the postgraduate dean, had been granted.

Sir David Innes-Williams, Director of the British Postgraduate Medical Federation at the time, expected that postgraduate training would have to adapt to overseas doctors' needs under the new conditions. But the only active response was the Overseas Doctors Training Scheme (ODTS), an idea that Williams had launched in 1984 together with Sir Ian Todd, Professor Peter Bevan and Mr David Evans. The DoH provided financial and strategic support.[31] Under the ODTS, overseas trainees are sponsored by one of the royal colleges. In addition, sponsorship through individual consultants is still possible, for example in psychiatry, though it was more widespread before 1994.

The ODTS was founded on good intentions but never really flourished. In 1994, Tessa Richards summarised: 'The Overseas Doctors Training Scheme has acquired a bad name.'[32] Only 40 per cent of overseas doctors have come under this scheme to Britain, which has often meant little more than some help in finding the first job. In the vigorous debate following the publication of Richards' article in the *BMJ*, the Royal College of Psychiatrists took pride in its good practice of ensuring that all its trainees under the scheme were placed 'in approved training rotations for the duration of their stay, not just for finding their first job'.[33] However, most doctors under the scheme were left in a position similar to unsponsored doctors.

The ODTS has become 'bogged down' in the last two to three years through ever growing waiting lists of overseas applicants.[31] By the end of 1998, the general shortage of training posts at SHO level had become acute, with about 50 to 100 applicants per post, and more than 100 in some specialties.[34] The majority of the royal colleges, including psychiatry, has now ceased sponsoring under the scheme. The Royal College of Surgeons, however, which was involved in launching the ODTS, is still committed to the scheme. The problem of overseas doctors' training placements is currently being reviewed by the NHS Executive.[35]

Until 1993, the Home Office more or less automatically allowed switching from permit-free status to that of a work permit holder. But overseas doctors *and* their employers were not aware that this happened only at the discretion of the Home Office since it had never been communicated to them.[36,37] Following a consultation exercise between the DoH and the Home Office in September 1993, procedures had tightened,[38] very much to the inconvenience of trusts.[39]

Immigration rules for doctors were changed again in 1997, allowing them now, as a rule, up to six years permit-free postgraduate training (section 3 (2) of the Immigration Act 1971; changes stated in the House of Commons on 2 April 1996, published 27 February 1997, to take effect from 1 April 1997). This change occurred following the reform of higher specialist training, usually referred to as the 'Calman reforms' (after the then Chief Medical Officer, Kenneth Calman). The impact of these reforms on overseas doctors is discussed later.

British emigration

The NHS was never entirely popular with British doctors. Given the considerable emigration of young doctors since the inception of the NHS, it is arguable whether it was 'all but an eccentric fringe of the medical profession' that resisted, or rather resented, its introduction.[22] In 1948, a young doctor wrote a letter to the *BMJ*, stating that '[m]ost of the young doctors have a fair idea of what is going on … The wisest of us have either left the country or are busy packing our bags.'[40]

Increasing numbers of graduates from British medical schools mistrust their prospects in the NHS. According to a recent survey only 78 per cent of the doctors who qualified in 1996 definitely or probably intended to pursue a career in the UK.[41] This is an even lower percentage than the 'historical low' of 83 per cent in the 1993 cohort.[42]

The USA, Canada and Australia are the preferred destinations of British émigré doctors. The same applies to aspiring foreign doctors who regard Britain as a transitory stage in their career, as well as to those who re-emigrate for other reasons. Emigration of British doctors counts as loss, but given the greatly increased international medical migration, this may not be a valid perspective. British doctors' emigration is part of a global scenario of exchange that has been called the '"medical carousel" in which doctors seem to be continuously moving to countries with a perceived higher standard of living'.[16] On closer inspection, the motives for migration in each country are much more complex than just the perceived living standard. The global trend away from rural areas is a decisive factor in *all* countries.

In the UK, the NHS is a gigantic organisation with the inherent flaws of bureaucracy, struggling at the same time with the historic legacy of under-funding. Implementation of clinical governance* and the recent pledge of the British government to increase funding to the level of other European countries are addressing this. However, even in a successfully rejuvenated NHS, young British doctors would still emigrate. Medical migration is a firmly established professional tradition, going back to ancient centuries, involving the usual scientific channels and the activities of agencies and professional bodies.

The receiving system in Britain

The supplementary report on the implications of the Calman reforms on overseas doctors conveys the impression that British immigration rules for doctors were predominantly designed to protect sending countries from a brain drain.[43] This is certainly not their sole purpose. Lister[4] has indicated that in the early 1980s, for

---

* From the large body of literature on the topic see, for example, Heard S. Educating towards clinical governance. *Hospital Medicine* 1998; 59 (9): 728–29.

example, fears of British doctors' unemployment was the driving force behind the introduction of the work permit for overseas doctors in 1985. In the long term, immigration rules are simply changed according to the interest of the host country.

The output of British medical schools has never met the long-term manpower needs of the NHS. The ideal of a nationally self-sufficient system has no basis in either policy or practice. The official rationale is rather an equilibrium of the medical two-way flow. However, the insufficient output of British medical schools plus British doctors' emigration does not fully explain the high demand for foreign doctors in the NHS hospital service. There are basic structural reasons, to be understood in historical context. Reflecting on the results of the social survey on overseas doctors, which had been commissioned by the DoH following the Merrison Report,[14] Richard Smith, the editor of the BMJ, remarked: 'One thing that emerges from studying overseas doctors' problems is that they are in many ways the problems of the whole profession.'[44] This is as true today as it was then.

Early days of the NHS

When the NHS was introduced, politicians made compromises in order to attract specialist skills to the new service. Consultants were 'offered many fresh inducements, without being expected to sacrifice too many of their traditional privileges'.[22] The system of distinction awards, a considerable enhancement of the pensionable salary, was created in 1948. The decisive part of the historic 'deal' was the concession of private practice, which is newly contested.

Perhaps even more important, the role and the working practice of consultants did not change. Until very recently hospital doctors' working arrangements were based on the sub-structure of the 'consultant firm', meaning 'a consultant leading a team of 'his own' junior doctors of various grades'.[46] This tradition goes back to pre-NHS times when doctors worked unpaid in hospitals. To be appointed a hospital 'consultant' was proof of competence and trustworthiness, an honour that in return attracted patients to the private practice.

The underlying rationale of the 'firm' was to ensure continuity of patient care and the provision of an apprenticeship-style training – the latter being one of the oldest traditions in the medical profession, especially in surgery, and not unique to Britain. Until the Calman reforms, apprenticeship had been the prevailing concept in British medical training , though surviving only as learning 'on the job' or 'random exposure to clinical work[6] of variable relevance and ad hoc (or no) supervision'.[47]

More recent developments

The historic compromise on the consultant role left a permanent mark on the hospital service and contributes to some of its most intractable problems. The report of the Audit Commission, *The doctors' tale*,[46] highlights this. The hospital service is built around consultants as the pinnacle of an elaborate support system, carried by nurses and junior doctors, whilst the ultimate responsibility for patient care rests with consultants. Before the Calman reforms it could take up to 15 years to qualify as a specialist in Britain. This meant that junior doctors were kept in the support role twice as long than in the rest of Europe and the US.

The NHS hospital service is consultant-led rather than consultant-provided. For more than ten years the Government has been trying to effect a shift towards a more consultant-based service. The three main initiatives have been: *Achieving a balance*[48] in the career structure, aiming at an improved consultant/junior doctor ratio; the *New deal*[49] for junior doctors, implementing in particular a reduction of their working hours and aiming to improve facilities; the Calman Report[50] on specialist training, implementing a shorter and more structured approach to postgraduate training.

These initiatives have accompanied the restructuring of the NHS. However, consultant posts have increased only moderately at an annual rate of 4 per cent over the last ten years.[1] Although necessary and desirable, increasing the number of consultants is not a magic key. The Audit Commission has addressed the *circularity* of the problem:

> *Consultant posts tend to create more clinical work. Unless this growth in clinical work is controlled or consultants are prepared to take on all aspects of this work, including that traditionally carried out by juniors, there is a pressure to increase the number of junior posts at the same time, and the net effect naturally is that the ratio of trainees to consultants does not change.*[46]

The consultant firm is an anachronism and rapidly vanishing, but 'many consultants still practise as individuals rather than as part of a team and the roles of the junior grades and the culture of the medical hierarchy remain essentially the same.'[46] This encapsulates a situation that has been allowed to ossify over decades.

The NHS needed overseas doctors in the past in order to expand and uphold the established system. As clearly stated in the supplementary Calman Report on overseas doctors, the NHS still wishes to attract them.[43] In 1997, 44 per cent of 7229 newly registered doctors (full registration) had received their early training in non-UK countries.[51] For the foreseeable future they will remain a feature of the hospital service, in fact a pillar of patient care. The dramatic trend away from general practice[41] makes further overseas recruitment predictable. Politicians and trusts are long reconciled with this state of affairs – one good reason to reflect more seriously on the *nature of the use* of these doctors, facing up to the problems that come with it.

The current hospital staffing structure

In 1999, 63,548 doctors were employed in the NHS hospital service. Of these 43,859 (69 per cent) have gained their primary qualification in the UK, 3810 (6 per cent) in the European Economic Area (EEA) excluding the UK, and a further 15,879 (25 per cent) elsewhere. Only the third group is referred to as overseas-qualified doctors or simply overseas doctors.

Table 2.1 Hospital medical staff by grade and ethnic origin in 1999

Ethnicity All countries of qualification	Total 63548 (100%)	Consultant 22017 (34.6%)	Staff Grd 3645 (5.7%)	Assoc. Sp. 1443 (2.2%)	Registrar Grp 12105 (19.0%)	SHO 14777 (23.2%)	PRH 3543 (5.6%)
	%	%	%	%	%	%	%
White	67.3	81.1	36.2	37.7	64.6	58.5	63.1
Black	3.8	2.1	9.1	5.8	4.7	4.9	2.9
Asian [Indian]	18.4 [13.8]	8.9 [6.8]	34.5 [26.0]	32.6 [27.4]	21.1 [15.2]	25.8 [19.6]	19.2 [11.3]
Other	8.3	6.0	17.8	21.4	8.1	9.0	8.6
Not known	2.2	1.9	2.4	2.4	1.5	1.8	6.1

UK-qualified
Total 43859
(69%)

White: 58.1   White: 72.6
Black: 1.0   Black: 0.7
Asian: 5.7   Asian: 2.4
[Ind.: 3.5]   [Ind.: 1.6]
Other: 2.9   Other: 1.7
Unknown: 1.2   Unknown: 1.3

Numbers and percentages retrieved from: Department of Health. *Medical and dental workforce census 1999*

Regarding the crucial white/non-white split, the statistical categories 'country of qualification' and 'ethnic origin' are overlapping. Therefore, one has to bear in mind that:

(1) the UK-qualified group includes around 10 per cent doctors of black, Asian (overwhelmingly Indian) and other ethnic origin
(2) the EEA 'other-than-UK-qualified' group will not be exclusively white
(3) the overseas-qualified group includes white doctors mainly from North America and Australia.

In 1999, doctors of Asian origin represented 18.4 per cent of all hospital doctors, 13.8 per cent of whom were Indian. Within the group of overseas doctors, 50 per cent were of Asian origin, of whom four-fifths were of Indian origin.

Distribution by specialty

NHS hospital doctors are distributed across the medical specialties. Medical graduates who opt for a career as a general practitioner (GP) receive 'vocational', as opposed to specialist training, in hospitals. About one-third of medical graduates become GPs, and around 42 per cent remain in UK hospital medicine.[46]

The following seven specialties account for 48 per cent of medical staff in hospitals: general medicine, general surgery, otolaryngology, trauma and orthopaedics, urology, anaesthetics, obstetrics and gynaecology.[46] There are now 55 acute specialties established – largely a development of the last 40 years – with enormous consequences for service delivery and training.

Statistics from the medical workforce census on the consultant group in selected specialties by ethnicity and country of qualification are illuminating (Table 2.2). The proportion of non-white consultants is highest in geriatrics (30.4 per cent), accident & emergency (27 per cent) and general psychiatry (24 per cent). Their numbers are lowest in general surgery (14.1 per cent).

Table 2.2 Selected specialties: non-white consultants in 1999

General medicine excluding subspecialties

Specialty Numbers	All non-white %	Black %	Asian %	Indian %	Other %	Not given %
Accident & Emergency						
All 3093	33.4	5.2	20.8	[16.1]	7.4	1.8
Cons. 438 (18.4%)	27.0	5.3	12.1	[10.3]	7.3	2.3
Anaesthetics						
All 6939	29.0	2.8	17.0	[13.6]	7.4	1.8
Cons. 3136 (45.2%)	17.0	1.6	8.1	[6.7]	5.2	2.1
General Medicine						
All 4915	36.0	3.1	20.6	[14.4]	8.6	3.7
Cons. 407 (8.2%)	20.4	2.7	6.4	[4.7]	7.9	3.4
General Psychiatry						
All 4581	35.5	6.0	17.7	[13.7]	9.6	2.2
Cons. 1569 (34.3%)	24.0	2.6	12.4	[10.0]	7.0	2.0
General Surgery						
All 4631	34.3	3.2	20.2	[13.8]	8.1	2.9
Cons. 1257 (27%)	14.1	1.7	7.1	[5.2]	4.1	1.2
Geriatrics						
All 2505	38.5	4.1	22.1	[16.0]	9.0	3.2
Cons. 719 (28.7%)	30.5	3.1	17.0	[13.5]	8.9	1.5
Paediatrics						
All 4566	35.6	5.2	20.5	[16.4]	8.0	1.9
Cons. 1313 (28.2%)	22.5	3.4	10.1	[8.4]	7.4	1.5
Obstetrics & Gynaecology						
All 4114	40.2	8.0	19.6	[14.8]	10.8	1.9
Cons. 1057 (25.7%)	18.1	3.2	5.4	[3.7]	7.8	1.7
Trauma & Orthopaedics						
All 3540	39.3	3.3	24.8	[19.2]	9.0	2.2
Cons 1142 (32%)	19.2	1.8	8.9	[6.7]	6.0	2.5

Numbers and percentages derived from: Department of Health. *Medical workforce census 1999,* file AH403.xls

The medical career ladder

Regarding ethnicity and racism in the given context, it is vital to have a sufficient understanding of what accumulates to a medical career in the hospital service. In 1999, 34.6 per cent of hospital doctors were specialist consultants, whereas 47.8 per cent of hospital doctors were employed in the training grades. In 1999, the overall consultant/junior ratio was 1:1.38. But within the specialties it varies greatly. In 1995, for example, it was 1:1 in anaesthetics but 1:2.5 in obstetrics and gynaecology.[46]

The consultant grade represents the top of a medical specialist career. There is a basic junior–senior divide between consultants and all training grades. There is an additional junior–senior divide within the training grades, which is of great significance regarding training opportunities and supervision.

Doctors' training starts at the pre-registration house officer grade (PRHO) over the first year after graduation from medical school. Following registration, specialist training occurs in two phases: general professional/basic specialist training, and higher specialist training (HST). The medical royal colleges have to approve of hospitals' suitability for training. The regional postgraduate deans have to approve of the training posts in hospitals and fund 50 per cent of the salaries of trainee doctors.

Specialist training is used to progress through three training grades: senior house officer (SHO), registrar and senior registrar, requiring three to four years in each grade. In the context of the Calman reforms, the specialist registrar grade was formally introduced on 1 April 1996, amalgamating the registrar and senior registrar grades. Only holders of the Certificate of Completion of Specialist Training (CCTS) constitute the 'pool' of future consultants, appointed usually in their late 30s. The royal colleges accredit consultants and they are represented on consultants' selection committees.

The associate specialist grade, which was introduced in 1981, and staff grade doctors with specialist skills, introduced in 1988, are sub-consultant grades. All non-training grades, i.e. consultants, associate specialists and staff grade doctors, are referred to as 'career grades'.

The training grades

Hospitals' primary function is patient care. As the Audit Commission has emphasised, training, important as it is, is secondary. Thus, once registered, everyone from the SHO grade to consultant is a 'valid' hospital doctor and most are vital to service delivery. The Audit Commission has briefly described how the work is distributed between all grades.[46] There is a clear divide between work on the wards and 'out of hours' emergency cover and the regular daytime/weekday work in operating theatres and out-patient clinics. In essence, ward work and emergency cover are largely left to the most junior doctors.

In 1999, just under half of all overseas-qualified doctors were employed in the training grades. The newly introduced category of the 'registrar group' in the official statistics unfortunately blurs the picture, because in the past there was always a marked difference between the senior registrar and the registrar grade. In 1992, 92 per cent (5300 of a total 5790 overseas doctors in the training grades) were employed as registrars and SHOs.[43] The three training grades are maintained in the statistics for 1996, reflecting the 'pre-Calman' situation. In 1996, 86 per cent of a total 5542 non-white, non-UK-qualified doctors in the training grades were employed as registrars and SHOs (Table 2.3). This is a minimum because many doctors did not state their ethnic origin, a second factor blurring the picture.

Table 2.3 White/non-white split in the senior registrar, registrar and SHO grades in 1996

| Total
24619 | Senior Registrar
5640 | Registrar
5206 | SHO
13773 |
|---|---|---|---|
| Non-white:
8210 (33.3%) | 1271 (22.5%) | 2033 (39%) | 4960 (35.6%) |
| [UK qualified:
2722 (11%)] | [476 (8.4%)] | [502 (9.6%)] | [1744 (12.6%)] |
| Not known:
1598 (6.5%) | 400 (7%) | 351 (6.7%) | 847 (6.1%) |
| [UK qualified:
1000 (4%)] | [251 (4.4%)] | [212 (4%)] | [537 (3.9%)] |

Numbers and percentages retrieved from: Department of Health. *Medical and dental workforce census 1996*

Recorded ethnic origin of hospital doctors

Six per cent of EEA-qualified staff did not state ethnic origin in 1997; and 6 per cent of *all* staff did not state ethnic origin in 1996. The assumption that nearly 100 per cent are non-white within the category 'not known' may be speculative, but it is not uninformed. In 1997, the country of qualification of 5000 doctors was not known, but 99 per cent of these doctors held limited registrations only.[52] It can be assumed that the actual figures are approximate maxima, i.e. the aggregate of 'non-white' *plus* 'not known'. This means that in 1996 the percentage of all non-white doctors in the registrar grade was up to 46 per cent and in the SHO grade up to 42 per cent. In 1996, between 27 per cent and 33 per cent of all hospital medical staff were non-white. Expressed in whole time equivalents, minimal 28 per cent and maximal 34 per cent of contracted time was provided by non-white medical staff.

The statistics for 1999 by ethnic origin have improved, with only 2 per cent of doctors having not stated their ethnic origin (Table 2.1). In 1999, the combined whole time equivalent of non-white medical staff, UK- and overseas-qualified, was 32 per cent of contracted time, excluding the category 'not known', and 34 per cent if the category 'not known' is included.

The employment pattern of overseas doctors applies also to UK/EEA-qualified non-white staff, especially Asian doctors. They are 'under-represented in the consultant grade, and over-represented at registrar [and] senior house officer levels'.[53] In 1999, 16.5 per cent of all consultants were overseas-qualified. In the staff grade and associate specialist grades, proportions are reversed: in 1999, overseas doctors represented 66 per cent and 65 per cent respectively in each grade. These are sub-consultant 'secondary' careers, with associate specialists providing much of consultants' routine work, and those on staff grade working shifts. It is contested whether their numbers should be allowed to increase. As the NAHAT survey[39] indicates, trusts wish it because royal colleges are not involved in appointment procedures. But trusts demand, at the same time, to allow access to continuing education to keep the consultant career as an option for these doctors.

Women doctors

In the years 1989 to 1999, hospital medical staff numbers grew by 35 per cent. In 1999, 34 per cent of all hospital medical staff were female. Of these, 51 per cent were employed in the PRHO grade, 44 per cent in the SHO grade, and 36 per cent in the registrar group; but only 21 per cent were consultants. The proportion of women in the junior grades indicates a further future rise in the consultant grade. However, women doctors are still under-achieving compared to men, for many complex reasons.[54,55]

Statistical results by country of qualification and gender have been available for the first time. In 1999, 22 per cent of all overseas doctors were female, and 35 per cent of them were SHOs. Hardly any other information is available for this group. There is anecdotal evidence that many female overseas doctors come to the UK as spouses of male overseas doctors (personal communication from Dr Mangalam Sridhar, consultant physician, Stafford).

Regarding race *and* gender, there are obvious parallels concerning career progress, and there must be a considerable overlap of problem areas in the lower training grades because of similar high proportions of women and non-white doctors, especially in the SHO grade. Major issues, addressed by the Audit Commission,[46] are part-time work, which is comparatively widespread in the consultant group but virtually non-existent for trainee doctors, and flexibility regarding exit from and re-entry to training.[56] 'Race' and gender issues are highlighted through the findings of McManus's most recent study on medical school applicants: 'The interaction between sex and ethnic origin was significant (P=0.049), women who were not white being less likely to receive an offer than expected.'[57]

The grievances

Postgraduate training is the single most important aspect of overseas doctors' employment in the NHS for two reasons: (a) training, not service, is still the official rationale to attract large numbers in the junior grades for the work permit-free period; (b) the amount and quality of training they actually receive determines their career.

Each *Statistical Bulletin* of the DoH on the medical workforce contains the remark that many of the overseas doctors will leave the UK 'on completion of their training'. This is misleading. Overseas doctors were not supposed to formally enter phase two of postgraduate training, i.e. higher specialist training (HST).

The revision of immigration rules in April 1997 appears to have been undertaken largely in response to trusts' pressure. In the NAHAT survey, the various facets of the issue of overseas doctors concerning recruitment, work permit and training, surfaces nearly on every page of the report, and it is explicitly stated that trusts want 'to see the permit-free period extended to cover the whole training period'.[39] This has been conceded. Overseas doctors who are not work permit holders are now allowed three years for basic specialist training, and – depending on the support of the regional postgraduate dean – a further three years as a rule for HST, but more if necessary for completion of training.

Access to training after the Calman reforms

The essence of the reforms is a structured approach to training as opposed to the traditional reliance on the amount of time spent in the different training grades and the related posts. HST occurs in teaching and general district hospitals. The training programmes and rotations for each specialty are constructed by regional specialty training committees. They follow a royal college curriculum and last about five years. The surgical specialties have opted for exit examinations.

The more formal aspect of the reforms is the introduction of a New Specialist List held by the GMC. Entry to the List is granted to holders of the Certificate for Completion of Specialist Training (CCST), and it is a requirement for appointment as a consultant. As indicated earlier, the most visible innovation is the introduction of the specialist registrar grade, amalgamating the previous registrar and senior registrar grades. Entry to the new grade is competitive. As a rule, candidates will have passed membership examinations for the royal colleges during their latter years in the SHO grade. The selection is mainly based on interviews. It had been assumed that appointment to the grade would 'almost guarantee a consultant career'.[58]

Regarding overseas doctors, it is unlikely that a pattern of failure will re-emerge that was characteristic of the period before 1985, when overseas doctors were not effectively barred from higher specialist training but often did not manage to qualify. As David Smith[14] has pointed out, many of the 'stuck doctors', as they were labelled then, did not achieve completion of specialist training and often left the hospital service frustrated after ten to 14 years to become over-qualified and not genuinely motivated GPs. The Calman reforms, plus the monitoring role of postgraduate deans, should secure the eventual award of the CCST, but of course only for those who are actually selected for higher specialist training.

Access to higher specialist training has become much more competitive. This does not bode well for non-white doctors since they have greater difficulties in obtaining training posts during basic specialist training, if they obtain posts with a training component at all. The collapse of the ODTS is proof of this. As was predicted,[58] the 'bottleneck' of transition from SHO to specialist registrar has become narrower for all junior doctors, and many of them are denied higher specialist training.

The Calman reforms have certainly improved higher specialist training and consultants' commitment to training in general. Trainee satisfaction has increased in all grades.[59] However, fully implementing them raises the question as to who will do the work even more urgently.[58] The Calman reforms make no provisions for the SHO grade. They have not led to a single training grade.[60] The junior–senior divide within the training grades is formally maintained and, post-Calman, the SHO has become 'the workhorse grade'.[61]

Senior house officers' training

SHOs receive 'service-based training', whereby within the day-to-day business, certain arrangements are supposed to secure a training effect, involving feedback, appraisal and set educational objectives. But often there are no such arrangements. SHO posts continue to be created primarily for the purpose of delivering service. SHOs represent 'cheap labour' to the NHS, and their number is rising. Even pseudo-SHO posts are created, meaning unapproved posts for training.[47] This is one example of how some trusts circumvent and undermine the intentions of the New Deal for junior doctors.

SHOs role as 'the resident "safety net", while partly designed to protect patients, also protects consultants, and in some cases higher trainees, from immediate out of hours service or directly supervising preregistration house officers'.[47] It is no polemic but a well-known and repeatedly admitted fact – confirmed in two reports of the Audit Commission[46,62] – that the most junior doctors receive too little training, in some posts none at all, and they work largely unsupervised. Studies on post-operative deaths have revealed that in deaths associated with surgical factors, inadequate supervision was implied.[63] The same applies to deaths associated with anaesthesia. Significantly greater mortality was found among patients with 'obstructing large bowel cancer operated on by registrars (31 per cent) than among those performed by consultants (12 per cent) which could not be explained by differences in the case mix'.[63]

Pass rates of royal college examinations highlight the difficult situation of senior house officers. Multiple attempts are allowed, with first-time pass rates in some specialties as low as 30 per cent. Though statistics on pass rates are not readily available,[65] overseas doctors' comparative under-achievement is no secret. According to a study in 1986 on behalf of the Royal College of Psychiatrists – one of the more accessible specialties for overseas doctors – ultimate pass rates (maximum of five attempts) for the MRC Psych were 75 per cent to 81 per cent for Indian/Arab candidates compared to 95 per cent for UK candidates.[66]

A large number of overseas candidates dropped out without making the allowed five attempts.[66] In addition, proportionately more overseas doctors made multiple attempts than UK candidates. The suggested reasons for this discrepancy were:

- less familiarity with examination techniques
- lack of interview skills
- lack of feedback after failed attempts.

The dean at the time explicitly excluded discrimination as part of the problem.[67]

Given the over-representation of overseas- and British-qualified non-white doctors in the lower training grades, it is evident that they are badly affected by the alarming deficiencies of 'junior' junior doctors' training. After 'Calman', postgraduate training remains a vexed problem, in which overseas doctors especially are caught up, although it is presumably true that they are not individually 'treated less well than British graduates, once they [have] secured a post'.[68] It is a convincing argument that in order to improve the training for overseas-qualified SHOs, 'attention should be paid to improving the quality of training for all SHOs.'[68] The review of the NHS workforce planning, *A health service for all the talents: developing the NHS workforce*,[69] has now put the 'drastic rethinking' of the SHO grade squarely on the agenda.[6]

Career progress, specialty choice and job satisfaction

Sufficient progress along the career ladder *plus* the free and right choice of specialty constitute the main factors of job satisfaction, which is significantly lower among overseas doctors. According to Anwar and Ali, only 20 per cent of them achieve job satisfaction compared with 44 per cent of white British doctors, and one in ten overseas doctors expressed disappointment because they had not been able to get into the specialty of their choice.[15]

Junior doctors have to compete for jobs, and they are required to move around. Career progress depends on the sequence of posts regarding amount and quality of training, as well as on the choice of specialty. SHOs are still largely left to their own devices in tackling a training programme that accumulates to career progress.

The medical job market is very complex. There exist hierarchies of hospitals by type and geographical location, and there exists a very marked hierarchy of medical specialties regarding prestige and popularity. In addition, informal networks for promotion impair open competition. All professions have limited 'career capacity', but the question is whether the established structures and procedures are at least fair and, in the case of medical practitioners, ultimately in the interest of patient care.

The most sought after training posts are in teaching hospitals. In the current recruitment crisis, teaching hospitals experience fewer difficulties because the 'combination of their ability to provide "in house" rotations and their general reputation are major advantages'.[39] Some general district hospitals are able to offer in-house rotations, but others have to share it with other trusts.[39] Teaching hospitals are considered to be the domain of the 'old boy network'. Patronage is neither unique to the medical profession nor is it confined to teaching hospitals, but it is very marked there. Many jobs are not externally advertised. Isobel Allen[70] and the reports of the King's Fund Equal Opportunities Task Force[71,72] emphasised the prevailing importance of personal references and patronage. Though widely accepted or seen as 'natural' by *all* doctors (patronage in medicine is not unique to Britain either), it puts non-white doctors, as well as women, at a general disadvantage, and they are increasingly aware of this.[70]

Geography too is decisive. Hospitals in less attractive areas depend even more on overseas recruits. For example, recruitment difficulties of the James Paget Hospital in Great Yarmouth, which serves a basic population of 220,000 – and twice that figure during the summer holidays – were reported in the national press (see, for example *The Guardian* of 23 April 1996). The results of an Equal Opportunities monitoring exercise in 1998 (see Tables 2.4 and 2.4a) reveal the very high proportion of non-white doctors: one-third of all doctors, and nearly 100 per cent in the sub-consultant career grades as compared to over 60 per cent nationally.

Table 2.4 Equal opportunities monitoring of medical staff by race and gender (Acute trusts)

Total numbers: 208

Trust ID 5

| | Current Medical Workforce | | | | Doctors appointed in 1997 | | | |
| | Ethnic Composition | | Gender Composition | | Ethnic Composition | | Gender Composition | |
Category	Ethnic Minority %	White %	Male %	Female %	Ethnic Minority %	White %	Male %	Female %
All Medical Staff	33	67	80	20	40	60	80	20
Consultant	19	81	85	15	20	80	60	40
Associate Specialist	97	3	82	18	100	0	100	0
Hospital Practitioner	1.50	98.5	100	0	–	–	–	–
Staff Grade	99	1	78	22	50	50	100	0
Specialist Registrar	50	50	49	51	37	53	33	67
Senior House Officer	43	57	78	22	44	56	88	12
House Officer	38	62	62	38	32	68	63	37

Source: James Paget Hospital, Great Yarmouth

Table 2.4a Analysis of doctors in the three largest specialties

	Male %	Female %	Ethnic Minority %	White %
Anaesthetics				
Consultants	77	23	8	92
Specialist Registrars	66	34	66	34
General Surgery				
Consultants	100	0	38	62
Specialist Registrars	66	34	60	34
Orthopaedics				
Consultants	100	0	20	80
Specialist Registrars	0	0	0	0

Source: James Paget Hospital, Great Yarmouth

Locum posts

It is hardly surprising that overseas doctors 'are more likely to have unplanned training experiences'.[43] In both social surveys,[14,15] in the supplementary Calman Report[43] and in the NAHAT survey,[39] much attention has been paid to the frequent locum experience of overseas doctors that is detrimental to their training and career progress. This is also addressed in a recent report of the Audit Commission, *Cover story: the use of locum doctors in NHS trusts.*[73] The majority of locum doctors have qualified overseas.

'Locums', although expensive, are frequently employed. They occupy, as a rule, temporary vacancies arising from multiple causes, for example holidays, study and maternity leave, or when trainees leave earlier than expected. Locums are also employed to circumvent the formal appointment procedures, especially for consultants. Since the nature of the work in hospitals implies, at times, urgency to the degree of despair, time-consuming appointment procedures are also an obstacle for proper replacement amongst the training grades.

A chain of locum posts is certainly the ultimate 'unplanned training experience' and not recognised as specialist training. With luck, doctors may be able to find locum posts that provide useful training, and it has been proposed to rename in such cases locum appointments to mark the difference. But it is agreed that '[a] planned training programme could not be largely or solely based on *fixed-term training appointments.* Further, such appointments could not be retrospectively identified as recognised for training.'[43]

Staff grade and associate specialist doctors

To retain doctors in the hospital service who had, for various reasons, no prospects of promotion to the consultant grade, sub-consultant career paths were created in the 1980s: the staff grade doctor and the associate specialist. The numbers of staff grade doctors have increased dramatically. In 1991, there were only 490 staff grades[74] whereas in 1999 there were 3640 of them in England.[1]

About two-thirds of doctors in both grades are overseas-qualified. However, for example in the Trent Region, over 70 per cent of doctors in the staff grade are overseas-qualified.[74] Dissatisfaction is widespread in the staff grade and most prevalent in male overseas graduates. Most have not buried their career aspirations. In the Oxford deanery, more than 50 per cent hold an 'eligible' postgraduate diploma and wish for promotion.[75] Involuntary and unpaid involvement in teaching is one major source of dissatisfaction, and findings from the study in the Trent Region suggest 'that the relationships between staff grade doctors [who wish to return to training] and the [accrediting] royal colleges are poor'.[74]

The principle of a sub-consultant career as such is contested. There is currently a heated debate because a planning error of training numbers occurred in obstetrics and gynaecology, which made a substantial number of fully-qualified specialist registrars 'redundant' and put their careers at risk because of a six-month cut-off period between obtaining CCST and promotion to the consultant grade.[76] It demonstrates that the solution of junior doctors' problems at every level are inextricably linked to the (promised) extension of the consultant grade and the change of consultants' working practice.

Specialty differences

The 'pecking order' of medical specialties is in many ways detrimental to the medical profession. Surgery, perceived as exciting and glamorous, ranks top, followed by general medicine, whereas psychiatry and geriatrics are the least popular specialties. Surgery is still largely the preserve of white male candidates.[70] Its popularity is ever increasing,[41] apparently rightly so since surgeons are 'the most happy with their choice and the least stressed' among all hospital doctors.[77] The high proportion of non-white doctors in general surgery in the James Paget Hospital only reflects its extraordinary recruitment difficulties (see Table 2.4).

In the past at least, psychiatry and geriatrics have been shunned by white British doctors to such an extent that both specialties offered real career opportunities to overseas doctors. Psychiatry is also one of the specialties with a high proportion of women[78] – in 1999, 32 per cent of consultants and 51 per cent in the registrar group.

In 1983 and 1985, 46 per cent of consultants in geriatrics and 26 per cent of consultants in psychiatry were born overseas.[15] The investigation of the Commission for Racial Equality into the appointment of NHS consultants and senior registrars reveals that the pattern has hardly changed, except that in psychiatry and geriatrics promotion may have also become difficult.[79]

In 1999, of all staff in geriatrics, 38 per cent were non-white doctors and 30 per cent of the consultants were non-white. In general psychiatry, the figures are 35.5 per cent of all staff and 24 per cent in the consultant group. Both specialties are medically attractive. Geriatrics is understood to be an extension of general medicine, and working conditions have certainly improved compared to the earlier decades of the NHS. General (adult) psychiatry is also chosen because of the large spectrum of diseases, however those actively avoiding general psychiatry do so because of poor resources, high workload and poor working conditions.[80]

Another 'stigmatised' specialty is Accident and Emergency (A&E), in which recruitment difficulties are currently exacerbated because a six-month stint in A&E is no longer required to pass the Royal College of Surgeons examinations. But, like geriatrics and psychiatry, it was an unpopular specialty previously. In 1983 and 1985, 35 per cent of consultants in A&E were born overseas, an even higher percentage than in psychiatry.[15] The prestige is low because of the patients it attracts, especially in inner city casualty departments. It is unpopular because of the excessive workload and the intensified stress through particular lack of supervision at night.[81]

As Hale and Hudson point out, it is not only illogical to leave the care of traumatised patients to the most junior doctors, but even more so 'to leave such patients in the care of overseas doctors who have a limited or heavily accented command of English, and who, for cultural reasons, lack an intuitive understanding of the patients the casualty department typically present'.[81] This is said not least with regard to the risks of verbal abuse and physical violence involved for the doctor. Language and culture-based communication problems have been a concern, and a source of criticism, in psychiatry and geriatrics too.

Prejudice and discrimination

Although the disadvantages of non-white doctors arise to a large extent from the shortcomings of the system in which they work, there is enough evidence that prejudice and discrimination exist as an additional burden. Prejudice influences selection in the context of training and recruitment, and discrimination is expressed in the fact that non-white doctors are clustered in the lower ranks.

A specific anti-Asian sentiment in British society[82] is reflected among hospital doctors. Doctors from India, Pakistan, Bangladesh or Sri Lanka and British-born, and qualified doctors of the same ethnic origin, are the largest identifiable group among non-white doctors that is affected by racial prejudice and discrimination. This starts at selection of applicants for British medical schools,[57,83] it is an adverse factor during postgraduate medical training, and it remains one afterwards.

Attitudes and climate of opinion

Although a very long time has elapsed since David Smith[14] published his survey report, it is still the most substantial and systematic effort so far that has probed into the climate of opinion.

Smith's analysis of attitudes towards Asian doctors is impressive. Now, as then, Asians, the majority of overseas doctors, are perceived as a group. Smith uncovers a considerable 'unanimity of opinion' and points to the unfortunate influence of the Merrison Report. Therein, it was stated that 'there are substantial numbers of overseas doctors whose skill and the care they offer fall below that generally acceptable in this country.'[14]

Smith concludes that the quasi-official generalisations in the Merrison Report, followed immediately by the withdrawal of reciprocity from Indian medical schools, were presumably factors that have influenced individual doctors more than their personal experience. Country of qualification and ethnic group are regarded as an indicator of competence, they influence doctors' judgement of their colleagues, and are used quite openly as selection criteria. The specific medical prejudice typical for a majority of white British doctors (60 per cent) is summarised as follows:

> Their view is that the general level of competence is lower among Asians, that there is among Asians a relatively high proportion of doctors who are below a minimum acceptable standard, that there is greater variation of competence among Asians, but there is not, among Asians, a relatively high proportion who are outstandingly good doctors.[14]

From results in an earlier study on employers at plant level,[84] Smith is able to compare them with doctors:

> Compared with employers, doctors are much readier to make generalisations about the competence of those belonging to a particular ethnic group, and the generalisations that they make are much more strongly critical. For a profession that is trained to take a cautious and analytic approach, this amounts to a very forthright expression of views.[14]

Whilst all grades of British-qualified hospital doctors are strongly critical of Asians, 'consultants are markedly more critical than those at lower ranks';[14] actually, a majority of 81 per cent. There is also an age-split, with 50 per cent of the youngest age group (under-30s) being critical of Asians compared to 78 per cent of the older ones. The study reveals such a strong prejudice that Smith argues 'it seems likely that [these] views have had, and will have, an effect on appointment committees' and 'that doctors make such generalisations so readily that to set them aside would require a considerable conscious effort'.[14]

At the same time, only a fifth of *all* doctors believe that this amounts to discrimination on racial or ethnic grounds. It is perceived as strictly 'medical', based on the strong belief in the superiority of British medical schools, with basic training in other white Anglophone countries ranking in the upper middle of the perceived pecking order, and the Indian subcontinent and Middle East (also Africa) lowest: 'thus, ethnic and racial differences tend to coincide with alleged differences in the value of basic training.'[14]

To my knowledge, this embarrassing attitude analysis was not explicitly discussed in the medical press. Richard Smith,[85] the editor of the *BMJ*, dedicated an article to the study without referring to aspects of attitudes and prejudice. However, the social survey on overseas doctors commissioned by the CRE built on these insights, which had 'confirmed the worst suspicions'.[15] Given the evidence from the nineties, all this is not a phenomenon of the past. As this survey revealed for the first time, the prejudice against Asian doctors is not confined to the overseas-qualified ones among them.

Discrimination of job applicants

Currently, prejudice surfaces most clearly with regard to locum doctors. There is 'widespread belief that locum doctors are of lower quality than permanent staff'.[73] A job advertisement at the Stafford General District Hospital attracted 224 applicants, of whom only three were UK-qualified and a further five had qualified in other EEA countries.[86] One is tempted to speculate whether a repeated survey on attitudes would still lead to such forthright expressed views. But undervaluing of medical qualifications and experience gained overseas remains an issue, not least with respect to the accreditation practice of the royal medical colleges.[79] This is also addressed in the NAHAT survey,[39] if from a different angle.

Individual doctors' prejudice may not be that strong and articulated. Job applicants' chances to overcome it are best at interviews. Discrimination starts at the stage of shortlisting. Names alone appear to be a 'sufficient' selection criterion.[87] A Nigerian doctor, Eunice Modupe Oluwemimo Abimbola Laleye, successfully uses the 'French-sounding' shortened form of her name, Eunice Laleye.[87] Anonymising medical school applications, however, has proved not to be such a success.[88]

Esmail and Everington took personal risks to provide evidence of racial discrimination.[89,90] They hold consultants collectively accountable for discriminatory practices. It is indeed they who shortlist and decide in interview panels, they assess juniors, report on them, and recommend them to other consultants. Juniors depend formally and informally on consultants for career progress.

Prejudice and discrimination as stress factors

Stress is pronounced in junior doctors for many reasons.[91,92,93] Consultants' behaviour can be an important source of stress. According to Hale and Hudson, consultants 'differ sharply' in their behaviour towards juniors. It varies between the extremes of 'surrogate parent' and functional treatment as 'another pair of hands', and 'education by humiliation' of juniors may not be as rare as one might be inclined to assume.[81] The hardships of the 'rite of passage' junior doctors have to go through allow for it, and some perceive consultants' powers over them as 'potentially despotic'.[81] Bullying and intimidation are experienced during medical training and need to be addressed as unacceptable behaviour.[94]

All this has a special meaning for overseas doctors, for whom it must be even more difficult to 'read' the behaviour of their seniors and colleagues correctly. Hale and Hudson suggest that an appreciable proportion of overseas doctors' distress may spring from 'unresolved ambiguities, embedded in the fine grain of culture and language'.[81] But sometimes they spring from obvious 'hostile situations … leading to waves of misery, homesickness, and resentment'.[91]

Hale and Hudson[81] describe in the 'Tavistock study' on junior doctors, which is a qualitative study, what must be the worst scenario. They focus on those qualified in Africa, the Middle or Far East, who have come as political refugees or for economic reasons, lacking sufficient command of English, and whose foreign appearance and self-presentation forms a considerable barrier:

> *In one sense, the difficulties encountered by such doctors are those of economic migrants and political refugees everywhere, and they can be construed as forming an 'under-class' within the NHS. They are assumed to have been relatively poorly trained in their home countries, are accepted on sufferance, and are allowed to fill only the jobs of lowest prestige.*[81]

Unfortunately, as a pattern, this is not confined to refugee doctors. Therefore, a recent initiative to help refugee doctors *into* work may not help them sufficiently *at* work[95,96,97] on the relevance of the UEB examinations for refugee doctors as the recommended alternative to the PLAB test.

Is the prevailing prejudice founded?

One has to ask the question whether the prejudice against Asian and other non-white doctors has some substance. Language deficiencies and cultural differences account for a certain amount of difficulties but should be anticipated. It is not helpful to deny that various problems may arise from the use of foreign doctors in any health service, but more important is how employers and colleagues respond to it. The 'small number of responders' to the NAHAT survey suggesting 'that for some posts the cultural background [of overseas doctors], if very different from that in the UK, could be an issue' may be the better employers.[39]

A common standard of assessment before entering the service can improve the situation but hardly eradicate all difficulties. The deeper-seated ones require conscious adaptation, as the example of Dr Sawran Singh highlights:

> *The other unsettling experience was the feeling of a loss of power that I initially experienced at work. In India doctors are at the top of the medical hierarchy, and the concept of consensus by a multidisciplinary team, many of whose members are in the lower ranks, is virtually non-existent. Multidisciplinary team meetings therefore seemed an annoying waste of time, besides allowing inaccuracies and diagnostic laxity. In addition, the Mental Health Act seemed an uncomfortable constraint as I was used to justifying my decisions only to my senior colleagues ... There is a lot that I have learnt in my two years and much that I now admire. The same multidisciplinary consensus method that I initially resented now seems admirable for the holistic care it provides ... I am glad that I came to Britain, to learn as much as to unlearn.[98]*

This quote emphasises the positive aspects of his experience, whereas his surprise and anger as a dedicated psychiatrist about the negative image of his chosen specialty remains unrelieved.

Focusing on difficulties of language and cultural adaptation easily blurs the picture and results in 'problematising' whole groups. These doctors are not used in the hospital service for being unsatisfactory, dysfunctional or disruptive. On the contrary, their use is an established solution to service needs. The NAHAT survey,[39] in particular, documents that trusts readily resort to recruiting overseas doctors. As far as overseas doctors may pose a problem, poor performance is much more related to the effects of a medical fringe existence that many experience during and after training, resulting in low job satisfaction, frustration and resentment, impairing standards and humanity of patient care.

Under conditions of long working hours to the extent of sleep deprivation exacerbated by poor facilities especially with regard to meals and accommodation for resident SHOs, junior doctors have admitted hostility towards patients 'such as the wish that a difficult patient would die rather than cause more work'.[63] In this respect, most overseas doctors may be better equipped for survival than their British colleagues:

> The prime virtue among [overseas doctors], men and women alike, is strength of will. They come from cultures where adversity is attributed to fate, and where anxieties are bottled up. As one said to us, 'our nature and build-up is different from the people here. What I can stand is 20 times, 50 times, what will give a doctor a nervous breakdown here.'[81]

Is this one of the more hidden reasons why they are so popular with the NHS? *

The issue of 'racism' is laden with contradiction and paradox. It is illuminating to compare David Smith's[14] attitude analysis of a strong tradition of the medical profession closely connected with self-regulation. Generally, doctors tend to turn a blind eye on under-performing or troubled colleagues, sometimes with lethal consequences for the patient, as highlighted by several scandals in the most recent past, in particular the Bristol case in 1998. Doctors are portrayed as 'quick to forgive', and 'non-criticism' is the norm.[99,100] How should one compare, for example, language difficulties? Seen in this context, the rather unforgiving criticism, especially of Asian doctors, is downright astonishing and can only be explained with white doctors' stubborn refusal to really accept non-white doctors as their peers.

---

* According to a later study by Hale and Hudson, overseas doctors have higher rates of suicide than other groups (Hale R, Hudson L. Doctors in trouble. In: Firth-Cozens J, Payne R L, eds. *Stress in health professionals*. Chichester: Wiley, pp. 219–30). This statement, referring to a study by Richings et al., is unfounded. Richings *et al.* have taken care to point out that only the very small sample of *female* overseas doctors – not more than ten in a study based on 54 cases, and seven only within the narrow definition of suicide – had a higher rate (Richings J C, Khara G S, McDowell M. Suicide in young doctors. *British Journal of Psychiatry* 1986; 149: 475–78).

The way forward

The open controversy on overseas doctors' competence in the aftermath of the Merrison Report has ebbed away,[101] but prejudice and discrimination prevail in various ways and affect many non-white doctors. Although racism in the NHS and the medical profession is now openly acknowledged, it has not become easier to eradicate it.

As evident from the analysis presented here, the patterns of the institutional or systemically embedded racism in medicine have hardly changed since the 1970s. The 'ethnic penalty' translates into non-white doctors being clustered in service posts with limited or no prospects. What needs to be said has been said, some of it a very long time ago. Both social surveys[14,15] were largely ignored, and the debate in the medical press was the most part fragmented, casual and futile.

The impact of the Calman reforms provides a clear focus, and there is a convergence in perception and analysis, as well as a new sense of urgency, within the frame of clinical governance. Acting on the evidence and the accumulated wisdom should imply central support from the NHS Executive and, at the same time, encouragement of local initiatives. It must be assumed that steps will now be undertaken to provide SHOs with better training, and it is almost universally agreed that the successful shift to a consultant-provided hospital service is key to problem solving.

However, problem solving in the given context also requires doing away for good with any hypocrisy and equivocation regarding overseas doctors. The historic concept of 'mutual benefit', with its roots in colonial-patrimonial attitudes, is definitely superseded. Many good ideas are offered and should be taken on board, among them as a short-term action, suspension of the PLAB test, and tying entry into Britain to a secure offer of a training post.[86] Sridhar proposes the creation of an organisation akin to the Education Commission for foreign medical graduates in the US to end a situation in which too many official and professional bodies are dealing with the same individual without any of them having to take ultimate responsibility.[102]

Even in an ideal system racism can survive. If the long-overdue conscious effort to eradicate prejudice among white doctors is ever to be undertaken, a specific educational component should be 'mainstreamed' into medical school as well as postgraduate training. Ways must be found to reach the royal colleges too. The NHS must value all of its doctors. Developing a supportive culture should not be denounced as 'management speak' but should be embraced as the way ahead to confine waste and abuse of staff, for which there is a potential in any organisation, to pockets that can be easier identified and targeted for remedial or innovative action.

References

1. Department of Health. *Hospital, public health medicine and community health service medical and dental Staff in England*. London: Department of Health; Statistical Bulletin 2000/9.
2. Williams D I. Overseas doctors and the staffing structure of hospitals. *BMJ* 1985; 291: 873–76.
3. Borman E, O'Grady P. Postgraduate training. *Medical Education* 1997; 31: 3–8.
4. Lister J. The impact of overseas graduates on service and training in the United Kingdom. *New England Journal of Medicine* 1986; 315: 1038–40.
5. Heath A, McMahon D. *Education and occupational attainments: the impact of ethnic origins*. Paper 34. Centre for Research into Elections and Social Trends, February 1995.
6. Biggs J. The Goodenough Report and medical education in 50 years of the National Health Service. *Health Trends* 1998; 30: 16–19; Biggs J. Both service and training demand attention in obstetrics and gynaecology. *Hospital Medicine* 2000; 61 (9): 664–67.
7. Beecham L. No evidence of racism in GMC complaints procedures. *BMJ* 2000; 321: 133.
8. Esmail A, Everington S. Complaints may reflect racism. *BMJ* 1994; 308: 1374.
9. Esmail A, Everington S, Doyle H. Racial discrimination in the allocation of distinction awards? *BMJ* 1998; 316: 193–95.
10. Rubin P. Distinction awards and racial discrimination. *BMJ* 1998; 316: 165.
11. Bennet S, McPake B, Mills A. *Private health providers in developing countries: serving the public interest?* Zed Press: 1997.
12. Thaver I *et al.* Private practitioners in the slums of Karachi: What quality of care do they offer? *Social Science & Medicine* 1998; 46 (5): 1441–49.
13. Yesudian C A K. Behaviour of private sector in the health market of Bombay. *Health Policy and Planning* 1994; 9 (1): 72–80.
14. Smith, D. *Overseas doctors in the National Health Service*. London: Policy Studies Institute, 1980.
15. Anwar M, Ali A. *Overseas doctors: experience and expectations*. London: Commission for Racial Equality, 1987.
16. Bundred P E, Levitt C. Medical migration: who are the real losers? *Lancet* 2000; 356: 245–46.
17. Loefler J P. Medical migration. Letter. *Lancet* 2000; 356: 1196.
18. Anonymous editorial. Medical migration and inequity of health. *Lancet* 2000; 356: 177.
19. Salt J, Kitching R T. Labour migration and the work permit system in the United Kingdom. *International Migration* 1990; 28 (3): 267–78.
20. Rees T. Inheriting empire's people. In: Kubat D, ed. *The politics of migration policies*. New York; Centre for Migration Studies: 89–107.
21. Seale J R. Supply of doctors. *BMJ* 1961, Dec 9: 1554–55.
22. Webster C. *Problems of health care. The National Health Service before 1957. The health services since the war, Vol. 1*. London: HMSO, 1988.
23. Lafitte F, Squire J R. Second thoughts on the Willink Report. *Lancet* 1960; 2: 538.
24. Medical notes in Parliament. *BMJ* 1961: 1579.
25. Overseas Conference. *BMJ* 1948; July 10; Supplement 39.
26. Sandford H A. Hospitality for overseas visitors. *BMJ* 1948, April 24: 809.

27. Doctors from overseas. Editorial. *BMJ* 1969; 22 March: 729–30.
28. Department of Health. *Report of the committee of inquiry into the regulation of the medical profession* (*Merrison Report*). HMSO, 1975.
29. Agarwal S K. Overseas graduates. Letter. *BMJ* 1962; 24 February: 555–56.
30. Patel V, Araya R. Trained overseas, unable to return home: plight of doctors from developing countries. *Lancet* 1992; 339: 110–11.
31. de Cossart L. Surgical training for overseas doctors: an historical review and proposals for the future. *Annals of the Royal College of Surgeon of England* (Suppl.) 1999; 81: 180–81.
32. Richards T. The overseas doctors training scheme: failing expectations. *BMJ* 1994; 308: 1627–31.
33. Caldicott F, McClelland R J, Robertson J. Overseas doctors training scheme. Letter. *BMJ* 1994; 309: 811.
34. Gupta R, Lingham S. The overseas doctors training scheme. *BMJ Classified* 1999; 9 January: 2–3.
35. Welsh C. Training overseas doctors in the United Kingdom. *BMJ* 2000; 321: 253–54.
36. Thompson J. UK immigration for overseas doctors. *Lancet* 1994; 344: 74–75.
37. Macdonald N J. UK immigration for overseas doctors. Letter. *Lancet* 1994; 344: 74–75.
38. Lowry S, Cope H. Postgraduate training for overseas doctors in Britain. *BMJ* 1994; 308: 1624–27.
39. National Association of Health Authorities and Trusts. *Hospital and community health services medical recruitment survey.* NAHAT, 1996.
40. Clark J S. Young Doctors. Letter. *BMJ* 1948; 28 Feb: 408.
41. Goldacre M J, Davidson J M, Lambert T W. Career choices at the end of the pre-registration year of doctors who qualified in the United Kingdom in 1996. *Medical Education* 1999; 33 (12): 882–89; Comment: 872–73.
42. Lambert T W, Goldacre M J, Parkhouse J. Intentions of newly qualified doctors to practise in the United Kingdom. *BMJ* 1997; 314: 1591–92.
43. Department of Health. *Hospital doctors: training for the future. A supplementary report by the working group commissioned to consider the implications for overseas doctors arising from the principal report.* (Supplementary Calman Report). London: Department of Health, 1995.
44. Smith R. Overseas doctors: coming to Britain. *BMJ* 1981; 282: 1045–47.
45. Beecham L. MPs say NHS consultants should do no private work. *BMJ*; 321: 133.
46. Audit Commission. *The doctors' tale: the work of hospital doctors in England and Wales.* London: Audit Commission, 1995.
47. Harris E, Ferreira, P. Training senior house officers. *BMJ* 1994; 314: 692–93.
48. UK Health Departments, Joint Consultants' Committee and Chairmen of Regional Health Authorities. *Hospital medical staffing: achieving a balance – plan for action.* London: Department of Health, 1987.
49. NHS Management Executive. *Junior doctors: the new deal.* London: Department of Health, 1991.
50. Department of Health. *Hospital doctors: training for the future. The report of the working group on specialist medical training. (Calman Report).* London: Department of Health, 1993.
51. Dowie R, Longman M. Staffing of hospitals: future needs, future provision. *BMJ* 1999; 30 October: 1193

52. Department of Health. Statistical Bulletin 1998; 27: 3–5.

53. Department of Health. Statistical Bulletin 1995; 14: 5.

54. Clay B. Medical workforce and the gender shift. *Hospital Medicine* 1999; 60 (12): 901–03.

55. McManus I C, Sproston K A. Women in hosptial. Medicine in the United Kingdom: glass ceiling, preference, prejudice or cohort effect? *Journal for Epidemiology and Community Health* 2000; 54 (1): 10–16.

56. Goldberg I, Paice E. Flexible specialist training compared with full-time training. *Hospital Medicine* 1999; 60 (4): 286–90.

57. McManus I C. Factors affecting likelihood of applicants being offered a place in medical schools in the United Kingdom in 1996 and 1997: retrospective study. *BMJ* 1998; 317: 1111–116.

58. Godwin R J, Biggs J S G, Bulstrode C J. The new hospital specialist training: seen dimly before the dawn. *Medical Education* 1995; 29: 322–27.

59. Paice E, Aitken M, Cowan G, Heard S. Trainee satisfaction before and after the Calman reforms of specialist training: questionnaire survey. *BMJ* 2000; 320: 832–36.

60. Leaver P K. Don't take your eye off the ball. *Hospital Medicine* 1998; 59 (11): 885–86.

61. Paice E, Leaver P. Improving the training of senior house officers. *BMJ* 1999; 318: 1022–23.

62. Audit Commission.*The doctors' tale continued: the audits of hospital medical staffing.* London: Audit Commission, 1996.

63. McKee M, Black N. Does the current use of junior doctors in the United Kingdom affect the quality of medical care? *Social Science & Medicine* 1992; 34/5: 549–58.

64. Campling E A, Devlin H B, Hoile R W, Lum J N. *The report of the national enquiry into perioperative deaths 1991/1992.* London: Royal College of Surgeons of England, 1993.

65. Sharif K, Afnan M. Quality control in postgraduate training. *BMJ Classified* 1998; 9 May: 2.

66. Cawley R H. Overseas graduates and the MRC Psych. *Bulletin of the Royal College of Psychiatrists* 1986; 10: 60–63.

67. White P. Why do overseas trainees fail? *Bulletin of the Royal College of Psychiatrists* 1986; 10: 59–63.

68. Paice E, West G. Senior house officer training: are overseas graduates treated differently? *British Journal of Hospital Medicine* 1995; 53: 203–06.

69. Department of Health. *A health service for all the talents: developing the NHS workforce.* London: HMSO, 2000.

70. Allen I. *Doctors' careers: a new generation.* London: Policy Studies Institute, 1994.

71. King's Fund Equal Opportunities Task Force. *Racial equality: hospital doctors selection procedures.* London: King's Fund,1990.

72. King's Fund Equal Opportunities Task Force. *The work of the equal opportunities task force 1986–1990. A final report.* London: King's Fund, 1991.

73. Audit Commission. *Cover story: the use of locum doctors in NHS trusts.* London: Audit Commision, 1999.

74. Baker M, Williams J, Petchy R, Flett A. Staff grade doctors and the consultant ladder: falling off of stepping off? *Hospital Medicine* 1999; 60 (11): 824–28.

75. Jefferis A, Davies G, Tunbridge M. Staff grades and associate specialists: their continuing professional development and aspirations. *Hospital Medicine* 1998; 59 (11): 887–91.

76. Wright C S W. Specialist training in obstetrics and gynaecology: have we got it wrong? *Hospital Medicine* 1999; 60 (4): 291–93.

77. Firth-Cozens J, Lema V C, Firth R A. Specialty choice, stress and personality: their relationship over time. *Hospital Medicine* 1999; 60 (10): 751–53.

78. Tait A, Platt J. Women consultants, their background and training: some myths explored. *Medical Education* 1995; 29: 372–76.

79. Commission for Racial Equalitiy. *Appointing NHS consultants and senior registrars: report of a formal investigation*. London: CRE, 1996.

80. Davies M, Schlich T. Determining whether senior and specialist registrars choose or reject a career in general adult psychiatry. A survey of factors. *Psychiatric Bulletin* 1999; 23: 607–09.

81. Hale R, Hudson L.The Tavistock study on young doctors: report of the pilot phase. *British Journal of Hospital Medicine* 1992; 47: 452–64.

82. Modood T, Berthoud R. *Ethnic minorities in Britain: diversity and disadvantage*. London: Policy Studies Institute, 1997.

83. McManus I C, Richards P, Winder B C, Proston K A, Styles V. Medical school applicants from ethnic minority groups: identifying if and when they are disadvantaged. *BMJ* 1995; 310: 496–500.

84. Smith D. *Racial disadvantage in employment*. PEP No. 544; 1974.

85. Smith R. Overseas doctors: future training and employment. *BMJ* 1981; 282: 1214–15.

86. Sridhar M. What is the future for training of overseas graduates? *BMJ* 2000; 321: 307.

87. British Medical Association. *The future of our doctors: a conference on racial equality in the NHS – are we getting the best person for the job?* BMA, 1998.

88. Lumb B, Vail A. Difficulties with anonymous shortlisting of medical school applicants and its effects on candidates with non-European names; prospective cohort study. *BMJ* 2000; 320: 82–85

89. Esmail A, Everington S. Racial discrimination against doctors from ethnic minorities. *BMJ* 1993; 306: 691–92

90. Esmail A, Everington S. Asian doctors still being discriminated against. *BMJ* 1997; 314: 1619.

91. Luck C. Reducing stress among junior doctors. *BMJ Classified* 2000; 28 October: 2–3.

92. Herzberg J. Can doctors self-manage stress? *Hospital Medicine* 2000; 61 (4): 272–74.

93. Moss F, Paice E. Getting things right for doctors in training. In: Firth-Cozens J, Payne R, eds. *Stress in health professionals*. Chichester: Wiley, 1999.

94. Hicks B. Time to stop bullying and intimidation. *Hospital Medicine* 2000; 61 (6): 428–31.

95. Mayor S. UK helps refugee doctors to practice in NHS. *BMJ* 2000; 321: 1178.

96. Cheeroth S, Goraya A. Refugee doctors. *BMJ Classified* 2000; 21 October: 2–3.

97. Eastwood J B *et al.* A training course for the UEB examination. *Journal of the Royal College of Physicians of London* 1999; 33 (2): 165–67.

98. Singh S. Cultural adjustment and the overseas trainee. *BMJ* 1994; 308: 1169.

99. Lens P, van der Wal G. *Problem doctors: a conspiracy of silence*. Amsterdam: JOS Press, 1997.

100. Smith R. All doctors are problem doctors. *BMJ* 1997; 314: 841–42.

101. Smith R. Overseas doctors: diminishing controversy. *BMJ* 1989; 298: 1441–44.

102. Sridhar M. Overseas trainee debacle. *Hospital Doctor* 2000; 5 October.

Chapter 3

The next generation, the problematic children: a personal story

Shahid Dadabhoy

He that would make his own liberty secure must guard even his enemy from oppression; for if he violates this duty, he establishes a precedent that will reach to himself.

Thomas Paine

The annoying truth

I think I annoyed someone once by telling the truth.

> *'What nationality are you?' asked the locum registrar from the Continent.*
> *'British,' I replied.*
> *'No ... but where were you born?' he continued.*
> *'Why, Scotland,' I naively answered.*
> *'No, no, but what I meant was ... what nationality are your parents?' he again impatiently asked.*
> *'British,' I replied, suddenly understanding his train of thought.*
> *'No, no, no, where is home?' he pressed me getting rather annoyed now.*
> *'Chingford, that's in London,' came my swift retort.*

Moments like this are priceless, but this got me thinking. Why was it so important for this chap to know what my racial origins were? More importantly, what did this have to do with the patient I was presenting on the ward round?

It is sufficient to say that this incident had a profound effect on me. I suddenly started to examine my own identity, its interface with my work in the NHS and ultimately the unproductive multi-system disease – racism – that has infected it at all levels. How did I, as a second-generation person of Pakistani origin, fit into all of this?

The point of reference

The simple and alarming revelation was that I didn't really fit in anywhere and certainly not into any neat category. To date, practically all the work on racial discrimination in the NHS has been on first-generation people from minority ethnic groups. Their sons and daughters, like myself, didn't get mentioned anywhere. Taxonomy of my first-generation peers and forebears is simplistic, using many euphemisms such as 'overseas qualified' and 'South Asian'. My black and Asian second-generation peers and I simply disappeared. Most of us were, and are, British citizens born in the UK. If it were not for our names and possibly appearance, on paper we blended in. There was at best a naivety, or at worst dishonesty, that if you were UK-born and educated, racism could not exist for this second generation. So why bother examining their situation?

Any journey needs a point of reference. This is my perspective. I am a general practitioner, a doctor, but I hope that I see the NHS landscape similarly to my other health worker colleagues. Born in the United Kingdom, the son of an Asian doctor who, after crossing continents, came to work for the NHS in the late sixties, I was surprisingly naive, like many of my second-generation peers, on issues of cultural and ethnic racism. Although my cultural and religious experiences were critical to me, I fundamentally saw myself as being British. When I was asked about a recent trip to Pakistan, described as 'home' by the questioner, I was frankly confused. My home was Britain; I'd never lived anywhere else and certainly never stayed in Pakistan for more than a few months. Ironically, I had no rights to gain Pakistani citizenship, even if I had sought it.

Collaborating with the Sepoy army

I had colluded with racism for a long time and denied that it applied to me. I had nothing to prove and had never lived in an openly racially stratified, colonial country as my parents had. To cite racism when not getting services or jobs, for example, was to appear weak; it was a fall-back position.

At my school there were a large number of Jewish children and we learned about the Holocaust, but I was never taught that this lesson from history had any relevance to all countries and all peoples, including the UK. It is bizarre that sub-consciously I was all too aware that racism in British society existed, but my denial was a manifestation of the disbelief that it could apply to me. To someone with similar qualifications, schooling and hobbies, I wondered how racism could exist. My schooling was at the beginning of the Thatcher years, when the days of the National Front were waning, rediscovered as xenophobia and racism; this appears to have found a haven in the prevailing political climate ever since.

In rugby and football, I supported Scotland (by accident the home country of my birth) and happily failed Norman Tebbit's 'cricket test' by supporting Pakistan. When the FIFA World Cup was on, I supported Algeria, the only good Muslim side playing. Watching matinee movies (when I wasn't learning the Koran), I was embarrassed and ashamed by the portrayal of non-white characters. They bore no resemblance to non-white people that I knew. On television and cinema, people from ethnic minorities were usually portrayed as victims waiting to be rescued by the white man from other non-whites, comic sidekicks or the evil enemy. The message to the young was that those wearing a turban, with a strange accent or swarthy of skin, were either evil or stupid.

On making career choices, the NHS, to anyone from a minority ethnic background, was, and still is, superficially tame. To many from an Asian background, including myself, seeking a career as a professional in public life, the NHS was the only institution that seemed to offer a worthwhile career. To me it looked like some great multiethnic volunteer army. In my case, my father worked for the NHS, as did his friends. Even in the then frankly racist television programming, you could at least see Asian and black people as doctors and nurses. You never saw people from minority ethnic backgrounds in the media, as an Oxbridge academic, barrister, judge, police officer, senior civil servant or politician. (A situation that unfortunately is still far too evident.)

Unfortunately, the fact that an organisation has many people from minority ethnic communities working for it does not necessarily mean that it values them. My parents' perception was that a medical career was attainable. I was given their blessing. The European colonial powers named their white-officered native-subject troops as *Askaris* or *Sepoys*. After many years, I have come to the conclusion that the multiethnic organisation I so admired from afar was probably a *Sepoy* army. Perhaps the safe bet was not so safe after all.

Getting into this career refuge at the level desired in the NHS was, and still is, pretty difficult. Indeed for many the problem commences in the school system. To one of my peers, careers officers would talk of every career in the NHS *but* medicine. A great deal of debate has raged in the *British Medical Journal* (*BMJ*) over the lack of success of minority ethnic doctors applying to United Kingdom medical schools;[1,2,3] there have been claims and counter-claims. I will leave the in-depth analysis to Dr Aneez Esmail, whose specialist field this rightly is. On a personal note, I recall the BBC Panorama programme in the late 1980s, which described how a computer programme thrust applicants at St George's in south London further down shortlists if they had names that sounded non-British. My anger was that racism was literally programmed into the system. As recently as 1999, Joe Collier, who worked at St George's, described how he was branded a traitor and ostracised in the *BMJ*.[4] Ten years on, and having been through what must have seemed like a journey through hell, the very institution that had isolated him, thanked him. Suffice to say I was deeply moved by his account and empathised with the frustration that he had felt, fighting what is now described as 'institutional racism'.

A Horizon television programme in 1986, 'Doctors to Be', said more about the selection panel at St Mary's Medical School than it did about the interviewees. Medical students were to be a certain archetype – white, middle class and certainly not deviating from an accepted norm. I watched as the interviewers privately derided a working-class Welsh applicant for his regional accent and pursuits. I felt sick, wondering how I would cope. If someone was given a hard time for being Welsh, albeit white, what chance did an Asian have?

Ironically, that same year I applied to five London medical schools and was rejected by all of them. I guess that I will never know whether it was racism or not. I pondered and agonised for many years on this same question; it was the uncertainty of not knowing more than anything else. The next year, in another round of applications, I applied to a medical school that did not routinely interview all its applicants – and succeeded. Although I initially went north with a heavy heart, in years to come I looked back and decided that I had, after all, learned more about life and not just medicine.

The difficulty of getting through finals as a minority ethnic student has also been highlighted.[5] We were asked strange questions when we went for jobs. Doctors of South Asian origin will remember the stock interview question in the early 1990s: 'What do you think of Salman Rushdie? What is your opinion on Saddam Hussein?' (Most of us gave the answer we thought the questioner wanted, probably successfully, as we got the offer of the job or position we were seeking.) In retrospect, I guess we colluded; in any case, to whom would we have complained?

Undergraduate, early overexposure

What happened during medical school training was also fascinating. I started to meet, as I would unfortunately continue to throughout my medical career, overtly racist patients. Some used racist expletives, whilst others would refuse to co-operate in medical teaching sessions. What horrified me most was the reaction of teachers and fellow students.

At best, I heard the excuses I would hear later in my working life: 'you are being oversensitive … it's not their fault, it's just their generation … what do you expect?' … I'm afraid they have rights as patients'. If we challenged those views, we were branded as troublemakers. The worst feeling was generated by the total denial that anything less than acceptable behaviour had just transpired. The silence screamed injustice.

This behaviour, however, was infinitely less painful than the openly racist language from medical educators. My medical student flatmate described to me with horror how a lecturer requested that his tutorial group should call a specific telephone number for information. The lecturer said that the alternative telephone number had 'some stupid Paki' on the line. Instances like this were isolated, but the fact that this was said in front of several medical students of South Asian origin beggars belief.

More insidious was the culture itself. Fellow white students marginalised people from ethnic minorities. My first social event in Fresher's week was like the first scene in the film *Animal House*, where the two new freshmen try to join one of their college fraternities and in trying to mingle and having gone round the room, end up exactly where they started. By default I was pushed towards Asian cultural activities, partly because these were the only places where I was welcomed. To some extent, this was a blessing. I met Asians from very diverse backgrounds and experiences, some of whom became my friends for life. Paradoxically, the Asians, brought together by exclusion, represented one of the most heterogeneous social groups.

In my second year of university I went on a sponsored walk for charity through several northern British cities. It was an education. I was amazed at the other side of the British minority ethnic experience, with its poor housing and squalor, and where for the first time I saw streets and areas where no white people lived and English was seldom spoken.

Of course, I made many white friends too, but it was much harder work. Though I had lived in the same areas – listened to the same music, read the same books – when it came to socialising I realised there was a galaxy of difference between us. The rules were different, particularly for a Muslim.

There was a culture of 'all or nothing'. You either mixed with Asians or you didn't. 'Coconut', a term meaning 'dark on the outside but white on the inside', was coined for Asians who mixed in predominately white circles. I did not drink alcohol and many student activities revolved around drinking. There were things I could not eat for religious reasons. If I went to a social gathering, how could I tell the exact ingredients of everything I ate? I was also initially uncomfortable in situations where there was male–female contact such as, say, dancing. These may sound trivial, but the differences mounted up brick-by-brick to form a concrete wall that was difficult to penetrate. When I succeeded in blasting a breach, I must say that the results were very satisfying.

However, there were many that lived in their fortress of stereotypes. I was surprised to find, about three years into my medical school, that I was thought of as an extremist misogynist by those select few to whom the wall of assumptions was a refuge. According to them, any observant Muslim, by definition, had to be. Those white friends, who knew me, knew better.

Much of this 'concrete wall effect' has followed me throughout my medical career and is one of the major reasons why I became a general practitioner. In my later medical life, I noted the compelling power to force conformity with the majority white attitudes. If you worked in hospital-based medicine, to be 'in' you had to socialise with white colleagues on their terms. If you didn't, you never got trained, were denied access to certain posts, rotations and, crucially, never got an advancement. When I went to training courses at teaching hospitals in my postgraduate years, I noted, amusingly, how members of hospital teams, from consultants to house officers, started to look like clones of each other. I was reminded why I had not considered law as a career; you had to work your way into the legal profession, hobnob with the right people, and it was not what you knew but whom you knew that mattered. Now I discovered that in the NHS Sepoy army, the perception was that you had to do something similar to get career advancement.

Much of the clinical teaching in medical school was on ward rounds, led by the consultant with his team of doctors and students going from bed to bed seeing patients. Medical students were quizzed on these rounds, in the presence of both patient's and peers. I remember how a 'Jekyll and Hyde' transformation took place on ward rounds when the teaching registrar addressed the minority ethnic students and then the white students. If we screwed up we hadn't learned our stuff, and were incompetent. If they did, they were in need of more teaching. The fact that the white students went out drinking with the senior house officers and registrars helped. If everyone got humiliated, irrespective of race, then I was perversely satisfied.

It was more or less at this point that I realised that a career in hospital medicine wasn't really going to work out for me. General practice became my default pathway, even before I had qualified. I was not prepared to change who I was to be a 'good boy' and get on.

The incident described in my introduction occurred during my third year. The cumulative racism of several years had aggravated me. I decided to take some action, albeit in a small way. During a paediatric attachment, students were expected to give a short presentation on some aspect of community child care. I chose to talk about the needs of minority ethnic children. I discussed the fact that there was a lack of cultural sensitivity combined with discriminatory practices that denied access to these children, and that the onus was on the doctor dealing with a minority ethnic family to ensure that there was effective communication. My white peers reacted negatively: 'He's off again!' some said. Others felt insulted that I could even consider that they would ever discriminate against anybody. Some groaned that they wanted a 'serious medical topic', which to them this wasn't. Most saw it as a political statement, bearing no relationship to their future in medicine. Thankfully, the consultant present saw the point.

Doing the rounds

After qualification, many of the themes I encountered during my undergraduate education continued. My work took me to the Midlands, where there were more patients from ethnic minorities. A new form of racism started to emerge, which in today's terms would be regarded as 'institutionalised'. I discovered the way that the NHS treated, or rather failed to treat, its ethnic patients. Things weren't explained; if there were language problems, the attempt to get a decent medical history was neglected. The all-too-familiar assumptions followed, such as an Asian family would automatically be able to care for its elderly relative without additional help.

As a junior doctor, if any of the nurses didn't like you, because of their own racial prejudice, your life was hell. You got bleeped more often for trivial matters, when for someone else common sense would have prevailed. For non-white doctors it was the letter of the law; for white doctors it was the spirit of the law. Sometimes I had to become a 'barrack room lawyer' to maintain my sanity. I quoted nursing regulations to avoid the endless calls for yet more never-ending tasks. I reflected, subsequently, that it could never have been good for all involved, especially the patients.

I was, however, more fortunate than another black colleague on a segment of his general practice rotation in hospital medicine. He made a small error on a prescription card. Ordinarily, this was the sort of mistake that would have been brought to his attention the next time he passed through the ward – corrected then forgotten. In his case, the nurses took the prescription card to a manager, without his knowledge. Before he knew it he was suspended and faced losing his job. His consultant, who could have retrieved the situation, decided not to support him.

Lip-service was also paid to improving access to services: translators were seldom available and I found myself translating frequently for patients who were bewildered and frightened. Hospitals can be a terrifying place when you cannot communicate with those around you. This was especially true for the simple things, such as asking for a bedpan. There is a British assumption, all too often seen in the NHS, that anyone who cannot speak English is both deaf and stupid. I remember trying to speak to a Somali patient with whom the only language I shared was my bad Arabic. It was comical, but you had to make the effort for the sake of the patient.

Language was my undoing once. The police dumped a German man in the psychiatric unit I was working in, after he had committed some petty theft, on the basis that he was behaving oddly and was German. Through my O-level German it turned out, however, that he thought he was 'The Crown Prince of Denmark' and was off to New York to help Bill Clinton! The man stayed in hospital for two months whilst I negotiated through the Home Office and his psychiatrists in Germany how to get him home.

Sadly it was in the same psychiatric job that I witnessed the racist attitudes of the police. I was called to admit a young black man who, after being arrested for stealing an ice cream, had been 'sectioned'; that is to say he was going to be admitted and detained under the Mental Health Act. He was mentally unwell. At least six policemen brought this six-foot-tall man to the ward, in handcuffs. Even the police admitted that he hadn't offered any resistance and had not been violent in any way. I was, however, unprepared for the sight of this black youth, face down on the floor of the examination room, hands cuffed behind his back, surrounded by six officers and being taunted about his sexuality. When he told me he was an escort at one point, one of the officers remarked, 'Homosexual escort, eh?' and laughed. The scene was so caricatured and bizarre, it was surreal. I mentioned what I saw to colleagues, but we all felt powerless, and to be honest I still feel moments of self-revulsion from the cowardice of not taking matters further.

Familiar racism from patients continued. If I spoke to a non-English speaking minority ethnic patient in their own language I was accused of giving preferential treatment and not the equity of access I was striving for. A patient's family openly refused to allow their paralysed mother rehabilitation in Hackney because 'there were too many black people there'. Racist remarks from some white patients to black patients were common; comments such as 'her over there and them people who visit her' often resulted in some minority ethnic patients being ostracised to the periphery of the ward.

Thankfully, thus far I found myself insulated from direct physical abuse. In A&E departments I became witness to this on several occasions, as frustrated patients took their aggression out on the minority ethnic nurses and other staff – the soft target. To add insult to injury, if any action was taken against this, there were counter-claims of assault from the perpetrator. The odds were stacked in the patient's favour, and the staff member faced the 'double whammy' of internal investigations and further emotional trauma.

What I did encounter was verbal abuse, and few racist patients would not even speak to anybody who did not look Caucasian. Many of my 'first-generation' colleagues took this as an occupational hazard, riding out the storm, thinking that the patient would leave anyway, and initially, as a neophyte, I did the same. Eventually fed up with this state of affairs, I started to challenge this but found there was no mechanism to confront the patients. Verbal abuse or no verbal abuse, they still got treated. Frequently, a familiar pattern repeated itself: if the stakes were raised, the patient threatened to put in a complaint and the doctor backed off. Powerless, we resorted to the familiar tactic of 'courteous containment', as described in a series of articles in the *BMJ* in 1999.[6] Management, to avoid hassle, gave little support. The patient/ customer/client was always right. The patients had rights, we didn't. We had to humble ourselves and apologise; they just kept on abusing us.

While never denigrating the increase in patient choice or a more user-focused health service, strangely, it is frequently these 'rights' that racist patients hide behind. Health professionals have extensive codes of conduct enshrined in the very fabric of the institutions representing them. There wasn't, and there still isn't, any onus on the patient to behave in a civilised non-racist way towards health workers. What frustrates me is the lack of sanction against such behaviour. The health worker who retaliates may lose his or her job and find the incident forever on an indelible criminal record.

Then, of course, there are times when a patient making a complaint relates the perceived incompetence of a doctor or his or her communication skills to ethnicity. I, the possessor of a public school English accent, personally recall the correspondence of a patient's wife whom I had never met, who stated, 'I noticed the doctor was not a white doctor. I wonder if he could understand my husband or speak proper.' The fact that I was not English was, for her, the prime reason for my competence to be called into question. Race was the lowest common denominator.

Second-generation gate-keeper

One-fifth of general practitioners are from a minority ethnic community. One of the roles of GPs since the NHS was founded has been the so-called 'gate-keeping' role.

On joining general practice, it came as no surprise to me that racism from patients was alive and well here too. What is worryingly common is the tendency for angry white patients to accuse minority ethnic doctors of denying them their 'birthright' with respect to services, an increasing trend in the era of tacit rationing. The 'birthright' was whatever they *wanted*, not I stress, *needed*, from the NHS. As far as they were concerned, the minority ethnic GP in his gate-keeping role stood between them (the white patient) and what was their 'right'. Comments such as, 'how dare a foreigner, and a Paki at that, deny them whatever they wanted from their health service?' were frequently heard. A middle-class English pensioner blamed her woes at a hospital out-patient clinic upon 'the little brown man' (not even acknowledging in any part of her tirade that he was a doctor) I had sent her to see. This was even more surprising as it was mentioned in my presence. Racism, not the inadequacy of service or resources, was the prime reason the NHS failed in this instance.

Many minority ethnic general practitioners work in deprived and low socio-economic class, inner city areas. Racist violence and verbal abuse can be part of life for these doctors who, ironically, hold together primary care services in these areas on a shoestring. In 1994, one inner city South Asian Birmingham GP provoked outrage when he planned to screen his prospective patients for racist views. The story was all over the BBC regional news. I understood, sympathised, but became even more outraged when the medical institutions distanced themselves from this. Although the Birmingham GP was a first-generation 'overseas' doctor, he had come to the same conclusion as many of the second-generation doctors that we had to 'put up with it'. Of course there was no reason why he had to put up with the racist behaviour of patients. It was brave enough to make a stand, but the institutions that represented him badly let him down.

In late summer of 2000, Dr Liam Fox, Shadow Health Secretary, dropped a bombshell. He suggested that overseas doctors should be subjected to language tests, implying that patients were at risk. Fast on the heels of a Conservative Party attempt to challenge so-called 'bogus' asylum seekers, it unfortunately struck a resonant chord with the darker forces of British society and denigrated several decades of achievements by minority ethnic doctors. I was incensed enough to write to a national newspaper stating that nice white doctors with perfect English could do far more damage to their minority ethnic patients than the reverse. To me it was as if the myth of the intrinsic fallibility of minority ethnic doctors had found credibility in political life. It also proved to me that Liam Fox, as a doctor himself, knew absolutely nothing about how the NHS worked or perhaps, more worryingly, knew all too well but was willing to use minority ethnic doctors as a whipping post for political gain. Instead of getting recognition for their immensely important contribution to the health service, the minority ethnic doctors were getting the opposite.

Apprentice general practitioners are termed 'GP registrars'. We usually met in a weekly teaching session. When I started my GP training, of the ten registrars present eight were from ethnic minorities. Nearly all of them were former hospital doctors, who had impressive credentials outside of primary care and were more experienced than myself. All had hit the 'concrete ceiling' in hospital-based medical careers. In my own registrar group, of the four course organisers, two were white, the other two Asian. All of them were enlightened, and championed the registrars. In this 'rainbow fraternity' I felt secure. We socialised on an equal footing. The rules from medical school had disappeared. I regret that all this lasted so briefly. Inevitably we moved on to the harsh world of general practice and were unable to recapture the magic.

Through my networks of colleagues I found out that many minority ethnic GP registrars faced problems with their GP trainers, their supposed mentors. One black registrar confessed that she could not do anything right. The last straw for her was when she ended up being told off for drinking Coca-Cola directly from the can at a practice meeting, a humiliating experience in front of the entire practice.

I heard of situations where there were two registrars, one white the other non-white, the old game of 'good doctor/bad doctor' was played. The non-white doctor was always denigrated for being less than adequate compared to his or her white peer. General practice training and certification relies heavily on the relationship between the registrar and his or her trainer. In fact, the test of competence relies heavily on the trainer's report. If your trainer did not like you, you were doomed.

Racism in the NHS institutions: the glacial pace of change

So far I have discussed the topic of racism at the NHS–patient interface, and have only mentioned the medical establishment in a cursory manner. The institutions have claimed that since racism is endemic in society, *ergo* it is only natural that it should exist within the NHS. To me, a second-generation doctor, this is about as convincing a defence as 'I was only obeying orders.'

In February 1997, the British Medical Association (BMA) organised a conference on racism. It was designed for the BMA to lead a systematic attack on the ingrained attitudes and prejudices that underpinned the discriminatory practices within the health professions. The 'glacial pace of change is unacceptable,' said Sir Donald Irvine, President of the General Medical Council.[7] For those of us whose careers could not wait for the glacier to melt, the *BMJ* included an article in its career section on how to outflank racism in the NHS when applying for posts.[8] I was initially horrified because it pandered to the *status quo*, but the pragmatic part of my mind understood the premise. Unfortunately, although second-generation doctors were promised a thaw, the speed of change finally speeded up through a tragedy, completely unrelated to the NHS.

The murder of Stephen Lawrence in 1993, a black second-generation teenager, followed by the inept, negligent and bungled investigation by the Metropolitan Police and the tenacious fight by his parents for justice, culminated in a public inquiry and subsequent publication of the Macpherson Report. The document that emerged legitimised the phrase 'institutional racism'.[9] I jumped for joy. For the first time, someone had actually decided to label and define the most insidious form of racism running through the institutions. The plague had a name. Finally, there was an acknowledgement of its existence and the damage it could do to society. An important piece of social history was made.

In a sobering moment, I then thought of all the thousands of patients from minority ethnic groups that the NHS had misunderstood, mistreated and possibly misdiagnosed. Without denigrating the horrific murder, weren't all of those nameless thousands also Stephen Lawrences in their own right?

The definition of institutional racism left many of the key organisations that comprise British society running for cover. We were promised there would be sanctions and these bodies would be 'named and shamed'. Some groups, such as the police, went into denial. They were only racist, according to them, with respect to the definition of the Macpherson Report. They continued to protest their innocence; it was to be business as usual.

The denial existed within my world as well. As it stands the figures still don't look good even today, and are compelling: 20 per cent of general practitioners are from ethnic minorities, yet ethnic minorities constitute but 10 per cent of the General Practitioners Committee, 14 per cent of the General Medical Council, 8 per cent of the Royal College of General Practitioners' council members, 8 per cent of BMA council members and only 3 per cent of elected primary care group and local health group members.

The Royal College of General Practitioners

The response from the Royal College of General Practitioners (RCGP) was just as disappointing. In September 1999, the College produced a discussion document co-authored by Dr Has Joshi and Professor Mike Pringle, *Tackling discrimination in general practice*.[10]

When I initially read this I was heartened, but the closer I looked the more worried I became. The figures quoted looked like an indictment. In the end it looked like a defence, rather than an agenda for change. However, in the course of writing this chapter, I looked hard for a similar document from other royal colleges, without any success.

The RCGP paper started with a preamble about the difficulty in defining ethnicity. Then it freely admitted that the RCGP has never really monitored ethnicity within its membership. As I applied for the college's membership exam in the spring of 1999, I was perhaps one of the first to complete the ethnic monitoring part of the application form. Until recently the College, like its peer medical bodies, used quaint euphemisms such as 'overseas-qualified doctors' to describe minority ethnic doctors. Again I became one of the lost second generation: the RCGP paper concentrates on 'doctors who migrated to the UK' and only 'considers' us. It got worse. I was also annoyed that the Overseas Doctors Association, advising the College, did not consult second-generation doctors like myself. We were either expected to conform with the mainstream or I guess the RCGP naively thought that racism could not exist for us.

The RCGP seems to be working to 'glacial' time as well. In 1989, its Leicester faculty raised concerns in College Council, the RCGP governing body, about under-representation from minority ethnic GPs. Yet in 1999, ten years and a 1992 working group later, the numbers still look bad.

In their defence, the RCGP are apt to use familiar arguments. They say they do not believe in quotas and that College Council membership is a democratic body – superficially worthy sentiments. However, what the RCGP never really makes apparent is that it does not advertise its faculties, the local arm of the College, to minority ethnic GPs. I only found out about my own local faculty through word of mouth – these things are not advertised very well. To its credit, the North East London faculty has many minority ethnic faces around the conference table, several of the examiners from ethnic minorities amongst them.

The RCGP, albeit through the 'fireball' of the Macpherson Report, has now begun some good work. First- and second-generation minority ethnic doctors have nothing to fear from the RCGP membership exam; the examiners seem to face as much scrutiny as examinees. For the first-generation doctors, who may be further from 'exam mode' than us, there is membership by assessment (MAP). As already mentioned, ethnic monitoring has started. The challenge will be to use the data creatively and change the working environment. The momentum must not be lost. Success will be achieved when minority ethnic doctors begin to acknowledge the royal college representing their speciality as truly their own academic representative body. Until this happens, the RCGP will itself suffer. It was with regrets that I recently heard a RCGP council member describe his organisation as 'a club' where 'he decided who was a member or not'.

The General Medical Council

The General Medical Council (GMC) has existed for over 200 years to police the profession and protect the public against substandard and dangerous medical practice. It is currently finding itself under constant fire for both the time it takes to deliver its decisions and also for its perceived failures. Among minority ethnic doctors it was, and still is, infamous for taking a disproportionate number of scalps from minority ethnic doctors.[11]

A recent Policy Studies Institute (PSI) report raised great controversy when it exonerated the GMC from discrimination. There were many explanations proposed: genuine under-performance, disadvantaged working conditions and, most worrying of all, deficiencies in the GMC's data recording and decision-making processes that masked potential racial bias.[12]

I must admit I was dumbstruck; tackling racism within the institutions had taken a step backward. The superficial conclusions of the report confirmed racist notions about minority ethnic doctors. The false message conveyed was that these doctors were actually bad. The institutions breathed a sigh of relief; citing racism was now being used as a defence for poor practice. What was not transparent, but spoke volumes to me, was the apparently shadowy way the GMC conducted its business. Like the RCGP, ethnic monitoring simply did not exist. Like any system, the quality of output was guided by the input. Nobody was putting in the data at the GMC.

During the media reporting of the Shipman Inquiry, I listened with trepidation for the consequences and damage done by this aberration to general practice as a whole. I secretly wept for joy, thanking fate that Shipman was not from a minority ethnic community. In a profession finding itself under fire, I still scan the media for cases of complaints against doctors, being very relieved if they are white. Like other minority ethnic doctors, I feel a constant pressure to over-perform and to exorcise the myth about our alleged incompetence once and for all.

Trusts, health authorities and other NHS institutions

Most NHS organisations have an attitude problem. I recall a primary care group (PCG) board member describing, in my presence, how in his locality they did not have the 'minority ethnic problem' that its neighbours had. The 'minority ethnic problem' as he described it was the fact that there were a large number of potential patients and doctors from minority ethnic communities. The problem as I saw it was his mind-set, and unfortunately he was not alone.

NHS organisations see all minority ethnic doctors as a problem. The label applies to both first- and second-generation doctors equally. Popular mythology has emerged: we are all allegedly inordinately bad prescribers, our premises are bad, and generally the quality of service we provide is lower than our white peers. Minority ethnic GPs are viewed as the weak link in the system. The evidence and literature does not support this. Data on prescribing, for example, refutes this.[13] The real problems that affect minority ethnic doctors are to do with inadequacies of resources, support and staffing. Many South Asian first-generation doctors are due to retire in the immediate future as they approach the retirement age of 70. A significant number of these doctors work in deprived inner city areas, many with poor resources. The alleged problems that these health workers are blamed for are due to mismanagement and inadequacies of NHS planning, not the incompetence of the doctors.

In 1999, the Department of Health, in collaboration with the King's Fund, commissioned a leadership development programme for general practitioners from black and minority ethnic communities.[14] This was a 'positive action' programme specifically for black GPs because it was perceived that many of these GPs were unable to attend such programmes either due to lack of funding or lack of support from their health authorities or lack of time, especially if they worked in single-handed practices. The programme was advertised nationally and letters were sent to all health authorities, informing them of the programme. It was interesting to note that of the 20 GPs who participated in the programme, the majority had found out about it through word of mouth, not from their health authorities. Again, I was doubly annoyed when I discovered that, apart from myself, only one other GP was a second-generation person. During the programme, I heard a health authority employee making openly racist comments about retiring Asian GPs, complaining of their surgeries and the 'unbearable stink' in their premises. It seemed that the Asian

GPs were seen by some health authorities as 'problem GPs', low on quality and competence and therefore not fit to send on leadership development programmes.

The reality is that many minority ethnic GPs, including myself, far from under-achieving, work harder and try much more conscientiously to meet targets. We do this to avoid having a finger pointed at us.

Health professional politics: a case study into collusion?

So far I have focused outwards. In this section I wish to turn my thoughts inward at a minority of first-generation minority ethnic health workers and discuss how both conscious and unwitting collusion with racism occurs in the NHS and the damage it does to all doctors, white and non-white. I will cite one example.

I became involved in medical politics early in my general practice career. I joined as a co-opted GP registrar representative of my local medical committee (LMC), one of the local groups representing GPs in a locality. The majority of LMC members are elected to their posts by local GPs. Each committee chooses the representatives to the General Practitioners Committee (GPC). The GPC then represents GPs nationally as the nearest thing to a trades union. The LMC negotiates with the health authority on issues such as pay and working conditions. It is also an important advisory body for the implementation of new initiatives. Generally speaking, a well-organised LMC can provide a powerful and positive impact on the health of the geographical area it is elected to represent.

In one LMC, their potential effectiveness was lost through racism. In previous years, a racial divide had emerged, with white doctors on one side and non-white on the other. The basis of this division was entirely due to past racist slurs and comments, which unfortunately had continued to the present, albeit to a lesser extent. The problem now was that every issue became a race/ethnic issue. Irrespective of the merit of the argument, the discussion was divided along racial lines. This also extended to elections. People voted for their LMC representatives along ethnic lines, rather than on the merits of the candidate. The end result was deadlock, and it seemed to me that racism had brought out the worst in health service political life. It stifled effective dialogue and communication, and resulted in all sides losing out. An isolated case you may argue, but there is evidence that this situation is not unique and is replicated in other parts of the country. It becomes obvious that racism has a bad impact on *everyone* within the NHS – the users and the workers.

The current climate of government NHS policy is for reform, and in the face of this the challenge is to innovate. Innovation, in turn, will need a true meritocracy;

without this, at every level of the health system, the NHS will be robbed of its greatest resource – the people who have dedicated their lives and their minds to it.

The wider world

A frequently cited defence against racism is that until it is eliminated from British society it will pervade the institutions. Whilst culture determines health care to a certain extent, I would argue that the institutions are a potential bulwark against racism and to some extent should define the norms in society. If racists and racist views can find refuge in British institutions, then this festering contagion will persist, never to be eradicated.[15]

There is a new emphasis on public health versus health care, and a welcome drive towards all public institutions co-ordinating their activities – so called joined-up working to achieve health. Inevitably, if one discusses health one has to consider the whole variety of public bodies whose activities impact on health, such as those governing housing, education and employment.

During my medical school years, through a community worker who was a friend, I discovered how institutionalised racism operated in areas outside the NHS, even though we did not have a label for it. He opened my eyes to how flaws in the housing system discriminated against ethnic groups. A good example was the way in which the larger Asian families were predominantly consigned to seedier parts of my university town, purely because the city council claimed that they did not build such houses in the nicer neighbourhoods. (It has since dawned on me that delivering effective health will require collaboration with a large number of public organisations who operate in an institutionally racist way.) I realised that the offensive against racism in health services would need to be on a much broader front. Racism should not find a safe haven anywhere in public life.

Many politicians seem to be completely out of touch, as evidenced by some of the unhelpful statements they make in the press. In 1998, for example, I recall sitting in a meeting of general practitioners, predominantly of South Asian origin, when the local MP was invited to speak on the topic of health reform. Trying to play to his South Asian audience, he launched into a speech on the subject of what the Government was doing on immigration issues. Naturally this did not go down too well, and I asked myself if I was being patronised or whether this chap was completely out of touch.

More alarming statements recently from high-level politicians (of which Liam Fox is sadly just one) from both sides of the political divide have taken race relations in the UK several decades back. While superficially (but still reprehensibly) aiming at those seeking political asylum in the UK, these statements were designed to tap into the rich vein of racism pervading some parts of British society. The tabloid press have colluded with this further, echoing the sentiments. The genie is well and truly out of the bottle. On the day I completed this chapter, William Hague, the leader of the Conservative Party, criticised the Macpherson Report and the 'political correctness' associated with it as the root cause in the rise in street crime. I fail to understand why there are still people in the mainstream who wish to turn the clock back. Tackling racism was never 'political correctness'; for me it was social justice.

The NHS has never formally acknowledged the important and valuable role minority ethnic health workers have played in the development of health services in the UK, particularly my co-workers who migrated here solely for the purpose of supporting it. To add insult to injury, in the new ten-year plan, it is apparent that doctors from developing countries will not be recruited. The reason given for this is to avoid denuding these emerging nations of medical staff. The fact that recruitment is encouraged from predominantly the West, has raised my suspicions. The Western incomes of many migrant health workers contributed large quantities of hard foreign cash to many developing nations. Is it altruism or prejudice that is the driver in this case? Diane Abbot MP raised similar fears a few years back about the recruitment of nurses from Finland.

More recently, my local RCGP faculty discussed the issue of integrating refugee doctors into the NHS. I never liked the word 'integration'; it always suggested to me an unequal marriage of two cultures. The proposal was that refugee doctors would be asked to summarise medical notes, an onerous task required by new changes in the NHS and something doctors pay medical students to do in exchange for education. I vehemently opposed the idea as it reeked of potential exploitation, even if the motives were sound. Two or three decades on from the first generation of minority ethnic doctors, I was not prepared to be involved in creating yet another medical underclass.

Taking stock

For the past decade or so I have struggled to seek answers to the questions I have posed in this chapter. My journey through the NHS has shown me the existence of many forms of discrimination that prevent this great institution from becoming even greater. Talent and ability have no racial, ethnic or cultural exclusivity. Racism robs the NHS of both.

The monitoring and endless reports from institutions are only a pathway to concerted policy and behavioural changes. These changes have been painfully slow in coming and there has to be a will to change so that the full power of the NHS can be harnessed to provide health care for all in an effective way. This will not be possible if the NHS remains a Sepoy army using minority ethnic health workers to provide mere manpower and denying the health rights of minority ethnic patients.

What some readers may find surprising is that I believe that I actually got off 'lightly'. The experience of other colleagues was far worse. I sometimes accuse myself of cowardice; I always took the path of least resistance. I saw many of my friends struggling against the system, mainly in hospital medicine. I sometimes ask myself what would life have been like if my father had not been a GP and I had not been educated in the public school system? I do know that I would not have got as far as I have, albeit a modest achievement. Like other people, I am an amalgamation of multiple identities, experiences, cultures, religious ideas, ideologies, thoughts and memories, all of them valid, all of which I am proud of. I have come through the denial and low self-esteem that marginalised me from the mainstream of NHS culture. Contemporary medical culture pushed me into a position of victimhood. I felt guilty that maybe the doors that were closed for me were a result of my own failings.

I compare my situation with my overseas-qualified father, who still seems inhibited about challenging racism. He still worries about the repercussions of confronting discrimination, whatever its source. He still thinks his position, as a GP in the UK, is as precarious as when he joined the Sepoy army of the NHS back in 1967. He was surprised when I threw a racist patient off my list, citing zero tolerance. I know, however, that he acknowledges that the NHS is not doing him a favour by letting him work for it. He knows he has rights and that racism in any way, shape or form is unacceptable to him or anybody.

The NHS itself, however, does have a case to answer, as I hope I have shown in this chapter. The task ahead does not seem easy and the current political climate in UK society has made it more difficult. Sometimes the barrier looks much as it did in my medical school days. I would therefore urge all those who are offended and hurt by the system, as well those who have succeeded in beating the system, to continue the battle, never to give in. We can then move beyond race in the NHS and take the organisation to its full potential, with a culture of equality and inclusion. The combination of experiences and diversity could lead to a powerful synergy of talent.

All I want is for Britain to give me the chance to get the best out of myself. When I face the prospects and future of challenging racism I ironically take heart in the words of the words of one of the last British Sepoy generals:

The British pride themselves on being good losers. I'm a damn bad loser. I'm going to win.

General Sir Claude Auchinleck

References

1. McManus I C, Esmail A, Demetriou M. Factors affecting likelihood of applicants being offered a place in medical schools in the UK in 1996 and 1997. *BMJ* 1998; 317: 1111–17.
2. McManus I C, Richards P, Winder B C, Sproston K A, Styles V. Medical school applicants from ethnic minority groups: identifying if and when they are disadvantaged. *BMJ* 1995; 310: 496–500.
3. Abbasi K. Is medical school selection discriminatory? *BMJ* 1998; 317: 1097–98.
4. Collier J. Tackling institutional racism. *BMJ* 1999; 318: 679.
5. Dillner L. Manchester tackles failure rate of Asian students. *BMJ* 1995; 310: 209.
6. Selby M, Neuberger J, Easmon C, Gough P. Ethnic dilemma: dealing with racist patients. Doctors are people too. Commentary: A role for personal values ... and management; Commentary: Isolate the problem; Commentary: Courteous containment is not enough. *BMJ* 1999; 318: 1129–31.
7. BMA Conference calls for less talk and more action to tackle racism in the NHS. *BMA Press Release*, 19/02/97.
8. Carnall D. Circumventing racism in the NHS. *BMJ Classified* 1997; 314 (7081): 2.
9. Macpherson Sir W. *The Stephen Lawrence inquiry report*. London: The Stationery Office, 1999.
10. Joshi H, Pringle M. *Tackling discrimination in general practice*. London: Royal College of General Practitioners, September 1999.
11. Dillner L. Ethnic minority doctors more likely to face GMC. *BMJ* 1994; 308: 875–76.
12. Godlee F. The GMC, racism, and complaints against doctors. *BMJ* 1996; 312: 1314–15.
13. Gill P S, Dowell A, Harris C M. Effect of doctors' ethnicity and country of qualification on prescribing patterns in single handed general practices: linkage of information collected by questionnaire and from routine data. *BMJ* 1997; 315: 1590–94.
14. Dadabhoy S. Redressing the leadership balance. *GP* 1999; 40, August: 13
15. Esmail A, Carnall D. Tackling racism in the NHS. *BMJ* 1997; 314: 618.

Chapter 4

Racial discrimination in medical schools

Aneez Esmail

*People are not better than the rest of creation.
The same principle which underlies human
beings underlies everything equally. Neither is
one person or one people better than the rest of
humanity. The same principle is everywhere.
One person is as worthy as the next. Why play
favourites?*

Lao Tzu

Introduction

Selection for medical school has always had its controversial side. Not only does the number of applicants far exceed the number of places, but also medicine is one of the few university courses that provides a vocational training. Applicants are expected to make medicine their career. Once qualified, medicine provides most graduates with a job for life. Entry into the medical course, therefore, is highly competitive, and much rests on the initial selection process. Selection becomes more difficult because there is no agreement on the balance of academic and non-academic characteristics that are needed to study medicine. Inevitably the lack of clearly definable criteria for admissions gives selectors huge discretion, not only as to how they select medical students, but also whom they select.

It is clear that, overall, minority ethnic students are over-represented in medical schools. This is true of all higher education establishments. In some medical schools nearly 40 per cent of the intake is from ethnic minorities. Does this justify selection bias against minority ethnic applicants? Many people argue that on the grounds of proportionality, minority ethnic candidates, and the Asian group in particular, are over-represented in the medical profession and therefore discrimination cannot possibly be occurring against this group of students. Absence of proportionality is one of the key pieces of evidence pointing to the existence of disadvantage. The under-representation of women in medicine in the past and the current under-representation of students from lower social classes in medical schools are often cited as examples of discrimination. So, the argument goes, 'if there are so many Asian students in medicine, how can we possibly be discriminating against them?'

It is important to counter these arguments for several reasons. In the United Kingdom, access to higher education is determined primarily on merit and on achieving minimum academic qualifications. Monitoring of gender, ethnicity and social class sometimes reveals structural problems that often point to discrimination against groups of students. However, there are often wider social and cultural reasons why, in some higher education institutions, the student body does not reflect the proportionality in terms of gender and ethnicity of the wider society. The high proportion of Asian students in medicine is almost certainly a reflection of the fact that a large number of Asian doctors work in the NHS as a result of immigration policies that encouraged Asian doctors to come and work in the NHS in the 1960s and 1970s. Nearly 20 per cent of doctors working in the NHS are from minority ethnic communities. As with white students in medicine, choice of profession partly reflects the views of their parents, and it is not surprising that Asian students are more likely to choose medicine as a career option. Furthermore, most minority ethnic applicants to medicine are children of immigrants to the UK, and professions like medicine have frequently attracted immigrants – children of Jewish immigrants in the 1940s and 1950s, and South Asians in the 1980s and 1990s, are examples of this trend (also present in the USA).

There are many structural reasons for this and it is beyond the scope of this chapter to discuss why this happens. The point to be made is that for a variety of reasons, South Asian students are attracted to medicine as a career option. In societies that aspire to be meritocratic, equality of opportunity is guaranteed, frequently in law – as exemplified by the Equal Opportunities Act and the Race Relations Act in the UK. If selection criteria are set and candidates meet those criteria, then why does it matter if a large number of students from minority ethnic groups are selected? The students affected are British citizens born in the United Kingdom, speaking English in all its regional dialects. When they qualify, most of their patients will be white and it seems to make no difference in terms of the clinical care that they deliver what the colour of their skin is. Many medical schools now have more women then men studying medicine – it shouldn't matter, provided that the selection process is fair and all applicants have the same equality of opportunity.

The diversity argument

One of the reasons that the proportionality argument has resonance in the UK is because of the experience of the United States and the role of affirmative action in shaping race-based policy and the use of the diversity argument to justify it. Within the US and with respect to medical schools and health care, there are three strands to the diversity argument. These include the utilitarian position of diversity being good for the university, the viewpoint that minority communities are better served by minority professionals, and that in a changing population, minorities in the professions are needed because they reflect the population at large.

The utilitarian position states that the purpose of an educational institution is to teach, not only through its professors but also through its student body. Using the utilitarian viewpoint, universities have the right to admit students who they judge to be more valuable to their educational purpose. A student who achieves high scores on a particular test has no right to attend a university, but the university reserves the right to admit the individuals it deems to have the most value, which may in present-day America include considerations of race. Within the United Kingdom, initiatives to improve access to higher education for students from lower social classes frequently use utilitarian justifications.

However, the problem with the use of race as a proxy for diversity is that it confuses race with both ethnicity and culture, and fails to take into account differences within groups. There is no doubt that every ethnic group, including European Americans, African Americans and Asian Americans, has distinct cultural attributes that may contribute towards a diverse student body. But to claim that there is a distinct 'minority viewpoint' or a 'black viewpoint' that contributes to diversity is questionable. In the American context, black views are probably no more liberal on issues such as abortion, the environment or the death penalty than those of the majority population. Racism, particularly the racism experienced by the black population in America has, however, been a powerful distinguishing feature of American society, and it is likely that it plays a role in shaping the experiences of millions of Americans. Therefore, there may be a justification for asserting that being black in the American context results in black Americans having a different life experience to white Americans. Whether this translates into having a different viewpoint on social and political questions is doubtful.

The second strand of the diversity argument states that minority ethnic communities are better served by minority ethnic professionals. This suggests that black doctors are better at giving care to black patients, are preferred by black patients, and as research also tends to suggest, that they are more likely to practise in socially deprived, inner city areas where minority communities are concentrated in larger numbers. The problem with this assumption is that once we allow the racial views of constituents to dictate the choice of personnel, we set a precedent that is ultimately more dangerous to black and minority communities. If racial preferences are justified by reason of social utility rather than compensation for past wrongs, there is nothing to stop white people from making the same arguments. What if patient satisfaction surveys found that white patients preferred to be treated by white doctors because they were more likely to 'relate better' to them? If Asian doctors are supposed to 'communicate more efficiently' with Asian patients, why should we not think that white patients will communicate better with white doctors? Although not made explicit in the UK, this point of view has frequently been put to me by senior people in the medical profession. Arguments are advanced along the lines that the wrong sort of people now go into medicine and that they do not understand the culture of the people that they will be treating. Implicit in these arguments is the feeling that there are too many Asians in medicine, they study medicine because they are forced into doing this by their parents because it is considered a respectable profession, and that there is no longer a sense of vocation by many minority ethnic applicants.

The related problem with using race as a *bona fide* occupational qualification is that it can pigeonhole ethnic minorities in certain slots. Minority ethnic academics will be told that they should concentrate on researching the problems of minority patients because somehow they understand the problems better. Similar justifications will also be used to deny opportunities to minority ethnic doctors in prestigious positions. The preponderance of Asian doctors working in inner cities in the UK and in non-teaching district hospitals provides ample evidence. This will result in black doctors being concentrated largely in inner cities and conurbations, such as in the north-west of England and the West Midlands. This 'ghettoisation' will ultimately deny opportunities to minority ethnic physicians in the sought-after specialties in medicine, such as cardiology and oncology, which will continue to remain predominantly white.

The other side of the same argument is that unless minority ethnic physicians who have expressed a desire to work in deprived areas are recruited, then people living in these areas will be denied care because white physicians will not practice in these areas. Whilst it is true that minority groups do receive care from minority physicians and that in many instances the absence of these physicians might result in a reduced level of care, the idea that health care to minorities is dependent on minority physicians is questionable. Health care to minorities is much more dependent on issues such as universal access and cost than on whether a particular group of doctors decides to practice in socially deprived areas.

The third strand of the diversity rationale is that minorities in the profession are needed because they reflect the population at large. This argument about proportional representation, which aims to increase the number of under-represented minorities in medical schools in the US, is based on the supposition that, had it not been for past discriminatory practices, we would expect to see minorities in the professions comparable to their numbers in the general population. There is, however, not a neat relationship between discrimination and under-representation because not all under-represented groups are defined by racial categories. The logic of proportionality in the diversity rationale advocates for the presence of all under-represented groups. For example, in some universities in the United States, where there is under-representation of people of a conservative political persuasion both in student and faculty numbers, this logic dictates that a university should specifically attempt to recruit conservatives because they would bring an important difference to the university.

In the racial context, using the diversity and proportional representation argument is already beginning to hurt Asians at some Californian schools. As they are over-represented in the higher education system, the diversity rationale that calls for their strict representation based on their numbers in the population is working against them. There is already evidence that Asian Americans now need higher scores than whites to be admitted to undergraduate universities in California.[1] Racial stereotypes of Asian Americans are widespread. Comments such as 'they are all premeds' or 'they don't participate in extra-curricular activities' are just as destructive as stereotypes of African Americans as 'lazy' or 'stupid'. Universities, rather than acknowledging that denying places to Asian Americans is prejudiced, and some would argue racist, can now justify their policies using the diversity argument that there are just too many Asians. As explained earlier, these views have some resonance in the UK.

However, the law in the UK is very clear. Discrimination is not allowed and selection criteria must be determined by principles of equality. The biggest problem for the majority of medical schools in the UK is that they have not defined their entry criteria in terms of equality of opportunity. This is probably one of the reasons, as will be outlined later in this chapter, why disadvantage is occurring against minority ethnic applicants. The issue is not that there are too many Asian students in medicine but that many continue to be denied equal opportunities in accessing the career of their choice.

The process of determining whether racial discrimination exists in the selection of medical students is a good example of how institutional racism operates. The next section of this chapter describes the historical background as to how the discriminatory selection process for medical graduates was investigated and exposed, and gives an example of one institution's attempt to make its selection process more transparent and ultimately less discriminatory.

Historical background

In 1986, two academics at St George's Hospital Medical School in south London wrote a paper in which they showed that black medical students applying for a place at the St George's Hospital Medical School were disadvantaged compared to white applicants.[2] This was the first piece of clear evidence that discrimination was a factor in the selection of medical students. Collier and Burke described how a computer programme that was being used at St George's to screen students with a view to selecting those students who would ultimately be offered a place, was systematically discriminating against minority ethnic and female students. Following the publication of their paper in 1987, the Commission for Racial Equality investigated the specific admissions procedure at St George's Hospital Medical School and found evidence for discrimination by race and sex.[3] In a damning editorial in the *British Medical Journal* (*BMJ*) at the time, Stephen Lowry described the St George's case as a blot on the profession.[4] As a result of the Commission's inquiry, in the autumn of 1989 the then Universities Central Council on Admissions (UCCA) began collecting routine statistics from applicants as to their ethnic origins. It is fair to state that most medical schools at this time believed that St George's was the case of a bad apple, and that in general, minority ethnic applicants were not disadvantaged when applying to medical school. There was, of course, no data to justify this belief, except for the fact that even in the late 1980s, minority ethnic applicants tended to be over-represented in medical schools compared to their proportions in the general population.[5]

The collection of data on applicants' ethnic origin by UCCA was in line with what many other public and private organisations in the late 1980s were trying to do under the guise of ethnic monitoring. Despite being a huge exercise in data collection, UCCA did not have a coherent strategy to analyse and report on this data. In the first few years of this data collection exercise, aggregate statistics were reported, which showed that minority ethnic applicants to medical school appeared to be disadvantaged when compared to white applicants. However, no attempt was made to analyse the reasons for this apparent disadvantage in a scientific manner. For example, UCCA had the data that would have allowed them to analyse the disadvantage by individual courses and universities, controlling for variables such as social class, type of school attended, GCSE and predicted A-level scores. Instead of proper scientific analysis of this data, a myth developed that was shared by many admissions officers during this period. This suggested that discrepancies between the minority ethnic and white candidates existed because minority ethnic candidates were applying for medical school places even though they did not have the right academic qualifications. There is, for example, a popular misconception that minority ethnic applicants are forced to apply for a medical school place by their parents even though they may not be suited for this. The assumption is, therefore, that large numbers of applicants from ethnic minorities do not have the required academic qualifications and therefore it was hardly surprising that there was a discrepancy between minority ethnic applicants and white applicants.

With the creation of the Universities and Colleges Admission Service (UCAS), the data from both universities and polytechnics were amalgamated and it became obvious to social policy researchers that this represented a rich source of data for the analysis of applications by ethnic minorities into higher education.

However, no attempt was made to analyse this data in a robust scientific manner, which would have allowed researchers and policy-makers to determine whether disadvantage was taking place. Studies reported by McManus *et al*. in 1989 and 1995[6] suggested that minority ethnic applicants may be disadvantaged because they had foreign-sounding surnames. However, McManus concluded at this time, that there was no systematic discrimination against this group of students. Despite the concerns raised by McManus, medical schools did not analyse the data that was made available by UCAS. The myth continued that racial discrimination was not a problem in selection of medical students because they were already over-represented, and that any discrepancies between applicants and acceptances was due to inappropriate applications by students who never stood a chance to pass the rigorous selection process.

Public release of information

In 1994, my then colleague Sam Everington and I began to take an interest in the issue of racial discrimination in medical school applications. We were receiving an increasing number of anecdotal reports from minority ethnic applicants with high A-level grades who were not getting admitted to medical schools. Medical schools vary greatly in their admissions procedures and much of the process remains a black box. Until recently, no criteria for admissions were ever publicly stated. Many schools selected on the basis of performance at interview following initial screening for academic and non-academic criteria. Several schools did not even interview candidates but used a points system derived from academic and non-academic criteria to determine which students to offer places to. It was our belief at the time that an analysis of the data showing disadvantage to minority ethnic applicants, if it existed, would provide useful evidence of good practice and would also start a public debate on the criteria that should be used in the selection of medical students.

Since UCAS already published aggregate statistics, we wrote to them in 1994 and asked them for a breakdown of their statistics by individual medical schools for one year. When we asked for this information, we were surprised to be told that this information belonged to individual medical schools and that we would have to seek their permission before UCAS could agree to release any data. We then wrote to a sample of medical schools asking them if we could have this data released by UCAS and were told that this would not be possible. It was only after we convinced a member of the then Labour Party's Shadow Health team, Dawn Primorolo, to help us carry out the investigation into discrimination in the selection of medical students that the medical schools agreed to release this data.

In 1995 we published an article in the BMJ[7] which showed that there were large differences in acceptance rates to medical schools between white and minority ethnic candidates. However, the use of one years' data made it difficult to draw conclusions on the differences between medical schools because of the small number of applicants in a single year. It also became apparent that we would require a release of much greater amounts of data from UCAS in order to understand whether racial discrimination was the only factor operating in differential acceptance rates. The publication of the information in the BMJ in 1995 was highly controversial because for the first time it named individual medical schools. The league table that we published (see Table 4.1) showed that some medical schools appeared not to discriminate against minority ethnic applicants, whereas others discriminated greatly. For example, a group of medical schools appeared not to discriminate against minority ethnic applicants (Edinburgh, Aberdeen, Liverpool, Manchester, King's College, St Bartholomew's, United Medical and Dental Schools of Guy's and St Thomas', Leicester and Southampton). The analysis of data from these schools showed that minority ethnic applicants had roughly the same chance of being accepted for a place compared to white candidates. Most other medical school appeared to discriminate against minority ethnic candidates, with some schools (Charing Cross and Westminster, Royal Free, Cambridge, St Mary's, Wales, Nottingham, Glasgow, Birmingham, Belfast, Royal London and St Andrew's) showing levels of discrimination which suggested that white candidates were between two and five times more likely to be accepted for a place compared to minority ethnic applicants. The research was important because, for the first time, an attempt was made to control for the A-level grade of the applicant, challenging the assumption that minority ethnic applicants were unsuccessful because they did not achieve the right academic qualifications. This is shown in the last column in Table 4.1. Although not a perfect study, the paper showed clearly that even controlling for the grade of the applicant, minority ethnic students appeared to be disadvantaged compared to their white colleagues when applying for medical school places. In our

Table 4.1 League table of likelihood of applicants being accepted for medical school compared to minority ethnic applicants (1994)

Medical School	Odds of acceptance for white candidates compared to minority ethnic candidates	Odds of acceptance for white candidates compared to minority ethnic candidates controlling for A-level grades	95% Confidence interval (a measure of the range of likely odds – if the range does not include 1, then the result can be considered statistically significant)
Liverpool	0.98	0.84	0.52–1.39
Manchester	1.01	0.83	0.59–1.18
King's College	1.05	0.99	0.61–1.62
St Bartholomew's	1.16	1.07	0.63–1.85
United Medical and Dental Schools of Guy's and St Thomas'	1.20	0.96	0.65–1.40
Leicester	1.37	1.06	0.64–1.79
Southampton	1.47	1.19	0.63–2.41
Newcastle	1.47	1.46	0.73–2.99
Bristol	1.50	1.22	0.66–2.45
Oxford	1.76	1.63	0.86–3.26
Dundee	1.78	1.76	0.80–4.47
University College	1.78	1.50	0.98–2.35
Sheffield	1.82	1.55	0.92–2.69
Leeds	1.98	1.61	1.01–2.60
St George's	2.02	1.85	1.23–2.83
Charing Cross and Westminster	2.02	1.93	1.30–2.95
Royal Free	2.08	1.88	0.90–3.93
Cambridge	2.12	1.88	1.21–2.97
St Mary's	2.14	2.03	1.20–3.56
Wales	2.18	1.79	1.00–3.38
Nottingham	2.28	1.98	1.04–4.14
Glasgow	2.39	1.81	0.51–7.72
Birmingham	2.54	1.88	1.12–3.26
Belfast	2.83	2.71	0.15–15.90
Royal London	3.02	2.77	1.89–4.31
St Andrews	5.40	3.83	1.12–20.53

The table shows the likelihood of acceptance of white applicants compared to minority ethnic applicants. Taking the example of the Royal London Medical School, the table shows that in 1994, white candidates were three times more likely (3.02) to be accepted for a place to study medicine compared to minority ethnic applicants. Adjusting for the grades of applicants shows that white applicants are still 2.77 times more likely to be accepted, despite having the same grades as minority ethnic applicants. The confidence interval shows that this is statistically significant.

analysis we showed that in fact white candidates with lower A-level grades were more likely to be accepted to study medicine than minority ethnic candidates. The argument that there were differential rates for acceptance because many minority ethnic students were applying inappropriately was therefore no longer tenable.

Realising that we needed to carry out a more thorough analysis of this data, which we felt should be in the public domain, we asked UCAS to release further information to us so that we could carry out a more in-depth analysis. This was refused. It was made clear to us by UCAS that medical schools were no longer prepared to release this data, partly because of the bad publicity that they had received following the publication of our paper in 1995.

We then started a long process of political pressure to try and get the data released into the public domain. Several factors contributed to the overwhelming pressure for the release of this information. First, the Secretary of the Council of Heads of Medical Schools and Dean of the Faculty of Medicine at the University of Manchester, Professor Stephen Tomlinson, was sympathetic to releasing this information. He used his position to try and convince the other deans that it was in the public interest to have the information released, so that independent researchers could assess whether minority ethnic applicants were disadvantaged when applying to medical school. He argued convincingly that if the whole process of medical school selection was more open then it would be easier to disseminate good practice and also, importantly, to rebut allegations of discrimination. Second, the Medical Practitioners Union (MPU), of which both Sam Everington and I were members, also wrote to all heads of secondary schools, informing them of the research we had published in the *BMJ* in 1995, which showed a differential disadvantage to minority ethnic applicants wanting to study medicine. In the letter to the heads of secondary schools, the MPU advised them to seek further information from the medical schools that students from their schools would be applying to. We pointed out to them that certain medical schools disadvantaged minority ethnic candidates to such an extent that there was little point in them applying. The MPU also asked the Secretary of State for Education and the Secretary of State for Health to directly intervene and support the release of this information in the public domain. Finally, impending legislation by the new Labour administration made it clear that this sort of information should no longer be secret and should be published in the public domain. Despite this pressure for the release of information into the public domain, the medical schools, through the Council of Deans, were reluctant to release the information. I was even threatened with legal action by the dean of a London medical school if we did not withdraw the letter we were sending to heads of secondary schools.

However, the case for release of this information was overwhelming. In early 1998, the Council of Deans finally agreed to commission an independent report by Professor Chris McManus to analyse this data. They also agreed that they would release this information into the public domain following publication of their commissioned report.

In the report published in the *BMJ* in 1998,[8] McManus carried out the most detailed analysis of applications to medical school, the relationship between a range of measures, and the likelihood of being offered a place at medical school. In his analysis McManus showed conclusively that applicants from minority ethnic groups were disadvantaged in some medical schools. He also showed that not all schools disadvantaged applicants from minority ethnic groups and postulated that there were structural differences in the process of selection, which resulted in minority ethnic applicants being disadvantaged. He was able to show that the degree of disadvantage did not relate to the proportion of applicants from minority ethnic groups and that the disadvantage occurred despite minority ethnic applicants having similar grades and academic qualifications as white candidates. His research was also important because the data that he analysed covered nearly 93,000 applications over a two-year period. The report was published in conjunction with a statement of aims from the Council of Heads of Medical Schools, which called on medical schools to critically assess their selection process to ensure that racial discrimination was not taking place. The Chairman of the Commission for Racial Equality, Sir Herman Ousely, also wrote a personal letter to all deans of medical schools demanding action. In a strongly worded letter, he told the deans to carry out an internal investigation on the application process in their medical schools. He also told them that he expected them to take the necessary remedial action if they were found to be discriminating against minority ethnic applicants. Failure to do this would trigger a formal investigation by the Commission for Racial Equality.

The preceding historical account gives the reader a chronological perspective leading from the collection of ethnicity data by UCAS through to the present day. Every medical school should now be in a position to provide a detailed breakdown of the outcome of applicants by age, gender and ethnicity, taking into account factors such as GCSE and A-level grades that may be classified as confounding variables.

It is worth briefly recounting the evidence before describing a plan of action, which could help institutions to monitor their admissions policy so that the chances of discrimination and disadvantage would be reduced.

The evidence

In terms of evidence there are *three key pieces of work*. Esmail and Everington's league table, which looked at the likelihood of acceptance to medical schools controlling for A-level scores for white candidates compared to minority ethnic candidates.[7] The importance of this data was that it listed each individual medical school and showed the huge variation that existed between medical schools. This research evidence showed that whilst it was possible to have in place selection policies that appear not to disadvantage minority ethnic candidates, some institutions still appeared to disadvantage ethnic minorities.

McManus *et al.* have done the other two key pieces of work in this area. Obviously, suffering from the same problem of UCAS not releasing data on ethnicity, McManus *et al.* first carried out research on ethnicity and medical school applications in 1989,[6] based on applicants to St Mary's Hospital Medical School. They showed that there may be a problem of disadvantage against minority ethnic applicants. In a more substantial paper in 1995, which was published at the same time as Esmail and Everington's study, McManus,[9] analysing offers made to applicants, showed that minority ethnic groups were significantly disadvantaged in nearly 50 per cent of medical schools. Rather than cite racial discrimination as a cause of this finding, McManus postulated that discrimination was occurring on account of the surname of the applicant. He suggested that admissions officers were biased against applicants with foreign-sounding surnames but were not responsible for racial discrimination. This was a peculiar logic because it was obvious that minority ethnic applicants were the main group of applicants affected by this finding. Within UK law it would be classified as indirect discrimination, and it was surprising that McManus was unwilling to attribute the finding to racial discrimination. However, the analysis was thorough, and although medical schools were not named individually, the findings confirmed the basic tenets of Esmail and Everington's work – that disadvantage was a feature in a substantial number of British medical schools.

McManus's work, published in 1998,[8] was by the far the most substantial research ever done on the issue of selection bias. Based on data released into the public domain by the Council of Deans, the analysis showed quite conclusively that some medical schools consistently discriminated against minority ethnic applicants. McManus was criticised because he failed to take into account predicted A-level or GCSE scores in his analysis. However, the differences and the disadvantages that he described between schools were so great that it was unlikely the differences could be explained away by differences in predicted A-level and GSCE scores. Most commentators accepted the basic findings that McManus listed. The most important factor is to consider the 1998 paper in the context of all the evidence that preceded, including work by Esmail and Everington, and McManus's earlier work. As I said in a commentary accompanying the article,[10] the time for excuses was up. He pointed out that if there was an identified problem then it was best that remedial action was taken by individual schools as opposed to it being imposed by the courts.

The challenge for medical schools is to move on from debating whether discrimination exists, and towards accepting that it is a problem. The onus is now on individual medical schools to examine their selection policies and show that minority ethnic candidates are not disadvantaged. The accusation that GCSE scores and predicted A-levels were not taken into account by McManus and Esmail can now be checked by individual medical schools and should be monitored as part of their review of admissions policies.

In the next section I will describe the lessons learned by an individual institution (where I work), which shows that there are lessons to be learned that can be applied to the advantage of all students.

Learning from experience

Manchester Medical School is the largest medical school in the United Kingdom. Annually it graduates over 300 medical students. Until 1995, Manchester had a system for selecting medical students that did not rely on interview. Candidates were selected on the basis of information provided on the UCAS form. A scoring system had been developed, which took account of both academic and non-academic criteria. The students who fulfilled these criteria were also asked to meet the minimum A-level requirements.

Until recently, the admissions committee did not routinely monitor statistics on gender or ethnicity. In the investigation carried out by Esmail and Everington in 1995, Manchester did not appear to discriminate against minority ethnic applicants. Nearly 40 per cent of the medical school intake was from ethnic minorities.

The publication of the McManus Report in 1998, suggested that Manchester appeared to be one of the schools that seemed to discriminate against minority ethnic applicants. This was of particular concern to the admissions committee because in 1995 it had changed its admissions policy to include interviews of potential applicants. The reasoning behind this change was to try to better assess applicant's ability to last the duration of the course. The course was also undergoing fundamental review and it was felt that it would be difficult to assess candidates for a totally different type of course. The admissions committee therefore developed explicit criteria on which candidates would be assessed. In effect, a job description and a person specification was created for potential applicants to Manchester. The system was devised so that all applicants were treated in exactly the same way, with consistency in terms of selecting academic and non-academic criteria. When the McManus Report was published, and showed that Manchester may be discriminating against minority ethnic applicants, the dean agreed to set up an internal inquiry into the admissions process.

As its brief, the inquiry had to determine whether Manchester was discriminating against minority ethnic candidates and in particular to take into account the variables that McManus could not readily integrate into his own analysis. Specifically, this included consideration of the applicants' predicted A-level and GCSE scores.

At the time of the inquiry, Manchester operated a policy in which all applicants were first assessed for minimum academic criteria. If those minimum academic criteria were fulfilled, the application form was then assessed independently by two medical assessors, who used a pro forma listing non-academic criteria to score the application form. Information from the head teacher's report and from the UCAS form were then scored. If candidates achieved a minimum score they were then invited for an interview. The interview was carried out in a standard manner and every candidate was assessed across five dimensions. If the candidates passed the interview stage they were then given an offer of a place, subject to attaining a minimum A-level score.

The investigation carried out in Manchester looked at all applications to the university over a one-year period. The analysis took into account GCSE scores, predicted A-level grades, actual A-level grades, gender and type of school. The investigation confirmed the main findings of the McManus Report and suggested that Manchester was probably indirectly discriminating against minority ethnic applicants. The analysis showed that discrimination was probably occurring at the interview stage but there was no information on how the discrimination was occurring. It was the first time that Manchester had reviewed its admissions policies in the context of the possibility of discrimination against specific groups of students, and the investigation was an important learning exercise for the institution and the admissions committee.

Several outcomes resulted from the internal report. Because the entire admissions process was reviewed, it became clear that there were structural problems that could easily have disadvantaged minority ethnic applicants. For example, in the assessment of non-academic criteria, points were given if the applicant had a position of responsibility in the school, such as being a school prefect. This would automatically have disadvantaged applicants who did not attend a school, for example if they attended a further education college or a State comprehensive school that did not have a prefect system. This was an obvious example of a structural problem, which may inadvertently have resulted in discrimination against minority ethnic applicants. It also became clear from the inquiry that the systems of monitoring were not robust enough and that, particularly at the interview stage, there was not a consistent attempt to monitor the results. A series of recommendations were made to the admissions committee, which included publicising admission criteria for the medical school on their web site, so that all students would know exactly what the medical school was seeking in potential applicants. The full process in the assessments of applications was described and even the questions that would be asked at the interview stage were listed on the web site.

It was agreed that the whole selection process would be monitored and a new system for monitoring was agreed. The most important result of the exercise was a realisation that a considerable amount could be gained from reviewing the selection process in a systematic way. Although the process sought to determine whether minority ethnic applicants might be disadvantaged, changes were made that, in fact, made the whole process more open and fair for all candidates. There were important lessons to be learned for the entire organisation. Interestingly, the lessons learned from this review, especially in terms of monitoring and selection criteria, were also taken on board by the university for other subject areas. The institution is now more aware of issues relating to access and discrimination, and paradoxically it is the medical school admissions committee which is setting the standards that other departments are now trying to emulate.

I cannot comment on the impact that these changes will have on future admissions to Manchester, but what is important is that there has been an organisational change in the institution. The admissions committee now realises the importance of monitoring and constantly reviewing the outcome of the selection process. Ethnic and gender monitoring, and on occasions monitoring the social background of applicants, will help Manchester assess whether it admission criteria are operating fairly. The monitoring system in place will help the organisation to continually refine and improve its admissions policies to the ultimate advantage of all future applicants to the medical school.

Concluding thoughts

For nearly a decade the mantra from medical schools has been that there cannot be discrimination in the selection of medical school applicants. No evidence was ever presented for this assertion and, despite systems for monitoring, little was done to understand or investigate whether this was reality or not. Almost no medical schools published information on their admission processes, and attempts to get information into the public domain were almost always thwarted. The cultural and organisational changes came about because of the publication of research evidence obtained against the wishes of the medical schools. A combination of naming and shaming through the effective use of league tables, together with political pressure, ultimately led to the recognition of a substantial problem that could not be ignored. The recent decision to release information on admissions into the public domain by the Council of Deans will finally bring the debate on admissions into the twenty-first century. For the first time we will be able to assess the differential impact of admissions policies of medical schools on social class, gender and ethnicity. We will be able to monitor the effect of policy changes in selection criteria on the types of students that are ultimately selected. Inevitably, the selection process will become more transparent.

Researchers will be able to study the whole process of medical selection. Those institutions with a desire to learn more about the selection process will be encouraged to review their admission criteria and, as shown in the example of Manchester, have the potential to learn an immense amount from the exercise. The process of organisational learning that has taken place because of this has been immensely useful and the continuing desire to question and re-examine the process will inevitably lead to a more open and fairer system. Hopefully the manner in which medical students are selected will now be open to a much wider public discussion, backed up by facts and figures. The debate should now shift away from the disadvantages suffered by minority ethnic applicants to the overall criteria for the selection of medical students in general. This is ultimately the most important question: 'what are the personal characteristics that make the best doctors and how do we select those people in a fair and consistent manner?'

References

1. Applebome P. Gains in diversity. *New York Times* 1995; 4 June; and Lubman campuses mull admissions without affirmative action. *Wall Street Journal* 1995; 16 May. In: Kahlenberg R D. *The remedy. Class, race and affirmative action.* New York: Basic Books, 1996: 77.

2. Collier J, Burke A. Racial and sexual discrimination in selection of students to London medical schools. *Medical Education* 1986; 20 (2): 86–90.

3. Commission for Racial Equality. *Report of a formal investigation into St George's Hospital Medical School.* London: Commission for Racial Equality, 1988.

4. Lowry S, Macpherson G. A blot on the profession. Editorial. *BMJ* 1988; 296: 657–58.

5. Vellins S. South Asian students in British universities. *New Community* 1982; 10: 206–12.

6. McManus I C, Richards P, Maitlis S L. Prospective study of the disadvantage of people from minority ethnic groups applying to medical schools in the United Kingdom. *BMJ* 1989; 298 (6675): 723–26.

7. Esmail A, Nelson P, Primarolo D, Toma T. Accceptance into medical school and racial discrimination. *BMJ* 1995; 310 (6978): 502.

8. McManus I C. Factors affecting likelihood of applicants being offered a place in medical schools in the United Kingdom in 1996 and 1997: retrospective study. *BMJ* 1998; 317 (7166): 1111–16.

9. McManus I C, Richards P, Winder B C, Sproston K A, Styles V. Medical school applicants from minority ethnic groups: identifying if and when they are disadvantaged. *BMJ* 1995; 310 (6978): 496–500.

10. Esmail A. League tables will help. Commentary. *BMJ* 1998; 317 (7166): 1116–17.

Chapter 5

General practitioners, ethnic diversity and racism

Paramjit S Gill

When will justice come to Athens?

Justice will come to Athens when those who are not injured are as indignant as those who are!
Thucydides

The aim of this chapter is to provide an understanding of the role of general practitioners (GPs) from black and minority ethnic groups (BMEGs) within the National Health Service (NHS). Many of these doctors are known as 'overseas doctors' as they obtained their first qualification from outside the UK. There are two misconceptions that need stating: first, that overseas doctors equates to Asian* doctors primarily and, second, that they are non-white doctors only. These have arisen as, despite the fact that these doctors came from all over the world, the majority of them were from the Indian subcontinent (ISC). Furthermore, the General Medical Council (GMC) stopped recognising the primary qualifications of many of these doctors, especially those from the ISC, while continuing to recognise those from white Commonwealth countries, such as Australia or New Zealand. This chapter draws together the disparate literature and data on BMEG doctors, but concentrates on Asian doctors as the published literature to date has focused heavily on them, choosing to ignore doctors who have qualified from elsewhere.

The first section of the chapter puts general practice into a historical context and the second deals with the concepts of 'race', ethnicity and culture, and their pragmatic use within the health service. Data on the ethnicity of GPs is not collected; instead, proxy measures are used. The third section describes the migration patterns of the different communities to the UK and compares this with doctors' origination from

---

*Asian refers to individuals originating from the Indian subcontinent (India, Pakistan, Bangladesh, Sri Lanka).

the ISC. The fourth section outlines some characteristics of GPs, the utilisation and quality of their consultations, as well as the racism they face.

The chapter finishes with a discussion about the increasing number of refugee doctors and the difficulties they face in obtaining the right to practice in this country.

General practice: development and reform

This section provides an overview of the historical development of general practitioner services, as it lays the foundations for understanding the role of doctors who qualified overseas. It is also important to note that primary care, of which general practice is one element, has a pivotal role in the NHS.[1]

The term 'general practitioner' came into use at the beginning of the nineteenth century and arose out of a trade dispute between physicians and surgeons on the one hand, and apothecaries on the other.[2] The physicians and surgeons gained control of the hospitals, including the teaching hospitals, and the apothecaries had control of the patients. Hospital specialists saw patients by direct referral from the apothecary. This division laid the foundation of British general practice.

Prior to the establishment of the NHS on 5 July 1948, medical services were provided through inclusion on the 'panel system'.[3] This was introduced by the National Insurance Act of 1911, which initially covered workers between 16 and 70 years of age who earned less than a specified amount. Dependants of these workers and the financially better-off were not covered and had to pay a fee for medical services.

The NHS, funded by general taxation, set out to provide comprehensive health care to all, based upon need rather than the ability to pay. It was assumed that the introduction of the NHS would eliminate ill health. It was also believed that the initial high demand would diminish and costs would be stabilised. However, only four months into the new system, Aneurin Bevan, the Minister of Health, informed the Cabinet that the costs of the services would be higher than expected.[3]

Until 1948, the majority of GPs practised alone and had large list sizes to maximise their income, as the 1911 Insurance Act provided an incentive for GPs to increase the number of patients on their list. There was strong opposition by GPs to a salaried system and so to ensure their participation in the new health service they were granted 'independent contractor' status.[3] Under this arrangement, GPs remained self-employed, with central government contracting services from them. This meant that there was little control over the behaviour of these GPs, who were to be the main providers of health care as well as the gate-keepers to hospitals.

The next major change came in 1966 with the introduction of the 'Family Doctor Charter', which improved the remuneration of GPs, encouraged them to work in under-provided areas, and provided finance for improving surgeries and employing practice staff.

'Race', ethnicity and culture

As the concepts of 'race', ethnicity and culture have been covered in detail in Chapter 1, a brief overview is given here to highlight the complexity in defining ethnic groups. Indeed, no data on general practitioner ethnic groups exists, except for a number of proxy measures.

Both race and ethnicity are complex concepts that are appearing in increasing number of publications.[4] Social scientists have been debating for some time on what different ethnic groups should be called:[5,6] the so-called 'battle of the name'.[7] The debate has also featured in health services research.[4,8,9,10]

'Race' first appeared in biological literature in 1749[11] and was explicitly regarded as an arbitrary classification, serving only as a convenient label and not a definable scientific entity. Race, however, carries connotations of genetic determinism and possibly of relative worth.[12] Race was therefore a taxonomy based on an ideology that views some population groups as inherently superior to others on the basis of external physical characteristics or geographical origin.[13] It is known that 85 per cent of all identified human genetic variation is accounted for by differences between individuals, whereas only 7 per cent is due to differences between what used to be called 'races'.[14]

In the United States, the collection of data on race is well established and used extensively for epidemiological, clinical and planning purposes.[15] However, the current consensus is that 'race' has no scientific value,[16] as there is more genetic variation within groups than between them.

Ethnicity is also a multidimensional concept that is being used commonly in medical research.[9] It is neither simple nor precise, and is not synonymous with 'race'. The dynamic nature and fluidity of ethnicity as a concept has been stressed.[13,17,18] Ethnicity is replacing race within the UK,[19] due to the increasing importance of social and cultural factors in health and disease, the social taboo surrounding the word 'race' and dismissal of race as a category.

What is culture?

'Culture' has been defined as a set of guidelines that include 'how to *view* the world, how to experience it *emotionally*, and how to *behave* in it in relation to other people, to supernatural forces or gods, and to the natural environment'.[20] These guidelines are passed on from generation to generation to provide cohesion and continuity of a society.

'Culture' is further complicated by societies consisting of *subcultures*,[20] in which individuals undergo *acculturation*, adopting some of the attributes of the larger society.[21] Hence, culture, too, is a social construct that is constantly changing and notoriously difficult to measure.[22]

Although an individual's cultural background has profound influence on his or her health and health outcome, it is only one of a number of influences, others being social, political, historical and economic, to name but a few.[4,21,23] It has been argued that research questions do not arise in a vacuum: they need to be answered within particular social, economic, professional, theoretical, ideological and historical contexts.[23] Pearson[24] began to address the complex politics of 'race and health research' so that there is now a move from the 'ethnic sensitivity' to the 'anti-racist' approach.[25] In the former, 'cultural differences' are offered as solutions to inequalities in health and health care,[24] resulting in the belief that the problems rest with minority ethnic groups,[26] whereas in the latter, 'racism' is the starting point that acknowledges differences within minority ethnic groups and links it to other forms of disadvantage, for example deprivation and unemployment.[25]

Operationalising ethnicity

As discussed above, all three concepts are problematic, with race being of unscientific value. Both ethnicity and culture are multidimensional social constructs that are also difficult to measure. Ethnic monitoring in organisations is now increasing and guidelines exist for its use.[27] It is also accepted in government surveys.[28] Ethnic monitoring is mandatory for the secondary care services, but the data collected thus far is incomplete and of variable quality.[29] There is no statutory requirement to record ethnic groups within primary care, although it is feasible[30] and has been advocated.[17,31]

As no ethnic group data is collected on general practitioners, two proxy methods have been used in routine statistics to identify a practitioner's ethnic group:

i) country of birth and qualification

ii) 1991 Census question on ethnic group

Country of birth and qualification

The country of birth has been commonly used as a proxy for ethnicity.[32] It is an objective but crude method of classification, and does not take into account the diversity of the country of birth. For example, the children of immigrants are not identified by this method.

There are limitations, too, with the country of qualification, as this includes a heterogeneous group, for example a significant minority of doctors qualifying in the UK were born overseas. These doctors are therefore classified as trained in the UK. With the increasing numbers of black and minority ethnic group graduates from medical schools, this classification of categorising on the basis of country of origin is becoming obsolete.[33]

1991 Census question on ethnic group

Despite the inclusion in the 1920 Census Act of 'race' as an issue upon which questions might be asked, an 'ethnic question' was not included until the 1991 Census.[34] This is a pragmatic question and despite conceptual limitations, was found to be acceptable.[28] Everyone is a member of (or claims membership of) an ethnic group, and this question is for everyone.[17]

Senior and Bhopal[13] have highlighted the fluid nature of self-determined ethnicity, so that results of studies cannot be generalised across time, generations, or populations with different histories of migration. It is also of limited use as a measure of socio-cultural differences. The Census ethnic question may not meet the needs of all researchers and health care providers, and several authors have suggested that as much information as possible should be collected to describe the groups being studied.[13,18,27] This method of classification is being used for ethnic monitoring and was introduced in the NHS in 1995.[17]

History of migration

Migration to Britain is not new, with the earliest immigrants originating from central Europe.[35] West Africans and Indians have been in the UK since the sixteenth and seventeenth centuries respectively.[36] In the sixteenth century, a number of resident Indians were renowned for their theatrical performances, and among the gentry it soon became fashionable to employ Indian servants. Beyond these isolated individuals, significant communities of African, Asian and Arab seamen settled in seaports over 200 years ago,[37,38,39] and it was they who laid the foundation for the subsequent mass migration and settlement in the UK. The reasons for this mass migration are complex and specific to each ethnic group.[40]

The main driving force was the shortage of labour after World War II, particularly in the poorly paid sectors of the economy, such as the railways, buses and hospital services.

Under the British Nationality Act of 1948, citizens of the British Commonwealth were allowed to enter Britain freely to find work, to settle, and to bring their families. Many chose this option as a result of employers' and government-led recruitment schemes. In the 1940s, the first significant migration started from the West Indies, with Indians from the subcontinent following in the 1960s.[40] However, successive immigration policies since then have significantly reduced this option for persons from the New Commonwealth.[41]

Political changes in East Africa ('Africanization') stimulated a flow of Asian refugees in the late 1960s and early 1970s.[42] The more recent migrants have come from the Sylhet region of Bangladesh, but most migration during the past 30 years or so has consisted of families of the earlier South Asian migrants, coming to join their mainly male relatives.

The above contrasts with the origins of overseas doctors, the majority of whom have come from the Indian subcontinent.[43] As the Indian subcontinent is vast and has a rich diversity of culture and language, these doctors will not necessarily be familiar with the language and culture of South Asian patients in their care in the UK.[42] Furthermore, there can be a significant social divide between these doctors – who are mainly from the educated middle classes – who could afford to pay for their medical education in the ISC, and many of their poorer patients, who are largely from rural India.

Doctors from the Indian subcontinent have been practising in Britain since 1872,[38] and were actively recruited in the 1950s to meet the shortfall from British medical schools and due to increasing demand for doctors in the NHS.[43]

This influx of overseas doctors was not foreseen and arose from the poor forecasting of the Willink Report of 1957,[44] which underestimated future medical manpower requirements. This has been described in detail in Chapter 2.

These doctors came to the UK mainly to gain postgraduate qualifications, with the intention of returning home afterwards. This pattern of migration was made possible by the General Medical Council, which recognised the basic qualifications obtained from foreign medical schools, including many in the ISC. Furthermore, immigration controls introduced from the 1960s did not apply to these doctors.[43] This pattern was curtailed with the publication of the Merrison Report in 1975, which concluded that:

> We could not fail to be aware of a widespread conviction that the standard of overseas-educated doctors allowed to practice in this country is lower than that of home-educated doctors.[45]

The Report questioned the competence of overseas-trained doctors and was based on subjective and 'objective' evidence from the medical royal colleges and practitioners. The objective evidence was based on the lower pass rate of the Royal Colleges of Psychiatrists' and General Practitioners' postgraduate examinations. For the latter, only three out of 49 overseas-qualified doctors passed the college examination. Although the numbers involved were small, the committee of inquiry concluded that, 'this is a disturbing indication of the quality of such doctors entering general practice'.

This subjective evidence was based on the belief that the standard of overseas-educated doctors is lower. These beliefs were prevalent in the medical journals, in the GMC and even the British Medical Association, who 'had expressed disquiet with the present standard of overseas doctors'.[45] This view of the poor standard of overseas doctors is still being expressed overtly today.[46]

A study has shown that the Royal College of General Practitioners' postgraduate examination does not systematically discriminate against Asian doctors.[47] However, Asian doctors born and trained overseas, and 'other' Asian doctors, performed badly. This could be due to the college examination measuring the effects of poor training or training that is not congruent with general practice in the UK.

The Merrison Report led to the establishment of the forerunner of the Professional and Linguistic Assessment Board (PLAB) test.[48] This test is still mandatory for overseas doctors and enables them to apply for limited registration for postgraduate training in hospitals. Many of these doctors were working in peripheral hospitals in the least popular hospital specialties, where postgraduate teaching was sparse. Consequently, it was difficult to obtain postgraduate qualifications, although a number succeeded and then failed to continue with their chosen specialty owing to discrimination.[43,49] These doctors reluctantly entered general practice in the 1960s, when general practice was unpopular, and many of them have ended up in single practices in the so-called 'undesirable' inner city areas.[43,48]

Many of these Asian doctors trained under the worst, rather than the best, training practices, and usually had to construct their own vocational training schemes, as competition for these was intense.[48] Discrimination in the battle for training posts[50] also occurs against British-trained doctors from minority ethnic groups.

Racial discrimination still remains in selection to medical schools[51] and continues in the postgraduate studies of Asian doctors, many of whom are second- or third-generation immigrants.[52]

Registration with the GMC

To practise in the UK, doctors who qualified overseas must first gain limited registration with the GMC through one of four routes:

- sponsorship
- membership of a royal college
- passing the PLAB test organised by the GMC
- 'requalification' through the United Examining Board.

Sponsorship is open only to those returning to their country of origin and is organised by the royal colleges. The United Examining Board does provide an alternative mechanism and candidates have to sit a preliminary examination that is used by universities to decide who might benefit from a clinical attachment prior to taking the qualifying examination. Places for these attachments are limited and the pass rates for college and board exams remain low. Most overseas doctors opt to take the PLAB test. This is a two-stage process, with the first stage requiring the candidate to achieve a good pass in the prerequisite International English Language Testing System (IELTS).[53] Subsequently, candidates sit a clinical exam, which has been reformed to reflect current undergraduate practice[54] by including an Objective Structured Clinical and Oral Exam (OSCOE). The OSCOE format is not familiar to many overseas-qualified doctors, so their chances of passing become limited.[55]

It is interesting to note that doctors qualifying from the European Economic Area are exempt from these language and 'fitness' to practice tests, whereas all other overseas doctors have to take them. In fact, politicians have recently fuelled racism by calling for even 'tougher medical tests' for overseas doctors, which casts a slur on the overall competence of overseas doctors.[46] What the public and politicians fail to realise is that the PLAB test is extremely tough and the pass rate is very low. This has been demonstrated by the fact that only one out of 100 British-trained doctors passed the test.

Characteristics of GPs in the UK

There is a dearth of literature and data on the ethnic origin of general practitioners, and the only information available is from routine statistics and one-off surveys, which have used proxy measures for recording ethnic group, i.e. country of birth and qualification (see above).

For the years 1988–92, only the country of birth of unrestricted general practice principals was recorded (Table 5.1) and the majority of these GPs were from the Indian subcontinent and constituted 20 per cent of the total number of GPs. As the country of first qualification data is available, a trend in the number of GPs from overseas is shown in Figure 5.1. The data is provided in aggregate form as qualification within the UK, EEA or elsewhere. Furthermore, information is only provided at regional authority level to maintain anonymity (Table 5.2). For comparison, data on ethnic groups is available for hospital medical staff, of which BMEG doctors form a third of the workforce (Table 5.3).

The unequal geographical distribution of GPs is well documented[56] and is particularly marked for overseas-qualified GPs. A high proportion of the latter reside within London, the West Midlands and the North West. A smaller proportion can be found in the South Eastern and South Western regions.

Many of these overseas-qualified doctors are working in smaller practices, particularly single-handed practices, and are concentrated within conurbations (Table 5.4).[43] It is known that doctors who qualified from the Indian subcontinent have more patients on their lists who attract deprivation payments.[57] There is also greater inequality in the distribution of other primary care professionals, such as practice nurses, practice staff and opticians,[56] which increases pressure on these doctors to deliver optimum care. This is another example of the 'inverse care law',[58] in that the provision of health services varies inversely with the need for them. Access to good quality primary care services varies more within urban areas, such as London, than anywhere else.[59]

Overseas-qualified doctors are older than their British-qualified colleagues when they enter general practice, which is not surprising as they came to Britain initially to complete their postgraduate training (Table 5.5).

History is about to repeat itself as these older GPs come up to retirement. There will be a large manpower shortage again in many health authorities in England.[60] These practitioners are, and will continue to be, very difficult to replace as they have coped with relatively high patient needs in designated deprived areas.[57] It is becoming evident that the recent increase in medical student intake will not be sufficient to fill this shortage.[61]

General practice consultations

Contrary to expectations, nearly all South Asian people are registered with a GP; non-registration seems to be higher amongst African Caribbean men than in South Asians and the white UK population.[62,63]

Studies have found that between 66 and 80 per cent of Asian patients consult with a doctor of Asian origin.[62,63] Ahmad *et al.*[64] found that linguistic and cultural concordance between patient and doctor was more important in the choice of GP than their gender. The Health and Lifestyles Survey confirms this and estimates that between 40 and 60 per cent of Asians communicate with their GP in one of the South Asian languages.[63] But others have found that proximity of the practice to the patient's home is more important than the doctor's sex or ethnic origin.[65] Recent data shows that up to a quarter of white respondents preferred to see a white doctor (Table 5.6) due to difficulties in understanding non-white doctors and their preference to see someone of their own colour. Some comments made by these patients were overtly racist:

> I'm prejudiced against them, they're in the wrong country. If you were in their country I wouldn't object but they're in my country.

Studies have found that consultations with general practitioners are higher amongst Asians and increase with age.[62] It is not possible to determine whether these patterns reflect differences in morbidity, varying thresholds and perceptions of illness, differential uptake of services, or a combination of these factors. The Fourth National Morbidity Study[66] attempted to control for morbidity and showed that there were no significant differences in the overall consultation rates amongst the different ethnic groups. However, the consultation rates for serious conditions were higher among Indians, Pakistanis and Bangladeshis of both sexes.

The only recent survey that provides a different picture from the above is the secondary analysis of data from the North West Thames RHA Health and Lifestyle Survey.[67] This found that reported consultations within the previous two weeks were 17 per cent for Asians, 16 per cent for African Caribbeans and 18 per cent for Europeans.

Studies have also shown that many white GPs hold negative attitudes about people of South Asian origin. They generally believe that South Asian patients consult more frequently, often have 'trivial complaints' and 'ill-defined conditions', require longer consultations, are less compliant and increase their workload.[68,69] This is not confirmed by more recent data.[66]

Explaining patterns of general practice utilisation

It is not surprising that variations exist in the use of primary health care services described above. Many factors influence utilisation of services. Some of these, such as age and sex, are common to all ethnic groups, although their effect may be different in a particular group, hence the differential uptake of services.[70]

Gillam[71] produced a critique of the literature, and Smaje[70] has gone further by providing a framework to explain health service utilisation by minority ethnic groups in which he highlights the role of:

- health beliefs that have been studied using specific diseases or problems
- lack of knowledge, low expectations and perceived administrative barriers to services
- social structure of the extended family, which may partly explain the low uptake of community services. Of course, these social structures are not static and vary between ethnic groups including successive generations of the ethnic communities
- distribution and access to health services. Tudor-Hart[58] stated that the provision of health services varied inversely with the need for them. Access to good quality primary care services varied more within urban areas, such as London, than elsewhere[59]
- racism as a pervasive feature of British society and its institutions, such as the NHS.

The above are exacerbated by the effects of poverty and social structures of BMEGs that have not been taken into account in health services research.[23]

Measuring the quality of consultations

The measurement of quality within general practice and in health care at large is difficult in conception as well as practice.[72,73] It is both a multidimensional and a relative concept that can always be improved upon.[74] This is at the heart of all quality initiatives. Inequalities exist in both accessing and in the use of health services.[75]

Black and minority ethnic groups are more likely than whites:

1. to find physical access to their GP difficult
2. to wait longer in the surgery
3. to feel that the time spent with them was inadequate
4. to be generally less satisfied with the outcome of the consultation.[63,76]

They are also less likely to receive a follow-up appointment or to be referred for further investigations.[77,78] There is no evidence that smaller practices provide poorer quality of care than larger practices.[73]

Barriers to communication are obviously important and there is tremendous linguistic diversity in the languages spoken by individuals,[79] with nearly 600,000 people unable to speak sufficient English to communicate adequately with health professionals.[80] Obviously high-quality medical care requires effective communication between the patient and health professional, and has been linked with improved health outcomes.[81] Despite this evidence, there has been little movement towards the provision of adequate interpreting services within primary care and information about services offered in appropriate languages and media.[82,83]

Figure 5.1 Number of general practitioners in England

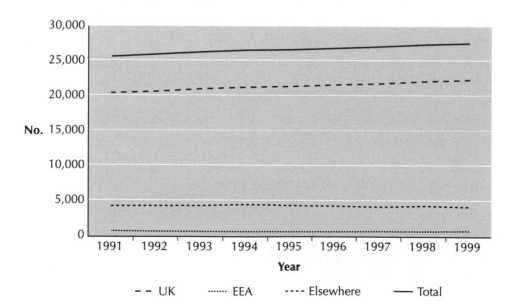

Source: NHSE Headquarters. Statistics (Workforce) GMS. Leeds, 1999

Table 5.1 Country of birth of general practitioners (England & Wales)

Country of birth	1988	1989	1990	1991	1992
Great Britain	19927	20197	20167	20375	20852
N Ireland, Eire & Channel Islands	811	756	706	628	574
India, Pakistan, Sri Lanka & Bangladesh	4366	4428	4469	4430	4344
Australia, Canada & New Zealand	114	119	132	118	116
Other Commonwealth countries	749	797	835	838	819
European Economic Community	86	85	86	91	90
Other European countries	267	244	215	184	173
Elsewhere	601	613	647	669	676

Source: NHSE Headquarters. Statistics (Workforce) GMS. Leeds, 1999

Table 5.2 Unrestricted principals by country of first qualification (October 1999)

Region	UK	EEA	Elsewhere	Total
Northern Yorkshire	3019	110	463 (13)	3592
Trent	2305	75	398 (14)	2773
Eastern	2461	118	377 (13)	2956
London	2518	167	1262 (32)	3947
South Eastern	4199	141	439 (9)	4779
South Western	2912	60	69 (2)	3041
West Midlands	2175	79	639 (22)	2893
North West	2769	109	727 (20)	3605
England (Total)	22358	859	4374 (16)	27591
Wales	1444	55	262 (15)	1761

Source: NHSE Headquarters. Statistics (Workforce) GMS. Leeds, 1999

Table 5.3 All hospital medical staff by ethnic origin (England at 30 September 1999)

All ethnic groups

	No.	%
White	42777	67.3
Black	2412	3.8
Caribbean	390	0.6
African	1480	2.3
Other	542	0.9
Asian	11760	16.8
Indian	8781	13.8
Pakistani	1565	2.5
Bangladeshi	288	0.5
Chinese	1036	1.6
Any other ethnic group	5307	8.4
Not known	1382	2.1
All	63548	100

Source: Department of Health, www.doh.gov.uk/stats/d_results.htm

Table 5.4 Number of doctors in the practice by type of area (%)

Size of practice	Total (British- and overseas-qualified)	British-qualified			Overseas-qualified		
		Total	Conurbation	Other	Total	Conurbation	Other
1	11	10	13	8	22	28	18
2	15	13	13	13	32	32	33
3	23	23	15	26	17	15	18
4	21	22	22	22	14	14	15
5–6	23	25	23	25	10	9	11
≥7	6	7	11	5	2	2	2
		1	3	–	2	1	3
Not stated	1						

Source: Smith D J. *Overseas doctors in the National Health Service.* London: Policy Studies Institute, 1980

Table 5.5 Age and sex characteristics of GPs

Age (years)	British-qualified	Overseas-qualified	All GPs
≤29	4	–	4
30–34	15	8	14
35–44	24	57	28
45–54	33	24	32
≥55	24	11	22
Sex			
Male	87	82	86
Female	13	18	14

Source: Smith D J. *Overseas doctors in the National Health Service.* London: Policy Studies Institute, 1980

Table 5.6 Preferred ethnic origin for doctor by gender

	White	Caribbean	Indian	African Asian	Pakistani	Bangladeshi	Chinese
Men	21	12	26	21	34	29	*
Women	29	11	33	20	49	54	*
Total	26	12	34	20	41	42	31

*small base numbers in the cell make the estimate unreliable

Source: Nazroo J Y. *The health of Britain's ethnic minorities.* London: Policy Studies Institute, 1997

Racism against doctors

Not only are black and minority ethnic doctors discriminated against in selection for medical school, postgraduate training and examinations, but they also face verbal and physical abuse from their patients. This direct and institutional racism continues when applying for practice partnership. Many BMEG doctors end up in single-handed practices in the inner cities, and with a heavy workload.[84] They also tend to have poor standard practice premises.[85]

Once in practice, overseas-qualified doctors are more likely to be referred to the various stages of the GMC conduct procedures than UK-trained doctors. The latest study commissioned by the GMC concludes that:[86]

- there is no evidence of overt or covert racial discrimination or bias within the GMC
- public bodies referring proportionately more overseas-qualified doctors to the GMC is a major factor in explaining why this group of doctors are over-represented in the GMC's procedures
- although there was no evidence of discrimination or bias, there were unexplained inconsistencies in the later stages of the complaints process.

It recommended that the current complaints model should be underlined by principles of transparency, consistency, fairness and freedom from discrimination, as there were limitations in the existing GMC model.

Doctors from BMEGs are still under-represented on decision-making boards, such as health authorities and trusts,[87] which is surprising when one considers the high proportion of BMEG GPs in the UK. The reasons for this are unknown, although institutional racism must play a part.

Refugee doctors

Another group of minority doctors is the refugee doctors, who face enormous difficulties in practising as doctors in the UK. They are considered separately from other overseas-trained doctors and are confronted with additional hurdles to register with the GMC.

Refugees and asylum seekers have been increasing in number during the past few years. The plight of refugee doctors is not new, with earlier waves of exiles, particularly from Germany and central Europe in the 1930s, having encountered similar difficulties.[88] Yet it has to be acknowledged that refugees have made substantial contributions to professional life in Britain.

The exact number of refugee doctors in Britain is not known, although estimates suggest there are at least 2000. The majority of these reside within Greater London. As described previously, they too are required to demonstrate their competence to practice in the UK. Refugees are disadvantaged, however, in comparison with other overseas doctors seeking registration for several reasons:

- extreme financial hardship
- psychological distress associated with loss and persecution
- the ambiguity of their legal status
- the cost of exam fees
- lack of opportunity to prepare for clinical exams, especially due to the haphazard provision of clinical attachments

- long waiting lists for retaking the PLAB test
- unhelpful feedback after failure
- racism.[88]

Box 5.1 STEPS FOR FACILITATING INTEGRATION OF REFUGEE DOCTORS INTO THE NHS WORKFORCE

Establish network of clinical attachments through collaboration between the regional postgraduate deaneries, the royal colleges, health authorities and trusts.

Ensure appropriate careers advice through colleges and deaneries and non-governmental organisations such as World University Service and the BMA.

Provide more bursaries for travel and subsistence for clinical attachments and cost of the Professional and Linguistic Assessment Board's (PLAB) test.

Provide revision courses and 'mock' exams for the Objective Structured Clinical and Oral Exam (OSCOE) 7.

Reduce waiting lists to take and retake the PLAB test.

Provide constructive feedback on areas of deficiency after the PLAB test.

Review the role and practice of the United Examining Board.

Continue to expose and challenge racism.

Source: Berlin A *et al.* Refugee doctors in Britain: a wasted resource. *BMJ* 1997; 315: 264–65

Given the repeated findings of racial discrimination against Asian graduates from British medical schools, it seems reasonable to infer that graduates from overseas schools must face even greater discrimination in their search for careers advice, clinical attachments and, having secured limited registration, employment.

Workforce predictions indicate that 500 additional new doctors are required annually in Britain.[89] Training each doctor costs around £200,000.[90] A training package could be developed, costing a lot less, to integrate more refugee doctors into the workforce (see Box 5.1). This would certainly go some way towards addressing the shortage of GPs.

The Health Minister John Denham launched the report of the working group on refugee doctors and dentists[91] in November 2000. It was encouraging to see that the Department of Health (DoH) endorsed the recommendations of the group that included the establishment of a database of refugee doctors and dentists, and ensured that they received language skills and training opportunities. A steering group has been established, chaired by Professor Lesley Southgate, to implement the report, and the DoH has provided £500,000 towards the initiative.

Conclusion

We can see that BME doctors (UK- and overseas-trained) are an integral part of the frontline staff of the NHS. They have contributed enormously to the running of the NHS by providing their services in deprived urban areas that have been shunned by the majority of white UK-trained doctors.

There is still reluctance on the part of the medical establishment and the NHS to acknowledge that institutional racism exists within their organisations. These BME doctors have been victims of both direct and institutional racism, and it is critical that action is taken to reverse this.

References

1. Royal College of General Practitioners. *The nature of general medical practice*. London: The Royal College of General Practitioners, 1996.

2. Stevens R. *Medical practice in modern England*. London and New Haven: Yale University Press, 1964.

3. Klein R. *The new politics of the NHS*. London: Longmore, 1995.

4. Sheldon T A, Parker H. Race and ethnicity in health research. *Journal of Public Health Medicine* 1992; 14: 104–10.

5. Banton M. *The idea of race*. London: Tavistock, 1977.

6. Cole M. 'Black and ethnic minority' or 'Asian, black and other minority ethnic': A further note on nomenclature. *Sociology* 1993; 27: 671–73.

7. Banton M. The battle of the name. *New Community* 1987; XIV: 170–75.

8. Bhopal R S, Phillimore P, Kholi H S. Inappropriate use of the term 'Asian': an obstacle to ethnicity and health research. *J Public Hlth Med* 1991; 13 (4): 244–46.

9. McKenzie K J, Crowcroft N S. Race, ethnicity, culture and science. *BMJ* 1994; 309: 286–87.

10. Williams D R. The concept of race in health services research: 1966 to 1990. *Health Services Research* 1994; 29 (3): 261–73.

11. Montague A. *The concept of race*. Toronto: Collier-Macmillan, 1964.

12. Cooper R. Race, disease and health. In: Rathwell T, Phillips D, eds. *Health race & ethnicity*. London: Croom Helm, 1986.

13. Senior P A, Bhopal R. Ethnicity as a variable in epidemiological research. *BMJ* 1994; 309: 327–30.

14. Lewontin R C. *The doctrine of DNA: biology as ideology*. London: Penguin, 1992.

15. Hahn R A. The state of federal health statistics on racial and ethnic groups. *JAMA* 1992; 267: 268–71.

16. LaVeist T A. Beyond dummy variables and sample selection: what health services researchers ought to know about race as a variable. *Health Services Research* 1994; 29: 1–16.

17. Gill P S, Johnson M. Ethnic monitoring and ethnicity. *BMJ* 1995; 310: 890.

18. McKenzie K J, Crowcroft N S. Describing race, ethnicity, and culture in medical research. *BMJ* 1996a; 312: 1050.

19. Mackintosh J, Bhopal R, Unwin N, Ahmad N. *Step by step guide to epidemiological health needs assessment for ethnic minority groups*. Newcastle: University of Newcastle, 1998.

20. Helman C G. *Culture, health and illness*. London: Butterworth and Co Ltd, 1990.

21. Leach E. *Social anthropology*. Glasgow: Fontana, 1982.

22. Fernando S. *Mental health, race and culture*. London: Macmillan, 1991.

23. Ahmad W I U. Making black people sick: 'race', ideology and health research. In: Ahmad W I U, ed. *'Race' and health in contemporary Britain*. Buckingham: Open University Press, 1993.

24. Pearson M. The politics of ethnic minority health studies. In: Rathwell T, Phillips D, eds. *Health, race & ethnicity*. London: Croom Helm, 1986.

25. Stubbs P. 'Ethnically sensitive' or 'anti-racist'? Models for health research and service delivery. In: Ahmad W I U, ed. *'Race' and health in Contemporary Britain.* Buckingham: : Open University Press, 1993.

26. Burke A. Social work and intervention in West Indian psychiatric disorder. In: Coombe V, Little A, eds. *Race & social work: a guide to training.* London: Routledge, 1986.

27. McKenzie K J, Crowcroft N S. Guidelines on describing race, ethnicity, and culture in medical research. *BMJ* 1996b; 312: 1094.

28. Teague A. Ethnic group: first results from the 1991 Census. *Population Trends* 1993; 72: 12–17.

29. Lay-Yee R, Gilthorpe M S, Wilson R C. *An audit of ethnic monitoring.* University of Birmingham: Department of Public Health and Epidemiology, 1998.

30. Pringle M, Rothera I. Practicality of recording patient ethnicity in general practice: descriptive intervention study and attitude survey. *BMJ* 1996; 312: 1080–82.

31. Heath I. The role of ethnic monitoring in general practice. *Br J Gen Pract* 1991; 41: 310–11.

32. Marmot M G, Adelstein A M, Bulusu L, Shukla V. *Immigrant mortality in England and Wales 1970–78.* (OPCS studies on population and medical subjects: No.47). London: HMSO, 1984.

33. McManus C. Factors affecting likelihood of applicants being offered a place in medical schools in the United Kingdom in 1996 and 1997: retrospective study. *BMJ* 1998; 317: 1111–17.

34. Bulmer M. A controversial census topic: race and ethnicity in the British census. *Journal of Official Statistics* 1986; 2 (4): 471–80.

35. Commission for Racial Equality. *Roots to the future.* London: CRE, 1996.

36. Fryer P. *Staying power: the history of black people in Britain.* London: Pluto, 1984.

37. Little K S. *Negroes in Britain.* London: Kegan Paul, Trench, Trübner & Co, 1947.

38. Visram R. *Ayahs, lascars and princes: Indians in Britain 1700–1947.* London: Pluto Press, 1986.

39. Halliday F. *Arabs in exile: Yemeni migrants in urban Britain.* London: I B Tauris, 1992.

40. Peach C, Rodgers A, Chance J, Daley P. Immigration and ethnicity. In: Halsey A H, Webb J, eds. *Twentieth-century British social trends.* Basingstoke: Macmillan Press Ltd, 2000.

41. Martin I. The development of UK immigration control. In: Coombe V, Little A, eds. *Race & social work: a guide to training.* London: Routledge, 1986.

42. Taylor C. Asians in Britain – origins and lifestyles. In: McAvoy B, Donaldson L, eds. *Health care for Asians.* Oxford: OUP, 1990.

43. Smith D J. *Overseas doctors in the National Health Service.* London: Policy Studies Institute, 1980.

44. Willink H. *Report of the committee to consider the future numbers of medical practitioners and appropriate intake of medical students.* London: HMSO, 1957.

45. Merrison A W. *Report of the committee of inquiry into the regulation of the medical profession.* London: HMSO, 1975.

46. Toynbee P. The racist poison pill. *The Guardian* 2000; 30 August: 15.

47. Wakeford R, Foulkes J, McManus C, Southgate L. MRCGP pass rate by medical school and region of postgraduate training. *British Journal of General Practice* 1993; 28: 542–43.

48. Rashid A. Asian doctors and nurses in the NHS. In: McAvoy B, Donaldson L, eds. *Health care for Asians.* Oxford: OUP, 1990.

49. Anwar M, Ali A. *Overseas doctors: experiences and expectations – a research study.* London: Commission for Racial Equality, 1987.

50. McKeigue P M, Richards J D M, Richards P. Effects of discrimination by sex and race on the early careers of British medical graduates during 1981–7. *BMJ* 1990; 301: 961–64.

51. Esmail A, Nelson P, Primarolo D, Toma T. Acceptance into medical school and racial discrimination. *BMJ* 1995; 310: 501–02.

52. Esmail A, Everington S. Racial discrimination against doctors from ethnic minorities. *BMJ* 1993; 306: 691–92.

53. Cassell J, Goode L. Attaining competence in English. *BMJ Classified* 1997; 314: 2.

54. Whitehouse C, Roland M, Campion P. *Teaching medicine in the community.* Oxford: Oxford University Press, 1997.

55. Berlin A, Gill P, Stone R. Changes in PLAB examination will have implications for overseas doctors. *BMJ* 1997; 315: 1539.

56. Gravelle H, Sutton M. *Inequality in the geographical distribution of GPs in England and Wales 1974–1995.* Manchester: National Primary Care Research and Development Centre, July 1999.

57. Taylor Jr D H, Esmail A. Retrospective analysis of census data on general practitioners who qualified in South Asia: who will replace them as they retire? *BMJ* 1999; 318: 306–10.

58. Tudor-Hart J. The inverse care law. *Lancet* 1971; i: 405–12.

59. Boyle S, Smaje C. *Primary health care in London: quantifying the challenge.* London: King's Fund, 1993.

60. Mathie A G. *The primary care workforce – an update for the new millennium.* London: Royal College of General Practitioners, 2000.

61. Pereira Gray D. Fit for the future – are medical schools going to produce the doctors the health service needs? *Med Educ* 1999; 33: 872–73.

62. Johnson M. Inner city residents, ethnic minorities and primary health care in the West Midlands. In: Rathwell T, Phillips D, eds. *Health, race & ethnicity.* London: Croom Helm, 1986.

63. Rudat K. *Black and minority ethnic groups in England.* London: HEA, 1994.

64. Ahmad W I U, Kernohan E E M, Baker M R. Patients' choice of general practitioner: influence of patients' fluency in English and the ethnicity and sex of the doctor. *J Roy Coll Gen Practitioners* 1989; 39: 153–55.

65. Jain C, Narayan N, Pike L S, Clarkson M E, Cox I G, Chatterjee J. Attitudes of Asian patients in Birmingham to general practitioner services. *J Roy Coll Gen Practitioners* 1985; 35: 416–18.

66. McCormick A, Fleming D, Charlton J. *Morbidity statistics from general practice. Fourth national study 1991–1992.* London: HMSO, 1995.

67. Nzegwu F. *Black people and health care in contemporary Britain.* Reading: International Institute for Black Research, 1993.

68. Wright C M. Language and communication problems in an Asian community. *J Roy Coll Gen Practitioners* 1983; 33: 101–04.

69. Ahmad W I U, Kernohan E E M, Baker M R. Patients' choice of general practitioner: importance of patients' and doctors' sex and ethnicity. *Br J Gen POract Practice* 1991b; 41: 330–31.

70. Smaje C. *Health, 'race' and ethnicity. Making sense of the evidence.* London: King's Fund, 1995.

71. Gillam S. Ethnicity and the use of health services. *Postgrad Med J* 1990; 66: 989–93.

72. Toon P. *What is good general practice?* Occasional paper No 65. London: Royal College of General Practitioners, 1994.

73. Howie J G R, Heaney D J, Maxwell M, Walker J J, Freeman G K, Rai H. Quality at general practice consultations: cross sectional survey. *BMJ* 1999; 319: 738–43.

74. Maxwell R J. Quality assessment in health. *BMJ* 1984; 288: 1470–71.

75. Acheson D. *Independent inquiry into inequalities in health report.* London: The Stationery Office, 1998.

76. Nazroo J Y. *The health of Britain's ethnic minorities.* London: Policy Studies Institute, 1997.

77. Chaturvedi N, Rai H, Ben-Shlomo Y. Lay diagnosis and health-care seeking behaviour for chest pain in south Asians and Europeans. *Lancet* 1997; 350: 1578–83.

78. Smaje C, Le Grand J. Ethnicity, equity and use of health services in the British national health service. *Soc Sci & Med* 1997; 45: 485–96.

79. Baker P, Everseley J. *Multilingual capital. The languages of London's schoolchildren and their relevance to economic, social and educational policies.* London: Battlebridge Publications, 2000.

80. Carr-Hill R, Passingham S, Wolf A, Kent N. *Lost opportunities: the language skills of linguistic minorities in England and Wales.* London: Basic Skills Agency, 1996.

81. Stewart M. Effective patient–physician communication and health: a review. *Can Med Assoc J* 1995; 152: 1423–33.

82. Jones D, Gill P. Breaking down language barriers. *BMJ* 1998; 316: 1476.

83. Levenson R, Gillam S. *Linkworkers in primary care.* London, King's Fund, 1998.

84. Murfin D, Hungin P. Asian general practitioners and the RCGP. *Br J Gen Pract* 1993; 43: 139–40.

85. London Strategic Review Independent Advisory Panel. *Health services in London: a strategic review (the Turnberg Report).* London: Department of Health, 1997.

86. Allen I. *The handling of complaints by the GMC: a study of decision-making and outcomes.* London: Policy Studies Institute, 2000.

87. Alexandre Z. *Study of black, Asian and minority issues.* London: Department of Health, 2000.

88. Berlin A, Gill P, Eversley J. Refugee doctors in Britain: a wasted resource. *BMJ* 1997; 315: 264–65.

89. Medical Workforce Standing Advisory Committee. *Second report: planning the medical workforce.* London: Department of Health, 1995.

90. Richards P, McManus I C, Allen I. British doctors are not disappearing. *BMJ* 1997; 314: 1587.

91. Overseas Doctors Sub-Group. *Report of the working group on refugee doctors and dentists.* London: Department of Health, 2000.

Chapter 6

Career progression and job satisfaction

Is the selection process for becoming a consultant racist?

Lyndsey Unwin

Until the NHS takes the issue of racial discrimination and bullying seriously, there will continue to be many doctors who dedicate their lives to the NHS but who are ignored, exploited, sidelined and discriminated against in their working lives.

Anonymous

Introduction

Discrimination is done in such a nice way. So delicately done you can't blame a particular person.

The royal colleges have been responsible for blocking the career progression of thousands of overseas doctors.

I was once almost reduced to despair when about 25 applications for senior house officer posts and locums went either unacknowledged or without offer of interview.[1]

There is an on-going wish in the profession for there to be a non-consultant career grade because it is a way of restricting the number of doctors who have access to private practice.

These views, expressed by several doctors, confirm that there is undoubtedly institutionalised racism in the health service. Many overseas doctors claim that their skin colour and background are obstacles to their career paths. Others go further and accuse the medical profession's leaders of running 'a white man's register' and retaining 'jobs for the boys'. Whatever you believe, there is agreement on all sides that where discrimination exists in the recruitment of doctors it is often difficult to prove.

Much of this chapter's research is based on personal stories and experiences, which in many ways makes the evidence that racism exists in our health service even more compelling. Anecdotes abound – for example, the Asian doctor who attended numerous interviews to obtain a senior registrar post in paediatric surgery, all without success, although on each occasion the person appointed had less experience and fewer qualifications; or, the highly qualified overseas doctor who is stuck in a staff grade position with no sign of gaining the elusive Certificate of Completion of Specialist Training (CCST). And running through it all is the fear that if you speak out, the damage to your career will be irreparable.

So, is race – largely identified by country of origin or skin colour – a career obstacle? Could it be said that the selection process for becoming a consultant is racist? This chapter looks at the evidence suggesting that the medical establishment is discriminating against overseas doctors.

The system

There are currently nearly 10,000 non-consultant career grade doctors working in the health service. During the past decade, associate specialists, staff grades and non-standard grades, such as trust grades, have mushroomed to fill both senior and junior posts. Doctors from minority ethnic groups fill many of these appointments.

The increase in these non-standard grades is causing concern in some quarters. Speaking at a BMA conference on discrimination and bullying in March 2001, Greg Dilliway, Associate Specialist at St Helen's and Knowsley Community NHS Trust and Chairman of the North West Non-Consultant Career Grade Committee said:

> What I find particularly worrying is the increase in trust grade posts. These are created to fill a very specific need in a trust and often have little regard for the doctor in terms of their professional development and future in the NHS. We hear of many cases of bullying and racial discrimination from doctors in these grades.

Although they have not been through a recognised structured training programme, many associate specialists and staff grades are well-trained doctors. Most have the ability and the motivation to progress to consultant level, yet many of them have been and continue to be blocked earlier in their careers. Why?

To answer this question, we have to look at the whole system of training and career progression in the UK medical profession. We need to understand what happens to overseas doctors when they arrive in the UK.

The training requirements for doctors

The British Medical Association's (BMA) guide for doctors new to the UK[2] provides very clear information on the medical hierarchy and training system. It states that the medical royal colleges and their faculties are responsible for specialist training. A network of regional postgraduate deans administers and monitors the system. The Specialist Training Authority (STA) of the royal colleges issues CCSTs to doctors at the end of their training. The General Medical Council (GMC) keeps a register of specialists.

Once fully registered, doctors become senior house officers (SHOs). They usually stay in this grade for two or three years, and this is their general professional training. During this time, they will study for examinations set by the royal colleges, which are usually a requirement for entry to higher specialist training.

The higher specialist training grade is for new specialist registrars (SpR). Training programmes for this grade are likely to last from four to six years. Doctors compete on merit for places in the grade, and those who gain places will be given a National Training Number (NTN), which they will keep throughout their training. The end point of the training is the CCST.

Consultants are the most senior grade in a hospital and have ultimate clinical responsibility for their patients and for training the junior doctors in their team. It is a legal requirement for doctors to be on the GMC's specialist register before they can take up consultant appointments.

This is all very straightforward if you are a UK or EU graduate, but much more complex for doctors from other overseas countries.

PLAB

First, overseas doctors, like their UK and EU colleagues, must apply to be on the GMC's medical register before they can do any clinical work. Second, they are required to sit the Professional Linguistic Assessment Board (PLAB) test set by the GMC. There are many references to PLAB on the Internet, on which overseas doctors can register for professional training courses to help them be more prepared – but at a price. Some sites refer to the test as 'challenging' and urge candidates to take their revision 'seriously'. In fact, most PLAB candidates are unsuccessful because it is not simply an assessment of language skills and the ability to speak and write English, but is a tough test of clinical skills that all non-EU doctors have to pass before they can practise in this country.

An anomaly of the test is that it is only doctors from non-EU countries who must sit and pass it. EC law rules that doctors from within the EU do not need to pass the test. This means a surgeon from Bombay with reasonable English probably stands less chance of finding a job in the NHS than a Spanish doctor who cannot speak a word of the language.

Dr Neil Ashford, a psychiatrist at the Julian Hospital in Norwich and Deputy Chairman of the British Medical Association's (BMA) Non-Consultant Career Grade Committee, is a long-standing campaigner for a fairer training system. He explains:

> If your degree is from Calcutta or Bombay then I'm sorry, it doesn't count. You will have to sit the PLAB exam, which is more advanced than the medical finals I had to sit as a UK graduate. About two years ago, somebody tried the PLAB exam on 51 newly qualified British graduates in Manchester and 49, who according to the GMC were deemed to be qualified, failed.

The elusive CCST

Once the PLAB test has been passed, overseas doctors face two types of training programmes, known as type 1 and type 2 training. Type 1 training is defined as a higher specialist training programme which, if completed satisfactorily, will lead to the award of a CCST and entry to the specialist register held by the GMC.[3] Type 2 is defined as a higher specialist training programme or fixed-term training appointment. Here the doctor pursues an agreed training programme tailored to meet the individual doctor's training goals. This will usually last from six months to two years but may be longer to fulfil individual needs. The programme does not lead to the award of a CCST.[3] Type 2 appointments are specifically for overseas doctors who do not have rights of residence.

The majority of overseas doctors from black and minority ethnic communities are guided towards the type 2 training programme. Most are unable to become consultants and so become staff grade doctors or associate specialists. The BMA guide[2] defines staff grade doctors as 'a permanent career grade in hospital medicine, which doctors can enter from the senior house officer grade, i.e. instead of moving to higher specialist training'.

Associate specialists, on the other hand, are defined in the guide as being 'more senior hospital doctors, but who are still responsible to named consultants'. Until 1997, associate specialist appointments were usually personal appointments.[3] Now, however, associate specialist posts in England may be advertised and associate specialists recruited directly by competition. Appointment procedures are nationally specified, whether the post is advertised or not.

In the past, overseas doctors who had worked for many years in the UK but who could not apply to be a consultant became associate specialists. Today, most overseas doctors in this position join the growing army of non-consultant career grades or NCCGs. Neither associate specialists nor NCCGs normally have access to private practice because most private insurance companies require doctors to be in the GMC's specialist register. Statistics show that up to 70 per cent of doctors in these staff grades are from black and minority ethnic groups.[4]

Understandably, many overseas doctors who are stuck in NCCGs are disenchanted with the medical profession. Many of them express their views in the medical press. The following quotes are an example of the letters that have been published:

> *The fact is overseas doctors are used as extra pairs of hands in the NHS with absolutely no consideration for our training or future careers. We do not make the grade because of a misguided belief system and culture in the NHS, which takes delight in believing that we are inferior beings with little or no medical education, and whose presence should be endured and suffered. Meanwhile, we are expected to enjoy the great honour of slaving away in positions for which we are over-qualified, with the great hope that attaining a membership of one of the royal colleges will be the beginning of a promising career.[5]*

> *The struggle for overseas doctors to get equivalent training to non-overseas doctors is a very real one. We overseas doctors invariably spend our SHO years in district general hospitals, as teaching hospital posts are largely unattainable. After passing the relevant college exams, the next hurdle is getting a specialist registrar job without which it is impossible to get higher surgical training and the elusive Certificate of Completion of Specialist Training. Pick a specialty, then see how many overseas doctors are in specialist registrar posts. We can't all be that bad can we?[6]*

> *Racial discrimination is widely acknowledged, at least among ethnic minority groups, as a hindrance to the career aspirations of graduates from ethnic minorities.[7]*

Many NCCGs are outraged that they are working alongside specialist registrars doing identical work and gaining the same experience, yet their training is not recognised by the medical profession. One argument put forward is that type 2 training exists to produce an experienced workforce who will not be paid at a consultant level and have all the rights that a consultant enjoys.

Mr Mohib Khan, an associate specialist in urology at Huddersfield Royal Infirmary and Chairman of the BMA Non-Consultant Career Grade Committee, has attacked a system that favours one group of doctors over another. He claims it is 'disgraceful' that type 1 training is recognised when type 2 is ignored by the royal colleges, although doctors in both groups are doing identical work. He believes the medical establishment is expert at playing with words and has deliberately created a 'second grade workforce' to maintain the ratio of consultants and accredited CCST holders. He poses two questions:

- If a non-career consultant grade doctor is regarded as not having the equivalent training to qualify for a CCST, how can he or she treat a patient without supervision?
- If such grades only undertake supervised work, then does this not signify that it is a training post and should such posts not be recognised for CCST purposes?

Mr Awani Choudhary, an associate specialist at Bassetlaw District Hospital in Nottingham, Chairman of the Trent Region Non-Consultant Career Grade Committee and Deputy Chairman of the National Committee, is of the same opinion:

> *Why appoint a consultant when you can get three staff grade doctors for the same salary? The NHS would collapse tomorrow if the system was changed. Many surveys show that large numbers of consultants are fulfilling their NHS contracts, but at the end of the day they still want to get off for an afternoon here and a morning there to do other things including private practice, knowing that their patients are being safely looked after by very experienced senior hospital doctors who don't cost the trust a fortune. I don't think things will improve in the short term because the present system is so economical.*

Culture of fear

There are recurring themes that can be drawn from letters, personal stories and anecdotal evidence. The first is the culture of fear that many minority ethnic doctors live with. This fear was highlighted in a survey carried out by Dr Neil Ashford, who was asked by the BMA Racial Equality Committee to explore the range of racially motivated behaviours experienced by non-consultant career grade doctors (NCCGs).

To prepare the report, he firstly drew on verbal reports he had received informally and then contacted the regional NCCG chairs asking them to invite their members to write in with their experiences. He explains:

> *Initially, I was pleasantly surprised, perhaps naively, at the small number of letters I was receiving and indeed I have only received letters from 11 NCCGs to date. Perhaps things were not so bad amongst the NCCGs as I had thought. Then came the verbal reports from regional NCCG chairs. They told me that NCCGs hardly dared put pen to paper because they did not trust the BMA to keep their cases confidential. They feared that their allegations would somehow get back to their consultants and turn a situation of bullying, harassment and discrimination into one of downright victimisation or worse.*

As well as living with a culture of fear, many overseas doctors have to cope with verbal abuse and public humiliation because of their skin colour. Dr Ashford's report quotes examples of verbal abuse made by consultants in front of a multi-disciplinary team: 'You are not properly qualified'; 'You are lucky to have a job'; 'Why don't you go home?' Most endure the abuse simply because they think a complaint will impede their career progression.

Career advice

Many NCCG doctors also reported receiving 'career advice' from consultants when they were senior house officers (SHOs) or registrars. Some consultants were able to be open and honest in their advice, telling the doctor quite clearly that they would never get a consultant post in their chosen specialty because of their ethnic origin.

The survey cites other examples:

> *Some were advised to change specialty to one which was recognised as offering some minority ethnic doctors the opportunity of progressing to consultant. Some took this 'career advice' but still made no career progress. Another reported common piece of 'career advice' is to go 'home'. A candidate for a paediatric registrar job was told by a consultant that he did not get the job because 'he should go back to his own country to benefit the children there'. For British citizens who have lived in the UK for many*

years, have settled status and are married with children, this advice to go 'home' is even more upsetting.

Finally, there are the promises and more promises that NCCGs received to help further their career. Appointments at the bottlenecks of senior house officer, specialist registrar and consultant levels have proved impossible for most NCCGs. Yet many report the lengths they have gone to in order to gain a higher training post in response to advice and promises given by consultants.

According to the survey, these lengths might include anything from changing specialty and moving area to undertaking more training. Many NCCGs believe that they did everything and more that was asked of them and still were never appointed to higher training posts. At the time of the introduction of the Calman reforms, all registrars were supposed to be written to by the regional postgraduate deans to offer them a National Training Number, which would allow their training to be recognised for the CCST. It is alleged that many non-white registrars were never offered NTNs in this way.

Mr Mohib Khan, reflecting on his own career, comments:

> *I completed 15 years as a registrar but I was not allowed to progress to a senior registrar. I applied for jobs but didn't get an interview. The job went to the least experienced person each time. I was advised to change specialty to accident and emergency, which at the time was seen as having a lower status with no private work. I have been interviewed for senior registrar positions three times but was unsuccessful. In the majority of cases, after a panel interview where there was not a single non-white person, the job would go to a white doctor who had far less experience than me. At the time, there was no formal appeal mechanism. A lot of Asian doctors became GPs and now they are propping up the whole primary care systems in the inner cities.*

Dr Ashford, the author of the report, adds: 'When these doctors have done everything asked of them and are then not appointed, it is especially galling if the desired post is repeatedly left vacant when only minority ethnic doctors apply but is filled as soon as a white doctor applies.'

Hospital appointments

Research often quoted to support the argument that racism exists in the NHS is the retrospective study of 1500 doctors graduating from five British medical schools between 1981 and 1987, which suggested that those from ethnic minorities experienced disproportionate difficulty in obtaining hospital positions.[8]

Dr Aneez Esmail, head of the Department of General Practice at the University of Manchester, and a contributor to this book, and Dr Sam Everington, a London GP, carried out a pilot study to test the argument that British-trained doctors with foreign-sounding names were less likely to be shortlisted for hospital posts. These two doctors developed a CV for six equivalent applicants – three with Asian names and three with English names. All applicants were male, the same age, and educated and trained in Britain, with similar lengths of experience in district general or teaching hospitals. All were at the same stage of their career, applying for their first senior house officer post in a non-teaching hospital.

Each CV was tailored to a particular post by including a short paragraph explaining why the candidate was applying for the job. The medical school and secondary education were randomly changed so that shortlisting was not influenced by attendance at a particular school or university. The paired names used for each application were randomly selected from the panel of three Asian and three English applicants. The identical nature of the CVs was confirmed by two consultants, who were unaware of the purpose of the research and were asked to rate the CVs after the names had been removed.

Difference in shortlisting

Matched pairs of applications were sent for each post – one with an English name and one with an Asian name. The most noticeable result was the difference in the applicant's frequency of being shortlisted. When applicants were shortlisted, Esmail and Everington immediately cancelled any interviews.

Forty-six applications for 23 advertised posts in various specialties were sent. Eighteen applicants were shortlisted, of whom 12 had English and six had Asian names. Eleven English and 17 Asian applicants were not shortlisted. In one post, the English applicant was shortlisted and was subsequently withdrawn, after which the Asian applicant was shortlisted. The Asian candidate was never shortlisted unless the English candidate was also shortlisted.

Esmail and Everington had originally planned a survey covering around 100 posts and all hospital specialties, but were arrested by the fraud squad and charged with making fraudulent applications. Although not prosecuted, they were advised against continuing their work.

They wrote in the *BMJ*:

> *Our results are important and suggest that discrimination does take place against ethnic minorities, apparently at shortlisting. English applicants were twice as likely to be selected, and this difference would probably have been greater had we carried out the full study and been able to include posts in teaching hospitals. Doctors from ethnic minorities predominate in at least two of our chosen specialties (psychiatry and geriatric medicine), reflecting these specialties' comparative unpopularity – and the proportion of such doctors is much greater in district general hospitals than in teaching hospitals. It is remarkable therefore that despite these two biases we still found a twofold difference.*

Five years later, the study was repeated by Esmail and Everington, who again found that discrimination against ethnic minority candidates was still prevalent, despite numerous public commitments to deal with it by the profession's leaders and employers.

Their letter published in the *BMJ* in May 1997 stated:

> *The discrimination is being practised by consultants who are responsible for shortlisting for junior posts. These consultants have a responsibility to maintain the highest ethical and moral standards and their employers have the added responsibility to ensure that equal opportunity policies are being implemented and monitored ... Five years ago we suggested several mechanisms including standard and anonymised application forms, together with strict enforcement and publication of the results of equal opportunity monitoring, as a means of reducing the possibility of discrimination. Sadly, little seems to have changed, and it is an indictment of our profession that we still seem to tolerate a situation in which people's careers and livelihoods are jeopardised simply because they have the wrong name (and hence the wrong colour of skin).*[9]

White and ethnic minority doctors – comparison of careers

The CRE findings

Other research was undertaken by the Commission for Racial Equality (CRE). In 1987, the CRE compared the career developments of white and minority ethnic doctors with similar qualifications.[10] The study concluded that:

- overseas doctors waited longer for promotion to higher grades and had to make more applications for posts than their white British colleagues
- overseas doctors changed their specialty more often in order to enhance their career progression
- one in six of all consultants and SHOs were from minority ethnic groups, although DHSS statistics from 1981 to 1985 showed almost a third of NHS doctors were born overseas
- overseas doctors were concentrated in lower grades and unpopular specialties
- thirty-three per cent of the overseas doctors who had made more than one application for a higher post at the time of the survey had to make more than ten applications for any particular post.

The CRE report highlighted a number of cases, including one of two hospital doctors – Dr A, aged 25 and white with no post-registration qualifications, and Dr B, a Kenyan Asian aged 29 with a MRCP Part One (Membership of the Royal College of Physicians). Both were trained in Britain and had become SHOs in the previous six months.

Dr A obtained the new grade at the first application. Dr B had applied to become a SHO four times before he was successful, and even then the job had initially been offered to someone else and was only give to him six weeks later when the candidate to whom it was originally offered turned it down.

Referring to the study, Dr Hasan Mazhari, writing in *GP* magazine[11] claimed that racism and discrimination were rife in the health service:

> *Racial disadvantage and discrimination are daily reality for many members of the ethnic minorities. Doctors in the NHS are no exception. Racism is as prevalent in the medical fraternity as in the community. In the field of the health service, discrimination is not only offensive but harmful, as it destroys the careers of many capable doctors and demoralises a section of the medical workforce.*

In March 1992, the CRE decided to conduct a formal investigation of consultant and senior registrar appointments in the NHS, following persistent complaints that ethnic minority doctors were being discriminated against in their applications for senior posts in hospitals.[12]

The investigation focused on the success rates of black, Asian and white applicants for consultant and senior registrar vacancies between October 1991 and 31 March 1992, in five areas where ethnic minority doctors were known to be heavily under-represented – general medicine, general surgery, obstetrics and gynaecology – and in psychiatry and geriatrics, where they tended to be concentrated. During the period, a total of 418 vacancies were advertised, 251 for consultants and 167 for senior registrars.

Questionnaires were sent to seven regional health authorities, seven special health authorities, 13 teaching district authorities and 20 NHS trusts – a total of 47 NHS employers. The questionnaire asked the NHS employers to provide detailed breakdowns by ethnic group of the applicants for all the relevant vacancies, those that were shortlisted and those appointed. It also asked for information about their organisation's equal opportunities policies and practices.

Key findings of the study

Unsuccessful applicants

The study found that black and Asian doctors applied for more than half of the consultant vacancies and over three-quarters of the senior registrar vacancies. For consultant posts, 42 per cent of candidates were shortlisted. Fifty-six per cent were white applicants and 28 per cent were from ethnic minority groups. When it came to making appointments, overall 12 per cent of applicants were successful. Among white applicants, 18 per cent were appointed, compared with only six per cent of ethnic minority candidates.

For senior registar posts, 29 per cent of applicants were shortlisted. Among white candidates, 35 per cent were shortlisted, compared with 19 per cent of ethnic minority applicants. Seven per cent of the applicants were offered appointments. Among white applicants, 11 per cent were successful, compared with four per cent of ethnic minority candidates.

The study noted that when a shortlist was made up entirely of ethnic minority candidates, often no appointment was made. It also found that the proportion of unsuccessful ethnic minority applicants appeared consistently across the medical specialties.

The study confirmed that minority ethnic doctors were consistently less likely to be shortlisted for, or appointed to, senior registar or consultant posts than white applicants. The report states: 'We cannot rule out the possibility that applications from ethnic minority doctors are not being fully and fairly considered.'

Action to prevent discrimination

Although almost every respondent's organisation had an equal opportunities policy covering the recruitment and selection process, in almost every case there was a large gap between policy and actual practice. The report states:

> *That the largest employment sector in the country has been unable to put adequate procedures in place to ensure equal opportunities for all applicants can only be attributed to lack of will, because there is no shortage of detailed guidance on the subject. Taken together with the consistently low success rates for minority ethnic applicants for senior medical posts, the selection practices found among health authorities and trusts can give little confidence to minority ethnic applicants that their applications will be treated fairly.*

The European Specialist Medical Qualifications Order

No discussion of racial discrimination experienced by minority ethnic staff grade doctors would be complete without some mention of the European Specialist Medical Qualifications Order (ESMQO). This law came into force in the late nineties and implemented the UK's European obligations relating to the training of medical specialists and to the EU-wide mutual recognition of qualifications.

Under the Specialist Training Authority's transfer arrangements, over 3000 doctors applied to be given consultant status. When 1528 doctors in non-consultant posts were turned down and another 413 were required to do further training, claims of racial discrimination against both the royal colleges and the STA were widespread. The allegations continued when a breakdown showed that black doctors, largely from developing countries, had far less success than their white colleagues. Both the royal colleges and the STA vigorously denied charges that racism played a part in any of the outcomes.

Mr Mohib Khan, himself rejected by the STA, accused the royal colleges of putting too much power in the hands of a white, male, middle-class dominated elite. Interviewed in *Hospital Doctor*[13] he pointed to the lack of representation for ethnic minority doctors on college councils as proof of the way in which the system is skewed against ethnic minority doctors:

> *I put most of the blame on the royal colleges. If you are from an ethnic minority then your chance of a proper training post is not as good as a British white graduate. That is why there are so many non-consultants from overseas ... Some openly say it is jobs for our boys. They are first, you are last. It should be competency based on your experience and your qualifications. It has been purely on the colour of your skin.*

Dr Neil Ashford agrees:

> *The STA is made up largely of the presidents of all the royal colleges of medicine. If you bear in mind that Mohib Khan is the first non-white person to be on the Council of the Royal College of Surgeons of Edinburgh in its 496-year history, despite the fact that more than 50 per cent of its membership is overseas doctors, that will give you a clue to the skin colour of the presidents of the royal colleges.*

Many other doctors have also publicly criticised the STA decisions in various journals. A locum consultant urologist had been in the UK since 1974, after achieving his primary medical qualification in India. His application to join the specialist register was turned down and he was recommended to do a further 52 months' training and then take the intercollegiate exam. He did not bother to appeal:

> *They have asked me to do 52 months' training, ignoring the fact that I have been doing the locum consultant job for seven years successfully. It is very difficult to say it is not racial discrimination.*[13]

Another London-based locum consultant urologist with 11 years' training in the UK and six years' experience as a locum consultant in this country was asked by the STA to do six years' further training. Having worked in UK teaching hospitals after gaining undergraduate and postgraduate qualifications in India, he believes racial discrimination is behind the decision: 'If I was not trained properly, I should not have proceeded for six years doing a consultant's job.'[12] And one locum consultant pathologist, who was bringing an industrial tribunal action against the BMA for refusing to support his appeal to the STA, commented in *Hospital Doctor*:

> *Examinations serve one purpose – apartheid in the medical profession. You have no choice but to become an associate specialist and do the donkey-work, so white consultants can take the private work. I am good at my work; I don't know why I should not become a permanent consultant.*[13]

STA figures display a marked variation in career progression between developing countries and others. For instance, just 21 per cent of applicants who gained their primary medical qualification in India were accepted onto the specialist register without further training, compared to 86 per cent of applicants from Australia.

Table 6.1 Applications for specialist registration under the transfer arrangements[13]

Country	Total applications	Approved (%) subject to further training	Approved	Turned down
Canada	3	3 (100)	0	0
Australia	21	18 (86)	2	1
Ireland	52	32 (62)	6	14
UK	852	507 (60)	70	275
Egypt	203	48 (24)	30	125
India	819	175 (21)	137	507
Pakistan	250	49 (20)	42	159
Bangladesh	31	2 (6)	3	26
Total	3069	1128 (37)	413	1528

Note: Totals shown relate to figures from all applicants covering 50 countries, not just those highlighted in the table.

Some doctors believe that the assessment of non-consultant career grade doctors was completed in a casual fashion. Doctors were assessed in the wrong specialty, evidence from medical logbooks was ignored, and in some cases the assessor did not bother to look at the logbook.

Mr Mohib Khan explains:

> *Experienced doctors were demoralised. The majority did not take it further because of the high cost of an appeal. During appeal hearings, royal colleges were quoting the 'Bristol Case'. I would like to remind the colleges that the Bristol surgeons and other well-publicised cases were, in the eyes of the college, so-called 'properly trained' and went through college-recognised training programmes. They were accredited doctors. If the Government wants its modernisation programme to succeed, then in my opinion some of the medical establishment's power must be reduced in order to rectify this anomaly.*

Membership of the royal colleges

The royal colleges often come under fire because of the low number of council members from minority ethnic groups. In April 1999, *Hospital Doctor*[14] revealed that only five per cent of members of council of the UK royal colleges are from minority ethnic backgrounds – just 22 out of 434 council members nationwide. Six colleges had no representation at all, while the Royal College of Obstetricians and Gynaecologists had the highest at 13.8 per cent – almost three times the average of 5.1 per cent.

In the same article, Mr Raafat Gendy, at the time one of six non-consultant career grade representatives on the BMA's Central Consultants and Specialists Committee, said the figures came as no surprise:

> We are a significant number of the doctors in this country, but representation on councils is very poor. I don't think the royal colleges understand our problems and concerns.

Interracial discrimination

Whenever racial discrimination is discussed, it is assumed that it is the white workforce discriminating against minority ethnic groups. However, this is not always the case and it is an accepted fact that racism is not a prerogative of white people. Dr Shehnaz Somjee, Chair of the Locum Doctor Association said in *Hospital Doctor*[15] that rivalries exist between doctors from India, Pakistan and Bangladesh. Discrimination on the grounds of religion, for example, between Muslims and Hindus, is not unknown.

Accusations are often made that some overseas doctors become 'more British than the British themselves' when they are appointed consultants. However, this too can be described as an outcome of a system that requires doctors to behave in a certain way in order to get on. Most overseas doctors believe that the potential for discrimination between different minority ethnic groups is low and is only used as a 'red herring' to divert attention from the white/black racism debate.

Conclusion

> Ghandi once said that humans are the only species where an individual feels pride by humiliating his fellow creature. This is exactly what happens in medical practice. If you are not part of the hierarchy, the person above you will treat you as if you don't exist.

This quote from Mr Awani Choudhary, Deputy Chairman of the National Non-Consultant Career Grade Committee, sums up the frustration that many black and minority ethnic doctors feel about the medical profession. If you are on the recognised training path to becoming a specialist registrar and then become a consultant, with the status these positions bring, your career couldn't be better. But, if you are stuck in a staff grade position being told by the profession that you are not good enough to be employed as a consultant, then it is a different picture.

Clearly, there is evidence that career progression and job satisfaction for black and minority ethnic doctors is unsatisfactory. This is an important issue, which the medical world must address. The changes ahead will require moving from good intentions to firm commitments: for example, a review of PLAB and the entry procedures for types 1 and 2 training, and a concerted effort to increase the number of black and minority ethnic doctors in higher positions.

Education is critical in this process – racial awareness and anti-discriminatory training must be included in the medical curriculum, including postgraduate training. Senior medical staff should not be exempt from such training. Fair selection and equality of opportunity should be exercised in the recruitment process for all medical positions, and it should be the responsibility of all chairs and chief executives of trusts, health authorities and primary care groups to make this happen.

As one overseas doctor said ruefully:

> *Can you name any other industry where 30 per cent of the senior people are unhappy and that industry is still thriving? Although I am trained and have many years' experience, I don't have a certificate and my profession does not recognise my training. This situation must not be allowed to continue.*

References

1.   Effects of discrimination on careers of British medical graduates. Letter. *BMJ* 1991; 302: 235.
2.   British Medical Association. *Guide for doctors new to the UK*. London: BMA, 2001.
3.   Career progress of doctors committee. *Recruitment and selection of doctors: guidelines for good practice*. London: BMA, 2000.
     http://web.bma.org.uk/homepage.nsf/htmlpagevw/careers
3.   Department of Postgraduate Medicine and Dentistry North West Region.
     www.pgmd.man.ac.uk
4.   Department of Health Census 1998 England.
5.   Time to treat disease. Letter. *Hospital Doctor*; 17 May 1999: 28.
6.   NHS is racist as an institution. Letter. *Hospital Doctor*; 15 April 1999: 16.
7.   Effects of discrimination on careers of British medical graduates. Letter. *BMJ* 1991; 302: 235.
8.   Esmail A, Everington S. Racial discrimination against doctors from ethnic minorities. *BMJ* 1993; 306: 691.
9.   Asian doctors are stil being discriminated against. Letter. *BMJ* 1997; 314: 1619.
10. Commission for Racial Equality. *Overseas doctors' experience and expectation*. London: CRE, 1987.
11. Mazhari H. White doctors rule the NHS. *GP* 1993; 12 Feb: 63.
12. Commission for Racial Equality. *Appointing NHS consultants and senior registrars*. London, CRE, 1996.
13. Smith P. Is the selection process for the register racist? *Hospital Doctor*; 29 April 1999: 28.
14. Smith P. Colleges failing to elect doctors from minorities. *Hospital Doctor*; 29 April 1999: 4.
15. Dunne R. Why not all racists are white. *Hospital Doctor*; 13 May 1999: 30.

Part 2

Agenda for action

Chapter 7

Racial discrimination and health services

Shona Arora, Naaz Coker, Stephen Gillam

I am not interested in picking up crumbs thrown from the table of someone who considers himself to be my master. I want the full menu of rights.
Desmond Tutu

Introduction

Important differences in the health experiences of black and minority ethnic (BME) populations as compared with white populations are well attested. A significant proportion of BME communities carry a higher burden of poor health, premature deaths and long-term chronic ill health than other groups in the population. Asian groups in England and Wales are 60 per cent more likely to have heart disease and are up to five times more susceptible to diabetes. Early death from coronary heart disease in this group is around 50 per cent higher than the UK average. Black African Caribbean people are five times more likely on average to have high blood pressure and twice as likely to die of stroke under the age of 65. Babies born to Pakistani women are twice as likely to die in the first week of birth than those of British-born mothers. The rates of uptake of cervical screening amongst Bangladeshi women are less than half of those amongst the general population. Refugees and asylum seekers – who are one of the most vulnerable groups – experience multiple deprivation, which can have a severe impact on their health. Their experiences pre-asylum and post-exile make them a high-risk group for mental ill health, which is compounded by problems of displacement, resettlement, poverty and language difficulties.

These differences are only partly understood but reflect socio-environmental determinants rather than genetic ones. BME groups with the worst general health are also those who live in the most deprived localities and on the lowest incomes. Income alone, however, does not explain why BME groups are more often ill than white people. Racism in society acts as a major hurdle to health and wealth. The experience of discrimination and racism, and its impact on the health of black people, is well documented. Racism and particularly institutional racism in the NHS increase inequality and injustice, which in turn contribute to anxiety and avoidable ill health.

On the whole, people from all ethnic groups in Britain have much the same illnesses. Heart disease, cancer and mental health problems are the most important causes of avoidable morbidity and mortality, regardless of ethnic group. Some health problems are, however, specific to particular groups: sickle cell disorders, for example, occur more commonly in the African and African Caribbean groups. Many NHS trusts and primary care groups, including many individual health workers, have developed specific specialist services to meet the needs of some of the groups, but these often exist outside mainstream health care. Much work has been undertaken at the policy level by the Department of Health to ensure mainstreaming of good practice in the delivery of culturally competent services. Yet, there is still a huge gap in implementing policy into practice on the ground.

This chapter provides a brief explanation for the causes of ethnic health inequalities and suggests ways of developing integrated strategies for addressing and improving the health of disadvantaged and vulnerable groups. Primary care groups/trusts (PCG/Ts), with the pivotal role in the commissioning and development of primary and specialist care, are used to illustrate the ways in which the delivery of culturally competent services can be improved. The importance of better understanding the needs of their populations, involving users in service planning and the practicalities of service delivery, are particularly emphasised.

What causes ill health in black and minority ethnic groups?

A growing body of evidence exists on health inequalities experienced by those from some BME groups when compared to the majority white population. Survey findings are consistent with the impression that, for relatively young populations, people from black and minority ethnic groups experience a greater than expected burden of ill health.[1] A common misconception is that minority ethnic groups suffer primarily from rare 'exotic' diseases. Some diseases are more specific to certain minority ethnic groups. These include the haemoglobinopathies, which have a genetic basis.[1,2] Another example is tuberculosis, as black and minority ethnic populations experience a greater incidence of this disease than the white population. The reasons for this may include travel, migration, immunity and overcrowded living conditions in the UK.[4]

However, it is important to remember that the diseases causing the greatest burdens for ethnic minority groups are the same as those experienced by the white majority in the UK. These are cardiovascular disease, diabetes, mental illness, accidents and respiratory diseases such as pneumonia, asthma and bronchitis.[5,6] Cancer rates tend to be lower overall in minority ethnic groups compared to the white population, but in absolute terms they are still a significant cause of morbidity and mortality. Surveys have also shown the serious deficiencies in primary care provision for refugees and asylum seekers.

The relationship between ethnicity and health outcomes is complex and influenced by a combination of many factors (Figure 7.1).

Figure 7.1 Understanding the relationship between ethnicity and health

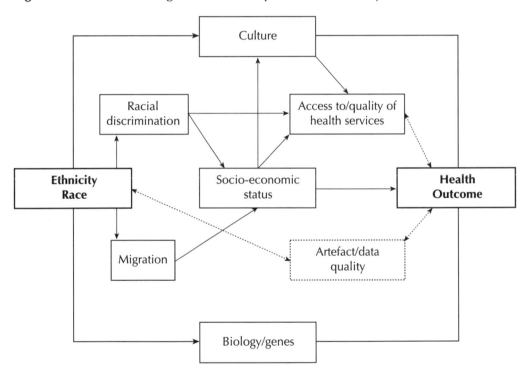

Dotted lines represent possible explanations for differences in health status that were not assessed by the National Survey.
Source: Nazroo J. *The health of Britain's ethnic minorities.* London: Policy Studies Institute, 1997

BOX 7.1   UNEMPLOYMENT BY ETHNIC GROUP

White	6%
Indian	8%
Black	19%
Bangladeshi and Pakistani	21%

Source: Khan V. *Ethnicity in the 1991 Census. Volume 4.* London: The Stationery Office, 1997

Generally, belonging to a certain ethnic group *per se* does not directly lead to better or worse health. Research increasingly shows that a considerable proportion of ill health in black and minority ethnic groups is more closely linked to their socio-economic status, environmental and employment conditions.[7] Black and ethnic minority groups are over-represented among the unemployed, low-income groups, school exclusions and those in poor housing.[8] All of these factors are associated with poorer health. Institutional racism, and indeed more widespread societal racism, cannot be excluded as factors that contribute to this picture of health inequalities and the disproportionate social exclusion felt by black and minority ethnic groups.[9,10]

Overt racism from individuals is also a very real phenomenon in the UK today, as suggested by findings from the Fourth National Survey of Ethnic Minorities, where about a quarter of white people interviewed admitted to racist feelings against those from Asia, Africa or the Caribbean.[1] Statistics recorded nearly 12,000 racist incidents reported to the police in 1994–95, compared with about 4000 in 1988. This is likely to be the tip of an iceberg: the 1992 British Crime Survey estimated that in 1991 there were 130,000 racially motivated crimes against Asians and Caribbeans.[1] Racism contributes much towards creating a climate of anxiety and fear. Nearly a quarter of all minority ethnic respondents in the National Survey worried about racial harassment. Such concerns can lead to increased social exclusion, have a major impact on lifestyle such as reduced exercise, and contribute to stress-related illness.

Inequalities in health care services

Use of health services and treatments is influenced by a number of factors, including patients' health beliefs and cultural influences[7] (Box 7.2). Although health beliefs may seem to be at odds with those held by health professionals, within every culture there will be norms and values that also promote good health. Health professionals need to learn to work with these positive aspects of different cultures.

Minority ethnic groups experience several barriers to accessing health care services, which may in turn affect health outcomes. For example, South Asians may be less

---

Box 7.2 FACTORS INFLUENCING UPTAKE OF HEALTH SERVICES

Demand side	*Supply side*
Health beliefs and knowledge	Distribution of health care resources
Knowledge of and attitudes to health services	Racism in service delivery
Social structure	Quality of care

Source: Smaje C. *Health, 'race' and ethnicity – making sense of the evidence.* London: King's Fund, 1995

---

likely to receive angiography or coronary artery bypass grafts (CABG) and may experience delays in referral for these procedures.[11]

In primary care, elderly Indian and young Pakistani women appear to consult less frequently than would be expected. Significantly lower use of primary care by the Chinese and African populations has also been reported. Higher consultation rates have been reported amongst Asians and by Caribbean women, but this may be appropriate as they seem to consult more for diseases such as cardiovascular disease and diabetes, for which they experience greater morbidity and mortality.[12]

The impact of intercultural communication on consultation rates has been debated.[12] Poor communication could account for both high and low levels of consultation with a GP. For example, the initial experience may discourage the patient from future attendance, or difficulties in communication may mean that they need to make several repeat visits to resolve their problem. Many black and minority ethnic patients register with a GP from the same ethnic group, which helps to overcome language barriers. However, since a higher proportion of the black GPs run surgeries on a 'drop in' basis, it results in longer waiting times, as illustrated in Box 7.3.[13] So, although for some groups the language barrier has been overcome by registering with primary health care professionals who can speak the same language, they end up waiting longer to see their GPs.

Reasons for differences in access to health care are not completely understood, but it is not due solely to patient preference or reluctance to take up interventions or services. Poor quality or lack of accessible information and negative experiences of the health service may be contributory factors.[14,15] It is these issues that should lead us to examine the extent to which health services may be vulnerable to institutional

---

Box 7.3 AVERAGE WAITING TIMES

Ethnic Group	Mins
Bangladeshis	50
Pakistanis	33
Indians	30
African Caribbeans	27
Average UK	18

Source: Health Education Authority. *Health and lifestyles: black and minority ethnic groups in England.* London: HEA, 1994

---

racism in delivering health care to an increasingly multicultural population, and how this might best be addressed.

Institutional racism and health care

Institutional racism represents the systematic and more covert forms of racism perpetuated by dominant groups, social systems and institutions. It is not always an indictment of individuals working within institutions, who themselves may not be racially prejudiced, but is a reflection of organisational processes, practices, actions and behaviours. In the UK, the Macpherson Report defined institutional racism as:

> The collective failure of an organisation to provide an appropriate and professional service to people because of their colour, culture or ethnic origin, It can be seen or detected in processes, attitudes and behaviour which amount to discrimination through unwitting prejudice, ignorance, thoughtlessness and racist stereotyping which disadvantage minority ethnic people.[16]

'Institutional racism' may operate at several different levels, either to exclude minority groups or to favour white majority groups. The ways in which institutional racism can impact on health care is illustrated in Figure 7.2.[17]

Tackling institutional racism is crucial to ensure equality. Cultural and Eurocentric bias frequently leads to crude (racist) conclusions about illness and need. The lack of dignity and respect meted out to patients through prejudice and negative stereotyping can be very distressing. There are three aspects to institutional racism, all of which need to be addressed. These are:

- the systems and processes within an organisation
- the culture of the organisation
- individual attitudes and behaviours.

Figure 7.2 Dimensions of institutional racism and health care

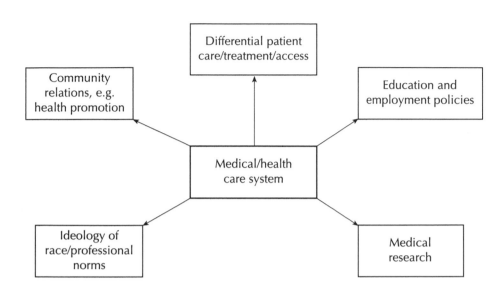

Source: King G. Institutional racism and the medical/health complex: a conceptual analysis. *Ethnicity and Disease* 1996; 6: 30–46

One way of tackling institutional racism is through the process of 'mainstreaming'.[18] This has been defined by the Department of Health as a:

> *Means of automatically considering the race equality dimension of everything that is done. Getting there involves equipping staff with the skills, knowledge, expertise and attitudes to do this so that they take responsibility for this as part of their professional practice.*

This contrasts with the notion of 'special provision', whereby services are established specifically for the use of minority ethnic groups but not integrated into core funding, planning and service development. Specialist provision has its place, in that it provides a chance to pilot and develop innovative services, often using non-core funding. However, the short-term nature of the funding means that services are frequently vulnerable to financial cuts and lack sustainability. Consequently, staff morale may be lowered and staff development limited. Furthermore, the health workers involved in delivering specialist services often lack the status of those working in mainstream services. The services also tend to get incorporated into specialist care packages, without ever stimulating a more strategic approach to the issue. It has been argued that this approach absolves mainstream services of their responsibility to deliver change.[19]

Senior level commitment and leadership are vital to the success of the mainstreaming approach, which requires *all* policy and planning processes to take account of local diversity and create opportunities for reducing disadvantage and inequality. In the next section, PCG/Ts are used as organisational exemplars. While they and their analogues in the rest of the UK have moved centre stage as commissioning organisations, they illustrate the challenges facing both commissioners and providers of services.

Taking a strategic approach: from intention to action

A strategic approach to addressing health inequalities requires planning and co-ordinated-action along several dimensions simultaneously. Tackling social exclusion and creating an environment where health, in its broadest sense, can develop, must be the key priorities for any strategic agenda. The main determinants of health – housing, employment, income, environmental pollution, crime, social injustice and discrimination – are important issues when tackling health inequalities.

An integrated organisational approach should address four main areas:

- tackling the root causes of ill health
- eradicating racism, both institutional and individual
- improving access to appropriate health care
- working with individual users and communities.

In the context of a mainstreaming approach, a comprehensive management strategy needs to specify 'diversity' within all areas of performance management, service development, monitoring and audit. This should include tangible goals and targets with clearly designated staff, who should be responsible for implementation within a given timescale. Mission statements are worthless if they are not reflected in the actions, systems and processes. In a PCG/T, all key initiatives and monitoring arrangements should acknowledge cultural diversity within the PCG/T population, for example in:

- The Primary Care Investment Plan
- The Health Improvement Programme
- The Clinical Governance Action Plan
- The User Involvement Strategy
- The Information Management and Technology Strategy
- The Annual Accountability Agreement.

A number of PCG/Ts have established ethnicity task groups, equal opportunities groups or inequalities groups to develop and lead on the implementation of the strategies. Such groups are usually led by a PCG/T board member with an interest in this subject. Some PCG/Ts may choose to develop a separate strategy to address black and minority ethnic needs. Others may choose to ensure that key strategic documents refer to this issue.

Developing cultural competence

A culturally competent organisation is one that can meet the needs of people of different cultural backgrounds, recognising what those needs may be and having the skills and resources to meet those needs through appropriate service development and delivery.[20,21] A model of cultural skills development is outlined in Figure 7.3.

Figure 7.3 Cultural competency development model

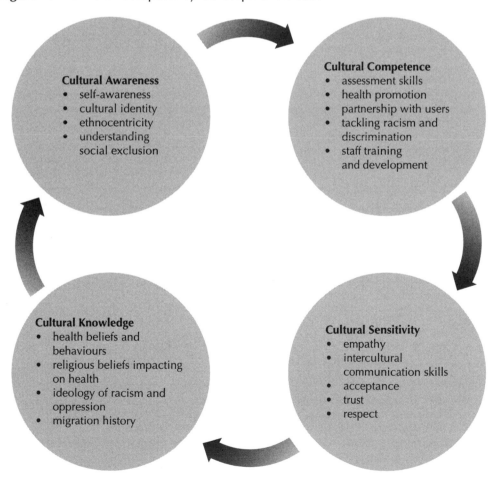

Adapted from: Papadopoulos I, Tilki M, Taylor G. *Transcultural care: a guide for health care professionals.* Salisbury: Quay Books, 1998

Cultural competence requires working in true partnership with users and empowering them to help shape the way services are designed and delivered. This model brings together both personal competences of health care professionals and organisational competence to deliver culturally competent services. Much work has been done, particularly in the USA, New Zealand and in the UK, on identifying the steps that an organisation and its members should take to become culturally competent.[20,22,23] These have been summarised in the flow chart below (Figure 7.4).

Figure 7.4 Steps to becoming culturally competent

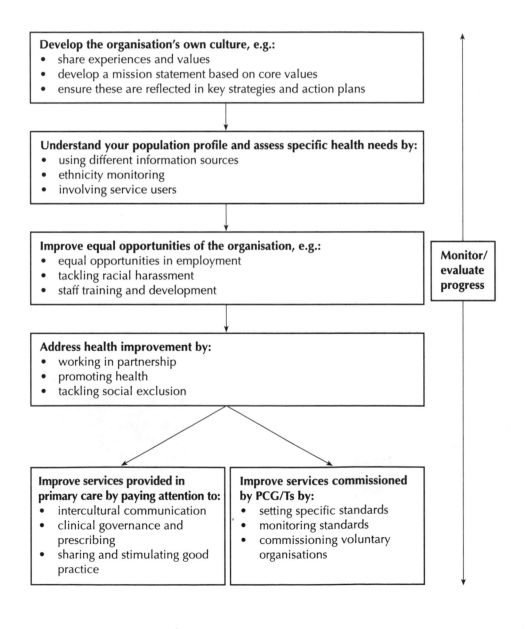

Core values

An important step at the outset is the generation of explicit value statements that will help to define the ethos and culture of the organisation. The process of bringing together a multidisciplinary group such as a PCG/T board or primary health care team to discuss and develop core values is an important part of organisational development, helping to create a shared picture of the future direction and culture of the organisation. These agreed values should underpin all the work of the trust.

Box 7.4 below sets out examples of some guiding principles that might be used for, or result from, this process. These principles were developed following an exercise of sharing stories and experiences between GPs, nurses, social workers and managers.[24]

Core values and the guiding principles need to be reflected in actions, systems and processes of the PCG/T. All services, policies, documents and monitoring arrangements should, therefore, acknowledge and reflect issues relating to cultural diversity in the PCG/T population.

BOX 7.4 SOME GUIDING PRINCIPLES FOR PCG/Ts AND PHCTs

A colour-blind approach suggests prejudice:
  We need to recognise that different people have different requirements – it is better to ask than to assume we understand and know everything
  One person is enough – everyone is entitled to fair access and appropriate health care services

We cannot deliver appropriate services on our own:
  Making connections and building up links is core business
  Local (non-statutory) community organisations can help

Organisations are discriminatory:
  If there are unequal patterns of care, we should assume these to be due to discrimination until proved otherwise
  It is an organisational/managerial requirement to uncover and engage with discrimination at the individual and institutional level
  Feedback mechanisms are needed to link individual and organisational learning

Communication is key to service delivery:
  Information enables individuals and organisations
  Advocates address imbalances of power

Source: Fischer M. *Developing appropriate services for all.* London: King's Fund, 1999

Understanding the population profile and assessing health needs

A prerequisite for deciding how to improve the health of the local population is a good understanding of who they are, where the burdens of disease and illness are greatest, and how they can best be reduced. This is the essence of health needs assessment. GPs and primary health care teams are close to the communities they serve, giving them invaluable insight into the health needs of their patients, but they tend only to see those who 'walk through the door' and demand health care. They may not be aware of those in their population with unmet needs. Also, health care professionals' perceptions of where the biggest gaps in service lie may not always coincide with patients' views on this.[14,25]

Traditional methods of health needs assessment are well developed and skills can be found in public health departments of health authorities. Health professionals based in the community, such as health visitors or district nurses, are also valuable sources of information and will most likely have such skills.[26]

Box 7.5 TECHNIQUES FOR ASSESSING NEEDS OF HARD TO REACH GROUPS

Routine data from the Census, local authorities and possibly trusts
Snowballing: certain individuals/key informants are used to identify other people to contact
Specific registers, e.g. ethnicity monitoring
Collecting information directly – verbally, e.g. a focus group, or via questionnaires (appropriately translated)

Source: Wright J, ed. *Health needs assessment in practice.* London: BMJ Books, 1998

The first step is to establish a population profile that includes a breakdown by ethnicity, age and gender. The Census is usually a good starting point, but obviously becomes out of date quickly, and is limited in its categories. In the NHS, trusts are required to collect ethnicity data, but for a large proportion of patients this is recorded as 'not specified', which makes the data difficult to use in any meaningful way. Until routine data systems capture more complete information on ethnicity, other methods for identifying the needs of minority groups will need to be used.[27]

In primary care, although ethnicity monitoring has been piloted for over a decade, there is currently no statutory requirement to carry it out. The reasons for introducing this are well rehearsed:

- To develop a more accurate profile of the practice population, and thus identify population needs.

- To help equitable distribution of resources. Ethnicity may eventually be included in national resource allocation formulae.
- To identify individual needs of patients and specific cultural aspects that might influence their medical care.

A number of nationally funded projects have looked at how the benefits of ethnicity monitoring in primary care can be optimised, and the costs minimised. Participating practices have generally found that the collection of ethnicity data is not as problematic as some thought. Staff training and explanation for patients were important in asking about what could be perceived as sensitive questions. Stressing to patients the confidential nature of the information being asked and explaining why it was being collected were particularly important.[28] Other sources of information that PCG/Ts have used include surnames on practice registers and/or data from schools. As well as ethnicity, other useful information to seek includes:

- religious and cultural needs
- preference for a male or female health professional
- particular times of year when it might be difficult to take medicines
- particular diet required if referred to hospital
- the need for interpreters
- the need for written information
- refugee/asylum seeker origin, i.e. from which country.

Collection of such information allows the practice to manage patient care more effectively and efficiently, tailoring services to meet their patients' needs.

Involving service users

Health services should involve users in planning and evaluating services. Many PCG/Ts have established user involvement groups (often led by the lay member) to understand why certain services, even when provided, fail to meet the local population's needs. A user involvement strategy needs to include reference to working with groups that might be 'hard to reach', such as black and minority ethnic groups whose first language is not English. Population profiling will help to identify ethnic groups within the PCG/T population.

The next step is to find ways of engaging with such communities. Religious or community leaders are often a useful first point of contact. There may be small community projects in the area, funded through Joint Finance, and therefore known to the health authority and local authority. The PCG/T board lay member should have links into local voluntary networks. A useful way of making contact with the voluntary sector is through the local branch of the National Council for Voluntary Services.

BOX 7.6 ASSESSING HEALTH NEEDS USING QUALITATIVE METHODS: AN EXAMPLE FROM EAST LONDON

GPs in Newham, where there is a high Asian population, commissioned a mental health needs assessment of young Asian women. They were interested in the management of deliberate self-harm (DSH), because there is some evidence nationally that suicide rates in young Asian women are higher than would be expected. The assessment used qualitative techniques such as focus groups with young Asian women, GPs and mental health service providers, as well as in-depth interviews with women who had self-harmed.

The study found that service providers believed that the main reason for DSH in this group was due to 'culture conflict' (balancing family traditions against the influences of Western culture to which they were exposed). However, this view was not shared by the young Asian women interviewed. They identified lack of information about available services, along with a sense of not being understood, being stereotyped or stigmatised by health professionals as barriers to using mental health services that should have been able to help them. For some women, culture conflict was a real issue, but by assuming that this was the main cause of DSH in this group of women (and therefore not one which health services could address), providers ignored the scope for other effective health service interventions.

There are a variety of methods available to promote user involvement. Those chosen will depend partly on the information being sought and the resources available. PCG/Ts are beginning to make use of a range of methods, including stakeholder events, focus groups and community meetings using a minority ethnic facilitator. When these work well, they produce remarkably good information. However, such meetings need careful thought and planning. Key questions to help the planning process are listed in Box 7.7.[29]

While some special consideration should be given to involving people from black and minority ethnic groups, the general principles underpinning public involvement still apply. It is important to be clear and explicit about:

- why you are asking people to be involved
- what you are asking of them
- how you might respond to their comments
- mechanisms for giving feedback to the people involved.

BOX 7.7 ORGANISING A PUBLIC INVOLVEMENT EVENT: KEY QUESTIONS TO ASK

Have you 'advertised' your meeting in places where people from minority ethnic communities are likely to go (e.g. local shops, cafes, clubs, places of worship)?

Will your chosen venue be acceptable and accessible to all potential participants? – Sometimes it might be more appropriate to go to, for example, a day care centre, rather than expect people to come to you.

Will the timing suit participants? – Working people will be less likely to attend during the day, but young mothers and children are unlikely to go to an evening event.

Do participants require training, confidence building or advocacy to take part?

Is any information you intend to disseminate written in plain English and translated into appropriate languages?

Will resources be available to provide, e.g. a trained facilitator, interpreter, crèche facilities, travelling expenses, cover carers' costs?

Adapted from: NHSE Northern and Yorkshire. *Public engagement toolkit for primary care groups.* Leeds: Department of Health, 1999

If little action results from seeking the community's views on services, 'consultation fatigue' will result, which will become a barrier to future involvement. Some black and minority ethnic groups have felt that consultation has had little effect in bringing about desired changes, and that their involvement has been tokenistic.

Assessing population need is a means to an end of providing more effective services. An example of where needs assessment in primary care has led to service changes is provided by Newcastle West Primary Care Group and Save the Children Fund Healthy Communities project (see Box 7.8).[30]

BOX 7.8 NEEDS ASSESSMENT IN NEWCASTLE-UPON-TYNE

In Newcastle-upon-Tyne, resident community members were trained to define and conduct qualitative research in their own communities. Community health needs in addressing psychological distress were identified, and practical recommendations for the re-orientation and provision of services were made. Changes implemented included:

deploying bilingual counsellors in non-general practice settings
providing information on service provision using bilingual leaflets in GP surgeries
proactive local programme of recruitment to expand training and availability of qualified Asian workers
racism and diversity training for local NHS trusts' staff and primary care workers.

Source: Kai J, Hedges C. Minority ethnic community participation in needs assessment and service development in primary care. *Health Expectations* 1999; 2: 7–20

Improving health

Health improvement is about reducing morbidity and mortality in the local population, and giving members of local communities opportunities and responsibility to improve their own health. Many health promotion strategies and health services are delivered in ways that benefit those people who already have a better understanding of the health care system or who already have a greater opportunity to change their lifestyle and circumstances, rather than those who are least enabled. This creates further inequalities in health. Health improvement strategies must, therefore, consider their likely impact on those who are most disadvantaged. Approaches that specifically target some groups will be needed.

As health status is also strongly influenced by factors beyond the remit of the NHS, working in partnership with other parts of the local community, such as local authorities, business and the voluntary sector, is important. Whilst the advantages of partnership working are self-evident, lack of experience and expertise in partnership working make the process excessively bureaucratic and achieve less than expected. The different cultures of organisations within the statutory sector and between the statutory and voluntary sector, coupled with varying resource allocation mechanisms, can generate much tension and conflict. Yet resolving these conflicts and finding ways to collaborate is critical.

Health promotion initiatives have sometimes focused too much on issues *perceived* by health professionals to be of great importance to ethnic minority groups, such as birth control and diet, rather than diseases such as cardiovascular disease, which are actually more common. Providing meaningful health promotion advice requires an understanding of culture and health-related beliefs on lifestyle. Communication is also critical, and health education materials may need to be translated into different languages. It is important to develop and pilot materials with members of black and minority ethnic communities to make sure that they are accurate and not likely to be perceived as insulting or patronising.[31] Leaflets and videos are useful adjuncts to, but not a substitute for, culturally sensitive face-to-face advice.[32]

Low rates of uptake for some preventative measures such as cervical cancer screening have been found for some ethnic groups.[33] Low attendance may be due to the fact that they are ill informed or are unaware of these services. They may feel badly treated when they attend, particularly if there is no-one to explain what is going to happen, for example when a cervical smear is taken. Access to health advocates (or at the very least interpreters) has been found to be of benefit.[34]

Tackling social exclusion via primary care

Socially excluded groups and communities include people who suffer from a combination of linked problems such as unemployment, low skills base, low income, poor housing, high crime environments, poor health and family breakdown. People from some black and minority ethnic communities, and recently arrived individuals and families such as asylum seekers and refugees, are excluded due to multiple factors. They are exceptionally concentrated in many of the deprived areas around towns and cities, and experience all the problems that affect other people in these areas. In addition, they experience the consequences of racial discrimination and racial harassment. Services that do not meet their immediate and long-term needs, language and cultural barriers, and a lack of general knowledge about how to access information to support services increase this isolation further. Consequently, social exclusion can be both a cause and an effect of ill health.

Primary care services, with their growing role in public health, are significant players in tackling social exclusion. PCG/Ts have already identified particular client groups as a health improvement priority. These include:

- children
- people with mental illness
- older people

The health of black and minority ethnic groups as a subgroup within these larger groups should not be forgotten. Refugees and asylum seekers, too, are a particularly vulnerable group. Given the extent to which other factors such as socio-economic deprivation, unemployment and racism impact on the health of many of those from minority ethnic groups, community development initiatives remain an important means of improving the health of black and minority ethnic populations. Primary care organisations have increasing opportunities to be involved with community development. Funding for such initiatives may come from Health Action Zones, Single Regeneration Bids, Healthy Living Centres and international funding sources such as the European Union.

For all PCG/Ts, the development of primary care services as the point of first contact for most of the population and gatekeepers to other services is a key task. The location of many ethnic minority groups in inner city areas means that they are vulnerable to the so-called inverse care law: they may have great health needs, but the health services available are less adequate than in more affluent areas. Many GPs working in inner cities are themselves from minority ethnic groups, and approaching retirement. The prospect of a GP shortage in areas that are already under-supplied creates a major challenge. Innovation in new forms of primary care delivery will be vital in responding to existing and future challenges. A number of PCG/Ts accommodate personal medical services pilots, some of which are nurse-led. Others have submitted proposals for walk-in centres. Finally, NHS Direct needs to be integrated into the 24-hour primary care services already offered, with its shape influenced by groups of GPs and other primary care professionals so that it can meet the needs of people whose first language is not English.

Intercultural communication

> **Box 7.9** ENHANCING COMMUNICATION
>
> GPs in Brent and Harrow use a 'body map' to enhance communication. This is a simple flip chart that illustrates parts of the body, with words translated into different languages. The body map enables shared and confidential understanding between patient and GP, and can be used to clarify what is going to happen during physical examinations. Practices have found this useful for many patients including children, and not just those who lack confidence in speaking and understanding English.

Intercultural communication at its simplest means being able to communicate with someone who speaks a different language. The consultation in primary care is central to the establishment of a successful therapeutic relationship. There is, not surprisingly, a link between patient satisfaction and levels of explanation received during a consultation.[32]

Effective communication may have many positive outcomes, including better patient compliance with treatment, fewer returns to surgery, and better understanding between patient and doctor of how best to manage illness.

Communication is not about the use of language alone; non-verbal communication is also important and may be influenced by attitudes towards and understanding of people from different cultural backgrounds. Finally, good communication is as much about listening and hearing as it is about talking. A non-judgemental approach and avoidance of stereotyping are important aspects of communication. It is also worth remembering, however, that some cultures do not have words to express 'mental illness', for example, or that some people may express physical illness in terms of general tiredness.[35] The best way to understand a patient's health beliefs is to ask about them.

Advocacy involves more than just interpreting, but also requires representing clients' needs. It is, therefore, more complex than straightforward interpretation. It usually involves the advocate building up a more long-term relationship with the client, meeting with them before they meet with the professional. Advocacy tends to be more costly than interpreting, but is extremely useful in some situations, particularly for disempowered groups such as refugees or those with mental illness. In areas that have developed good advocacy projects, such as east London, they have become an essential part of good service delivery.

A recent mapping exercise of advocacy in London revealed that, while there was great need for advocacy in primary care, many GP practices were not receptive to using advocacy services, believing that they were not required.[36] This even included areas where the health authority was funding these services – only one PCG out of the 66 in London had taken on commissioning advocacy services.

Box 7.10 Key areas to address for using linkworkers in primary care

strategic framework
assessing local need for linkworkers
defining linkworker tasks
management and supervision
funding
monitoring and evaluation
recruitment and selection
training
administration and support

Source: Levenson R, Gillam S. *Linkworkers in primary care.* London; King's Fund, 1998

There is considerable ambiguity over the meaning of the word 'linkworker'. Originally introduced as part of the National Mother and Baby Campaign, linkworkers can be found working in many settings, for many client groups, fulfilling a range of jobs from interpreting to advocacy.

However, linkworkers are often marginal to the health care organisations in which they work. They are often supported by 'soft' funding, and their jobs are therefore insecure and low in status, without much scope for development. The King's Fund has recently produced a checklist for PCG/Ts planning to employ linkworkers, to help make them more central to the organisation.[34]

Improving clinical practice

Clinical governance provides the framework for ensuring high-quality clinical care. Clinical governance action plans should, therefore, take account of black and minority ethnic groups. Health professionals can facilitate good self-management as part of chronic disease management, as well as reviewing their own clinical practice.

Prescribing practice may also be improved as part of the clinical governance agenda. Some drug treatments are inappropriate for specific communities: gelatine-based medicines, for example, are not suitable for vegetarians. Compliance may be affected by fasting and other cultural factors that influence when and how medicines can be taken. The evidence base for treatment effects in different black and minority ethnic groups is poor. Nevertheless, where it does exist, for example in the management of hypertension in African Caribbean groups, health professionals should be aware of this.

Prescribing may be used as one measure of poor performance. At least one study has shown that, contrary to common belief, Asian single-handed GPs do not prescribe higher volume, more expensive drugs than white doctors, or more than those Asian doctors trained in the UK, once population case mix has been taken into account. However, being single-handed does act as a barrier to participating in clinical audit, most commonly because of lack of time. PCG/Ts need to take account of the extra pressures on small practices when developing clinical governance strategies.

It is important to develop ways of working within the PCG/T that allow examples of good practice to be transferred and shared across practices. This might involve a range of communication methods (including electronic, meetings and paper media). Frequently, a small proportion of practices seem to deal with most of the black and minority ethnic patients in a specific area; many practices are reluctant to take on people from these groups as they are perceived to generate extra work. Such practices must be encouraged to undertake this work through the use of incentive schemes (see example in Box 7.11) and additional resources.

Box 7.11 AN INCENTIVE SCHEME FOR REGISTERING ASYLUM SEEKERS

South Kensington, Chelsea & Westminster PCG/T in London has developed an incentive scheme to encourage practices to register asylum seekers and refugees. Practices are awarded a small amount of extra money for carrying out a full registration and health check of people with refugee/asylum seeker status. A further amount of money is awarded to practices when a member of staff undertakes training in equal opportunities and the use of interpreting services. A primary care facilitator has been appointed for two years to support practice development across the PCG and link primary care services with other relevant services and organisations

---

Given that there is an association between ethnicity and deprivation, with significant black and minority ethnic populations living in inner city areas, extra support may be needed for the many single-handed or two-partner practices that serve these populations. In some areas, this may justify funding a facilitator or co-ordinator to work across the whole PCG/T (or even several PCG/Ts) to provide support and to catalyse change. The job description needs to ensure that someone with strong facilitating skills is identified. However, it is all too easy to marginalise such workers, and it is important that they are given authority and support to carry out their job effectively. Making sure that they have been provided with desk space, a telephone, and have a proper induction to the organisation, will ensure success.

Personal medical services pilots offer new models for extending primary health care to specific groups. Many are based in inner city areas and some have chosen to target minority ethnic groups as their priority. These are still under evaluation, but may provide some useful insights as to what kinds of services work best. Drop-in centres could also prove useful, especially in areas with highly mobile populations who are unlikely to register with general practices.

Commissioning health services

PCG/Ts will increasingly be taking on the contracting and commissioning roles from health authorities. Numerous checklists for commissioners already exist. These include *Facing up to difference* by Jeff Chandra[20] and a *Health and race checklist* by Yasmin Gunaratnam.[37] Both cover generic issues and specific services and disease groups. Commissioning and contracting can be a powerful tool, but can take a long time to change services. A pilot study of commissioning coronary heart disease and diabetes services for ethnic minorities in four health authorities found that:[6]

1. a strategic long-term approach is needed
2. high-level (executive) commitment is essential
3. involving a broad group of key players early, including community members, greatly improves the chance of successful change
4. locally relevant 'health intelligence' (knowledge of local health needs amongst those commissioning services) is a powerful catalyst for change; its absence is a hindrance
5. effective systems for monitoring service quality are challenging to establish.

The national service frameworks (NSFs) provide standards for services in primary and secondary care, covering prevention and treatment. The NSF for coronary heart disease makes specific reference to the need to meet ethnic minority health.[38] In commissioning services from trusts, PCG/Ts can include generic quality criteria in service agreements. The provider should:

- be an equal opportunities employer
- offer cultural awareness/anti-discrimination training programmes for its staff
- improve ethnicity monitoring
- provide access to interpreters as relevant, so that black and minority ethnic groups are not excluded from services such as cardiac rehabilitation because of linguistic reasons
- provide appropriate signage
- cater for specific food requirements
- offer a place of worship for non-Christian faiths
- have access to appropriate spiritual and religious advice.

Contracts may relate to specific services, some of which will be mainly used by certain black and minority ethnic groups, e.g. for haemoglobinopathy services. Such contracts may include, for example, requirements to maintain a register of those who suffer from sickle cell anaemia including their usual pain treatment, to offer universal antenatal screening and provide nurse specialists, counsellors and interpreters. Common diseases such as coronary heart disease may highlight specific problem areas: people whose first language is not English, for example, may not be offered cardiac rehabilitation. Such issues must be addressed through setting appropriate standards in the service agreement.

Longer-term service agreements provide an opportunity to focus on quality in contracts. In Southampton, a service agreement for coronary heart disease (CHD) includes group-specific outcomes (see Box 7.12). As many of the other outcomes will not be achieved without improving care for black and minority ethnic groups as well as for the white majority patients, this form of contract could have real benefit for patients with CHD generally.

BOX 7.12 OUTCOMES-BASED SERVICES AGREEMENT

Central Southampton PCG has developed a three-year outcomes-based services agreement covering both primary care provision and secondary care for coronary heart disease. Some of the standards for secondary care relevant to minority ethnic groups are listed below:

1. A culturally sensitive, locally based rehabilitation programme is offered to all patients following myocardial infarction or cardiac intervention.
2. Clear, culturally appropriate information for use at home is provided to all patients following admission for unstable angina or myocardial infarction.
3. All patients admitted to hospital can discuss with staff their requirements for religious worship during their stay.
4. The PCG and acute trust are also considering using a scoring system for severity of CHD in identifying candidates for revascularisation procedures like CABG and angioplasty.

Commissioning from the voluntary sector is sometimes the most culturally appropriate course of action. A small voluntary organisation may not always provide the cheapest care, but may provide high-quality care for certain clients (for example, day care for Asian patients with dementia). It is reasonable to expect some monitoring information from voluntary organisations commissioned to provide services, however it is important to remember that smaller organisations have much more limited administrative capacity than many GP practices and PCG/Ts.

Monitoring and evaluation

Box 7.13 A HEALTH AUTHORITY ACTION PLAN

Birmingham Health Authority's Action Plan for black and minority ethnic groups covers the following areas:

> understanding community needs
> commissioning and contracting
> Health Improvement Programme local targets
> organisational development.

The Action Plan contains targets and milestones relevant to PCGs and their staff, and cross-references to HImPs, PCIPs and Clinical Governance plans.

Being able to demonstrate success within the organisation is an important motivator. PCG/Ts are accountable to their populations and to their local health authority through the annual accountability agreement. Indicators will need to include some basic process ones as well as outcome-based indicators.[39,21] Careful thought will need to be given as to:

- what information is important
- how feasible it is to collect it.

Health authorities may agree with their PCG/Ts to review how ethnicity monitoring data is used. The PCG/T should set milestones for developing effective systems and processes across all practices for ethnicity monitoring purposes. Some of the action points listed in Box 7.14, modified from work in the USA,[40] may serve as useful indicators for PCG/Ts. Many of these apply equally well to primary health care teams, acute and community trusts.

> **BOX 7.14** ACTION POINTS FOR PCG/TS
>
> Does the PCG/T have processes to review policy and procedures systematically to assess their relevance for delivering culturally competent services?
>
> Does the PCG/T have policies and procedures to review periodically current and emerging demographic trends for its area?
>
> Does the PCG/T have structures and processes to ensure representative user and community participation in the planning, delivery and evaluation of services?
>
> Does the PCG/T regularly review the likely impact of policies and service provision on reducing inequalities?
>
> Does the PCG/T have methods to identify and acquire knowledge about health beliefs and practices of black and minority ethnic groups, including perceptions/knowledge of preventative services available?
>
> Does the PCG/T have policies and resources to support health promotion for hard to reach groups, e.g. translation of information, community outreach initiatives?
>
> Does the PCG/T have a strategy for providing intercultural communication, including resources for interpreting and translation?
>
> Does the PCG/T have policies and processes which support a practice model that incorporates culture in the delivery of services?
>
> Does the PCG/T have support and/or incentives to develop cultural competence at board, practice and individual levels?
>
> Does the PCG/T review its commissioning and contracting arrangements to ensure that the needs of black and ethnic minorities have been considered?

Conclusion

There is disturbing evidence that points to delayed and inferior medical care for some BME groups. Many minority ethnic communities, asylum seekers and refugees are trapped in a cycle of poverty, disadvantage, social exclusion and isolation, which results in excessive morbidity and mortality. This is avoidable. A growing body of literature documents the existence of inequalities in health and health care experienced by black and minority ethnic groups. Surveys suggest that varying and subtle forms of racial bias exist among some health care professionals. But there is currently little research to evaluate the extent to which different factors, such as socio-economic, cultural and organisational issues, especially racism and institutional racism, contribute to these differences.

It is important to recognise that the minority ethnic communities in the UK are not homogenous but comprise many different cultural and religious groupings, speaking a variety of different languages. Many health professionals are poorly informed on the health beliefs and needs of these communities. Designing and implementing culturally sensitive services will require a mainstreaming approach that acknowledges culturally diversity at all levels of planning and decision-making. Tackling racism and discrimination is a critical component of this agenda. A 'colour-blind' approach will not address inequality. Doctors and other clinicians must learn to see people as individuals and not through the negatively stereotyped lens of race.

In the USA, health care organisations have acknowledged the need to become culturally competent and gain the confidence of their users in order to survive in a competitive market. In Britain, too, this makes both good business and ethical sense, leading to a more efficient, effective and equitable health care service with greater job satisfaction for health care professionals and better health for service users. Arguably, achieving cultural competence is an essential requirement for a modern NHS delivering health to a multicultural and diverse population in Britain today.

In this chapter we have illustrated how health care organisations can transform themselves into culturally competent ones to better meet the needs of the people they serve. The examples provided by PCG/Ts show that, with senior level commitment and leadership, change can occur, even in relatively young organisations.

Parimala Moodley, a consultant psychiatrist describes a culturally competent service:[41]

> *An ideal service for ethnic minorities is one which the majority will use voluntarily because it is a place they can trust to provide them with care when they need it. It will have a racial and cultural mix of staff which will enable them to feel understood (not black staff in inferior positions). If the languages they speak are not spoken by the staff, interpreters will be easily available. Assessment of their difficulties will be carried out free of negative stereotypes and taking account of the cultural variations in their expressions of distress ... Goals of management will be set jointly with users, enabling them to take greater control of their lives.*

References

1. Nazroo J Y. *The health of Britain's ethnic minorities*. London: Policy Studies Institute, 1997.
2. *CRD Report 5: Ethnicity & health: reviews of literature and guidance for purchasers in the areas of cardiovascular disease, mental health and haemoglobinopathies*. York: NHS Centre for Reviews and Dissemination, University of York, 1996.
3. Chapple J, Anionwu E. Genetic services. In: Rawaf S, Bahl V, eds. *Assessing health needs of people from minority ethnic groups*. London: Royal College of Physicians, 1998.
4. Noone A. Infectious diseases. In: Rawaf S, Bahl V, eds. *Assessing health needs of people from minority ethnic groups*. London: Royal College of Physicians, 1998.
5. Mackintosh J, Bhopal R, Unwin N, Ahmad W. *Step by step guide to epidemiological needs assessment for ethnic minority groups*. Newcastle-upon-Tyne: University of Newcastle-upon-Tyne, Medical School, School of Health Sciences, Department of Epidemiology and Public Health, 1996.
6. Unwin N, Bhopal R. *Strategy for commissioning services for coronary heart disease and diabetes from ethnic minority populations in England and Wales. Lessons from a four-site pilot*. Newcastle-upon-Tyne: University of Newcastle-upon-Tyne, Department of Epidemiology and Public Health, 1999.
7. Smaje C. *Health, 'race' and ethnicity – making sense of the evidence*. London: King's Fund, 1995.
8. Khan V. *Ethnicity in the 1991 Census. Volume 4. Employment, education and housing among the ethnic minority populations of Britain*. London: The Stationery Office, 1997.
9. Ahmad W, ed. *'Race' and health in contemporary Britain*. Buckingham: Open University Press, 1993.
10. Social Exclusion Unit. *Bringing Britain together: a national strategy for neighbourhood renewal. Annex B*. London: The Stationery Office, 1998.
11. Chaturvedi N, Rai H, Ben-Schlomo Y. Lay diagnosis and health care seeking behaviour for chest pain in South Asians and Europeans. *Lancet* 1997; 350: 1578–83.
12. Goddard M, Smith P. Equity of access to health care. York: University of York, Centre for Health Economics, 1998.
13. Health Education Authority. *Black and minority ethnic groups in England*. London: Health Education Authority, 1994.
14. Yee L. *Breaking barriers: towards culturally competent general practice*. London: Royal College of General Practitioners, 1997.
15. Airey C, Erens B. *National surveys of NHS patients: General practice 1998*. London: NHS Executive, 1999.
16. Macpherson Sir W. *The Stephen Lawrence inquiry report*. Chapter 6: 'Racism'. London: The Stationery Office Ltd, 1999. Available at http://www.official-documents.co.uk/documents/cm42/
17. King G. Institutional racism and the medical/health complex: a conceptual analysis. *Ethnicity and Disease* 1996; 6: 30–46.
18. Department of Health. *The vital connection: an equalities framework for the NHS*. London: Department of Health, 2000. Available on the Department of Health web site: http://www.doh.gov.uk

19. Alexander Z. *Study of black, Asian and ethnic minority issues.* London: Department of Health, 1999.
20. Chandra J. *Facing up to difference – a toolkit for creating culturally competent health services for black and minority ethnic communities.* London: King's Fund, 1996.
21. Chirico S, Johnson M, Pawar A, Scott M. *The toolbox: culturally competent organisations, services and care pathways.* Bedford: Bedfordshire Health Promotion Agency, 2000.
22. Gardenswartz L, Rowe A. *Managing diversity in health care.* San Francisco, California: Jossey-Bass, 1999.
23. Carberry C. Contesting competency: cultural safety in advanced nursing practice. *Journal of the Royal College of Nursing Australia* 1998; 5 (4): 9–13.
24. Fischer M. *Developing appropriate services for all.* London: King's Fund, 1999.
25. Fassil J. *Primary health care for black and minority ethnic people: a consumer perspective.* Leeds: NHS Ethnic Health Unit, 1996.
26. Rawaf S, Bahl V, eds. *Assessing health needs of people from ethnic minority groups.* London: Royal College of Physicians, 1998.
27. Wright J, ed. *Health needs assessment in practice.* London: BMJ Books, 1998.
28. Silvera M, Kapasi R. *Primary care ethnicity project. Interim report.* Brent and Harrow Health Authority, 2000.
29. NHSE Northern and Yorkshire. *Public engagement toolkit for primary care groups.* Leeds: Department of Health, 1999. Also available via the Department of Health web site: http://www.doh.gov.uk
30. Kai J, Hedges C. Minority ethnic community participation in needs assessment and service development in primary care: perceptions of Pakistani and Bangladeshi people about psychological distress. *Health Expectations* 1999; 2: 7–20.
31. Buckinghamshire Health Authority. *Communicating with our ethnic minority communities – how should we do it?* Aylesbury: Buckinghamshire Health Authority, 1996.
32. Kai J. *Valuing diversity. A resource for effective health care of ethnically diverse communities.* London: Royal College of General Practitioners, 1999.
33. Kubba A. Sexual and reproductive health. In: Rawaf S, Bahl V, eds. *Assessing health needs of people from minority ethnic groups.* London: Royal College of Physicians, 1998.
34. Levenson R, Gillam S. *Linkworkers in primary care.* London: King's Fund, 1998.
35. Henley A, Schott J. *Culture, religion and patient care in a multi-ethnic society – handbook for professionals.* London: Age Concern, 1999.
36. Silvera M, Kapasi R. *Health advocacy for minority ethnic Londoners.* London: King's Fund, 2000.
37. Gunuratnam Y. *Health and race checklist.* London: King's Fund, 1993.
38. Secretary of State for Health. *The national service framework for coronary heart disease.* London: The Stationery Office, 2000.
39. Department of Health. *Good practice and quality indicators in primary health care: health care for black and minority ethnic people.* Leeds: NHS Ethnic Health Unit, 1996.
40. Office of Minority Health, Department of Health and Human Services. *Assuring cultural competence in health care: recommendations for national standards and an outcomes-focused research agenda.* Available at: www.omhrc.gov/clas/
41. Moodley P. Setting up services for ethnic minorities. In: Bhugra D, Leff J, eds. *Principles of social psychiatry.* Oxford: Blackwell, 1993.

Chapter 8

Racial harassment in the NHS

Mike Collins

The worst betrayal of intelligence is finding justification for the world as it is.
Jean Guéhemo

Introduction

Research to date clearly demonstrates that the racial harassment experienced by black and minority ethnic staff in the NHS is significantly higher than the levels of harassment experienced by other staff groups. It is important to view this widespread existence of racial harassment in the NHS within the wider context of the racist experience of ethnic communities in other aspects of life. The pervasive nature of racism is seen as a general part of everyday life for minority ethnic communities in Britain.[1] Being made to feel different in a variety of social situations and locations is largely seen as routine, and in some instances expected. What minority ethnic staff experience in the wider community will influence their responses to the behaviours they experience at work, and vice versa.

Over 8 per cent of directly employed staff in the NHS are from minority ethnic groups, making the NHS the largest employer of minority ethnic people in the country. As the NHS is also the largest employer of women and part-time staff, it is a unique employer with unique responsibilities. If the NHS is to ensure delivery of high-quality, fair, accessible and responsive services, then it has to build a commitment to equality and inclusiveness into everything it does.

The success of the NHS in tackling the problem of racial harassment is a touchstone of its success in making tangible progress in ending racial discrimination. Local studies show that the NHS is seen to be a racist employer by minority ethnic communities,[2] and that there is a high level of cynicism about the commitment of the NHS to tackle racism. The service needs to demonstrate that it is serious about tackling racism, both in terms of employment and service provision, if it is to assure minority ethnic communities of its commitment to providing services that are responsive to different needs, free from stereotyping and discrimination.[3]

This chapter explores the nature and extent of racial harassment within the NHS, its impact on both the individual and NHS employers, and the actions that need to be taken by NHS employers to tackle the problem. It draws on a study of the experiences of black and minority ethnic staff and describes the extent and nature of racial harassment. The impact of racial harassment on both individuals and employers is highlighted, and recommendations made for the development of policies and practices for health service employers.

In December 1998, the Government reaffirmed its commitment to tackling racial discrimination and racial harassment in the NHS by endorsing the national plan for action – *Tackling racial harassment in the NHS*. This plan for action provided a framework within which NHS employers were required to take sustained action to tackle the problem of racial harassment. The plan was drawn up following consultation with the service, including black and minority ethnic staff, recognising that racial harassment was a 'long-standing and widespread problem which has not yet been thoroughly recognised and addressed'.[4]

This plan for action had five key aims:

- To inform users of NHS services and those providing them that racial harassment would not be tolerated.
- To ensure this message was widely disseminated and visibly evident.
- To deter perpetrators.
- To ensure NHS staff have the knowledge, structures and skills to fulfil these commitments.
- To give black and minority ethnic staff the confidence and support to challenge harassment effectively.

A small number of national action groups, together with local networks of NHS employers, worked on the development of good practice guidance and practical tools to assist NHS employers in tackling racial harassment, and to meet the responsibilities expected of them in *Tackling racial harassment in the NHS*. The learning and outputs from this work has helped inform the content of this chapter.

Racial harassment defined

There is no hard and fast definition of racial harassment. It is a general term covering a wide range of unacceptable, and often unlawful, behaviour. Although the more overt forms of racial harassment, such as physical abuse, intimidation and threatening and abusive language, are more easily recognised, it is the less obvious forms of harassment that are more common, but invariably much more difficult to deal with in the workplace.

The Commission for Racial Equality (CRE) uses the definition of sexual harassment provided in the European Commission's Code of Practice on Sexual Harassment, there being at present no definition for racial harassment. The CRE defines racial harassment as 'unwanted conduct of a racial nature, or other conduct based on race affecting the dignity of women and men at work'.[5] As the CRE explains, racial harassment may be deliberate and conscious, but it can also be unintentional. Whilst the intention of the perpetrator may provide an explanation for the harassment, it can never be an excuse.

Box 8.1 sets out the definition of racial harassment developed for NHS employers, which included examples of racially harassing behaviours.

Box 8.1 DEFINITION OF RACIAL HARASSMENT

Racial harassment is unacceptable targeted behaviour motivated by racial intolerance affecting the dignity of women and men at work.

Racial harassment covers a wide range of unacceptable, and often unlawful, behaviour. There are the more obvious and overt forms of harassment such as racist language and physical intimidation. However, racial harassment is frequently more covert. These more subtle forms of racial harassment, such as deprecating the way people dress or speak, are equally distressing and can create an intimidating and unpleasant atmosphere at work.

Examples of racially harassing behaviours include:

  patronising remarks
  shunning or excluding people from normal workplace conversation or social events
  being condescending or deprecating about the way people dress or speak
  intrusive questioning about a person's racial or ethnic origin, culture or religion, or subjecting this to mockery
  unjustified criticism of work performance
  unfair allocation of work and responsibilities
  racist 'jokes', banter and insults
  display or articulation of racially offensive material, including racist graffiti
  denial of access to training and/or overtime
  black and minority ethnic staff being more likely to be disciplined than white staff
  threatening and abusive language
  physical abuse or intimidation.

Racial harassment may be deliberate and conscious, but it can also be unintentional, as when an individual is oblivious to another person's feelings and sensitivities.

Extent of racial harassment

For some years, most NHS employers have declared their opposition to racial and other forms of harassment in their equal opportunity policies, invariably providing a grievance procedure to address any problems that may arise. However it was not until the mid-1990s that employers began to more fully understand the full extent of bullying and harassment in the workplace, with a number of research studies showing that, when asked, between 10 and 20 per cent of workforces say they have experienced harassment or bullying in the previous six months.[6]

In 2000, Hoel and Cooper[7] published the findings of the largest ever study into the nature and extent of workplace bullying in the UK. This survey covered a wide range of employers, including several NHS trusts. Using the following definition of bullying, 10.5 per cent of the 5300 respondents reported being bullied in the previous six months. It is worth noting that less than 3 per cent of the respondents reported themselves as belonging to an ethnic minority.

> We define bullying as a situation where one or several individuals persistently over a period of time perceive themselves to be on the receiving end of negative actions from one or several persons, in a situation where the target of the bullying has difficulty defending him or herself against these actions. We will not refer to one-off incidents as bullying.[7]

In terms of general levels of harassment, there is nothing to suggest that the NHS is any worse, or any better, than other organisations in the public and private sectors. In a survey of 6000 RCN members conducted in 2000, one in six nurses reported that they had been harassed or bullied by colleagues in the previous 12 months.[8] Where local audits have been carried out to determine levels of harassment, the results have been consistent with these wider research studies.[9]

Until recently, there has been little quantitative information on the extent of racial harassment on staff within the NHS, or any other major employers in Britain for that matter, until in 1995 the Policy Studies Institute published the findings of a Department of Health-funded study into the experiences of nursing and midwifery staff belonging to minority ethnic groups in the NHS. This study included a postal survey to which some 1200 minority ethnic staff responded. One of the findings from this survey was that:

- 66 per cent of black nursing staff reported being racially harassed by patients
- 58 per cent of Asian nursing staff reported being racially harassed by patients
- 37 per cent of black and Asian nursing staff reported being harassed by colleagues, including supervisors and managers.[10]

The study concluded that racial harassment continued to be a regular feature of the working lives of minority ethnic staff. This was echoed in the Plan for Action in *Tackling racial harassment in the NHS*:

> *Racial harassment in the NHS was frequently described by people involved in drawing up the action plan as 'endemic'. So it has come to be expected and therefore, to some degree, to be accepted.*[11]

In 1999, a survey of attitudes and experiences amongst staff in all occupations in 34 NHS employers who participated in the piloting of the Positively Diverse initiative, found that 30 per cent of black and minority ethnic staff reported being racially harassed in the previous 12 months.[3] The survey of harassment and bullying experienced by nurses undertaken by the RCN in 2000 found that 16 per cent of white nurses had been bullied or harassed in the previous 12 months, and for black and Asian nurses the figure was significantly higher at nearly 30 per cent.[6]

One of the key objectives of the Plan for Action was to establish a more empirical knowledge base of the extent and nature of racial harassment in the NHS, so that the service would be able to make more informed judgements about the most effective actions necessary to tackle it. Whilst the general extent of racial harassment was understood, very little had been heard from black and minority ethnic staff about their experiences, their feelings and their views on the negative actions of others. There was, for example, little qualitative information behind the widespread non-reporting of incidents of racial harassment by black and minority ethnic staff, or the nature of the harassing behaviours experienced.

Evidence from focus groups

During the early part of 2000, some 500 black and minority ethnic staff took part in focus groups held within 53 NHS workplaces across the country, the purpose of these groups being to gather qualitative and quantitative information on the nature and extent of racial harassment experienced by black and minority ethnic staff, and the effectiveness of their employers in tackling the problem. The employers that participated in this study were members of seven local networks set up in the previous year to support the development of good practices to tackle racial harassment.

The experiences of participants in these focus groups confirmed that racial harassment was widespread in the NHS. Staff in front-line jobs were, not surprisingly, given their contact with service users and members of the public, more likely to have experienced racial harassment than other staff. In addition to experiencing racial harassment, participants commonly reported witnessing incidents of racially harassing behaviour. It is important to recognise that, for many staff, witnessing the harassment of a colleague could be as distressing as experiencing the harassment themselves.

The perpetrators of racially harassing behaviours were colleagues, managers, service users or members of the public. Staff reported somewhat higher levels of harassment from colleagues than from other groups. The experiences recounted showed that perpetrators existed at all levels in the organisations concerned, from senior clinicians and managers to front-line team members.

The experiences of black and minority ethnic staff

Racial harassment by colleagues

Many participants in the focus groups reported that racial harassment by colleagues had become subtler and less overt over recent years. The most common form of harassment by colleagues was verbal abuse, with a significant number of participants reporting being excluded or shunned by their colleagues. This exclusion often extended into social activities.

Some participants did not initially recognise some of the more subtle negative behaviours being described as racial harassment. This suggests that some staff, when asked to report whether they have experienced racial harassment in previous studies, may have failed to recognise certain behaviours as racially motivated.

Many participants gave examples of racist comments made in their company, or within their hearing, which whilst not being directed at them personally, were made with the intention of causing them offence. A number of examples were given of banter and comment that were clearly insensitive to strongly held religious views of Muslim staff, for instance.

When describing their own experiences of racial harassment by colleagues, many examples were also given of racial harassment of individual service users by staff, particularly derogatory remarks, and of perceived unfairness in service delivery to black and minority ethnic patients.

It was clear from the comments made by participants that, not surprisingly, black and minority ethnic staff draw parallels between the commitment of their employers to tackle issues of discrimination and lack of equity in service delivery, and their own experiences as members of staff, and vice versa. Where staff perceived that their employer was less than committed to addressing issues of discrimination and inequity in service delivery, and racial harassment of service users, they understandably expressed scepticism about their employers' commitment to tackling racial harassment of staff.

Racial harassment by managers

By far the most common form of harassment by managers reported by participants was denial of training or career development opportunities, with a number of participants feeling they had been discriminated against. The second most common form of harassment reported by managers was unfair work allocation. When raising these concerns, participants frequently drew comparisons with the more favourable treatment they perceived other staff to have received.

Racial harassment by service users

The most common form of harassment by service users (and their relatives or carers) reported by participants in the focus groups was verbal abuse. In some cases, staff believed that the verbal abuse they received was related to patients' medical conditions or the treatment they were receiving, and they often made allowances for behaviour in a medical context that they would regard as unacceptable in almost any other environment.

The second most common form of harassment of staff by service users was the refusal of care or treatment from minority ethnic staff. Less common, but nonetheless significant, were participants' experiences of being ignored or excluded by service users, and physical aggression and malicious complaints made about them.

In general, most staff who took part in the focus groups expected people, and in particular colleagues and managers, to know the difference between acceptable and unacceptable behaviour and, when they did not, took the view that most racially harassing behaviours are likely to be deliberate and conscious, and not unintentional.

The racially harassing behaviours most commonly identified by focus group participants are listed in Box 8.2.

Staff perception of managers

In addition to exploring the nature of the racial harassment experienced by black and minority ethnic staff, the focus groups also explored staff perceptions of the effectiveness of their employers in tackling the problem.

BOX 8.2 MAIN RACIALLY HARASSING BEHAVIOURS

verbal abuse
being excluded or shunned
unjustified criticism including malicious complaints
lack of training and/or development opportunities
unfair work allocation
stereotyping
unequal treatment
denial of authority
having to prove themselves v
ictimisation and intimidation
inappropriate management style
unfair performance review
physical aggression

In nearly every focus group, fears were expressed about victimisation, or being labelled a 'troublemaker' for raising concerns or complaints about racial harassment. The victimisation experienced was often quite covert, but nonetheless invariably caused further distress to the individual concerned. The fear of victimisation is clearly an important factor in the non-reporting of many cases of racial harassment.

There are no available figures to quantify the levels of under-reporting of racial harassment within the NHS, but the recent RCN survey into all forms of bullying and harassment showed significant under-reporting, with only one-third of the respondents reporting incidents of harassment by patients and relatives to a manager.[8]

The general experience of black and minority ethnic staff was that when incidents were reported, few were investigated or dealt with in a timely or effective manner. Many examples were given of managers not taking complaints or concerns seriously, and of trivialising matters. The experience of participants was that some managers were uncertain about how to deal with cases of racial harassment. Of particular concern was the fact that, in nearly every focus group, many white managers seemed ill equipped to deal with sensitive and difficult issues such as racism within the workplace.

Interestingly, most focus groups were able to identify individual managers in whom they had confidence in their ability to effectively deal with incidents of racial harassment. This demonstrates the importance of personal commitment on the part of individual managers not to tolerate racial harassment, and shows that committed and knowledgeable individuals are able to bring about behavioural changes, notwithstanding any policy or procedural weaknesses.

There is undoubtedly a strong association between the lack of competence on the part of many managers to effectively tackle racial and other forms of harassment in the workplace, and the level of training and support they receive. Very few of the NHS employers involved in this study could claim that their managers had received the training necessary for them to effectively tackle harassment at work. Subsequent work with a group of London NHS employers – to develop training for managers – demonstrated that many managers were unsure of their role and responsibilities, recognising that they sometimes mishandled complaints.[12]

Within this group of managers from London trusts, a number indicated they were unclear as to how best to deal with racial harassment on the part of service users, a view echoed by many of the focus groups. A review of the harassment policies in place in those workplaces where focus groups were held showed that only in a minority of cases were there clear policies on how to deal with harassment by service users, notwithstanding the incidence of racial harassment from this source. The 1998 survey of good equal opportunities practice in NHS trusts showed that 81 per cent had policy statements on harassment by staff, but only 59 per cent had policy statements of harassment by service users.[13]

The case for action

A recent survey has shown that black and minority ethnic people are more likely than they were ten years ago to believe that they have been unfairly treated by employers, with a quarter of African Caribbeans and over 40 per cent of Asians believing that their religion is a factor in the discrimination and harassment they face.[14] This study suggests that as many as 250,000 African Caribbeans and Asians experience racial harassment every year.

Racial harassment has a significant impact on a large number of black and minority ethnic staff, on individual health care providers, and on how the NHS is perceived by the communities it serves, both as an employer and provider of health services responsive to the needs of all.

Impact on individuals

The impact of racial harassment can be grave on individuals. It can destroy a person's self-confidence, their powers of concentration, their health, their peace of mind, and their trust in the people they work with. The effects of harassment are well described in a recent UNISON guide:

Harassment can and often does, undermine an individual's confidence and self-esteem. This can in turn lead to long-term problems with work and personal relationships. In particular, the recipient's health is likely to suffer as a consequence of stress. Common symptoms are stomach complaints and ulcers; inability to concentrate; exacerbation of asthma and ulcers and/or other health related conditions; depression; low resistance to infection; headaches; tearfulness; insomnia; palpitations and panic attacks. These effects can continue long after the harassment has stopped. In extreme circumstances they can lead to an individual leaving the organisation or even attempting suicide.

The situation may be even worse in cases where recipients do not feel able to report incidents of harassment. Because they cannot explain what is happening to them, it may lead to their being disciplined or dismissed on grounds of work performance and/or sickness absence.

Because of the loss of self-esteem, in some cases individuals will blame themselves, convincing themselves that they may have caused the situation to arise.[15]

Harassment is a major cause of stress. In turn, stress is one of the main reasons why staff take time off through sickness. Research suggests that bullying and harassment account for between one-third and one-half of all sickness absence due to stress.

Impact on the NHS

As well as harming the individuals concerned, racial harassment has damaging consequences for NHS employers, resulting in a waste of talent and potential, and if not tackled, making it that much more difficult to secure and develop a workforce that reflects and understands the diversity of service users and the community.

It is clear that racial harassment has a significant impact on the ability of the NHS to recruit staff from black and minority ethnic communities. Whilst there has been little large-scale empirical research into the recruitment of staff from minority ethnic communities, there have been several small-scale studies that highlight the difficulties of recruiting black and minority ethnic staff. Two key factors are evident in the literature on difficulties in recruiting minority ethnic staff. The first relates to cultural norms that may restrict some people from certain ethnic communities from pursuing careers specifically in nursing or midwifery. The second is the impact of institutional racism, including racial harassment, experienced by staff from minority ethnic communities.[16] The experiences of staff frequently deter members of their families or the wider community from applying for employment or training in the NHS.[4]

Racial harassment has also been found to be one of the main reasons why black and minority ethnic staff leave the NHS. The most important determinants of job satisfaction for black and minority ethnic nurses are the experience of racial harassment at work and having faced discrimination in promotion and training. Black and minority ethnic staff who report frequent racial harassment from colleagues are seven times more likely to be very dissatisfied with their job than those who have not experienced such abuse.[17] Shields and Price also found that nearly 20 per cent of minority ethnic nurses reported facing discrimination with regard to gaining promotion or access to training opportunities in their careers, which accords with the experiences of participants in the focus groups previously referred to.

Impact on trainees

There is qualitative evidence from several local studies of students experiencing racial harassment in training, both within the school and during clinical placements,[2,18] with examples being given of individuals leaving training as a result of the racism experienced. For instance, interviews with a sample of black and minority ethnic students in Birmingham showed that 75 per cent had experienced race-related difficulties on placements.[2]

There is no reason to suggest that the levels of racial harassment experienced by black and minority ethnic students in training will be markedly different from those experienced by registered staff, given that in the main staff and students come into contact with the same groups of perpetrators. It is important, therefore, that Training and Education Consortia work in collaboration with NHS employers and training providers to ensure that there are adequate policies in place to tackle racial harassment of students in training.

A survey of 18 Training and Education Consortia in 2000 found that two-thirds required their training providers to have effective harassment policies in place, with several others intending to make this a requirement. However, only two Consortia conducted any post-entry ethnic monitoring of students. Training Consortia need to monitor the levels of racial harassment experienced by black and minority ethnic students, the impact of harassment on attrition rates, and to ensure that training providers and NHS employers collaborate in making sure that there are effective policies, practices and support for students in place.

Knowledge that racial discrimination and harassment are significant problems in the NHS makes it that much more difficult to recruit staff from black and minority ethnic communities. In those parts of the country experiencing significant change in the ethnic profile of the local labour force, such as Birmingham and London, this could have a serious impact on the ability of the NHS to provide services of the range and quality required.

Impact on quality

Effective clinical governance is dependent on staff being able to raise concerns about the quality of clinical practice, including concerns about a colleague's clinical practice. However, staff who are being harassed or bullied at work are often reluctant to raise such concerns. For example, the recent inquiry into the physical mistreatment of mentally frail older people by staff at Beech House, St Pancras Hospital, details the racial harassment and victimisation of junior, and largely black and minority ethnic staff, who had raised concerns over the treatment of patients.[19]

When racial harassment undermines an individual's confidence and self-esteem, work performance invariably suffers, and for the NHS this will have a clear impact on the quality of care provided, with staff who suffer the effects of harassment being more likely to make mistakes. Employers need to create an environment in which individuals feel valued, in which differences are recognised, where the diverse talents of all staff are fully utilised in delivering service goals, and where racial harassment is not allowed to cause the opposite to happen.

Racial discrimination and harassment are expensive: they cost money and undermine staff morale and reputation. Employment tribunals are no longer constrained by limits on the compensation they can award victims of discrimination. The amount of compensation that courts can order can be substantial where it can be demonstrated that an individual's health has been damaged as a result of harassment.

Recommendations for action

Policies and procedures

It is important that policies to tackle racial harassment, and the support that staff experiencing harassment can expect, are well publicised and understood by staff and managers at all levels. Most staff who participated in the focus groups were unaware of their employer's policies and procedures for dealing with harassment, and it was rare to find any evidence of an employer being proactive in setting and monitoring the standards of behaviour expected of staff, or indeed tackling the organisational causes of racial harassment.

In 1993, the NHSE set out ten goals and supporting objectives for NHS employers to achieve in order to ensure equality of opportunity for black and minority ethnic staff. One of these goals was to ensure that 'NHS workplaces are free from harassment and discrimination, including racial harassment',[20] with employers being required to translate policy into positive action plans.

In a recent survey of 128 NHS trusts, reported in 2000, the CRE looked at the extent to which there were formal action plans or programmes to translate policy into practice.[21] This survey found that only 5 per cent of the trusts had fully implemented racial equality action plans, either separately or as part of a wider equality at work action plan. Certainly, in terms of tackling racial harassment, there has until recently been little evidence of NHS employers taking sustained actions to achieve the goal set in 1993 of ensuring workplaces are free from racial harassment. Little wonder that many black and minority ethnic staff are often sceptical of the commitment of the NHS to tackle racism and deliver equality of opportunity.

BOX 8.3 TACKLING RACISM IN A NHS TRUST

South West London and St George's Mental Health Trust is one trust where both staff and senior managers have recognised the importance of tackling racial harassment as part of a key service objective to deliver culturally integrated services, free from racism. The policy to tackle racial harassment has been supported by the introduction of staff support advisors. There is a mandatory rolling training programme, which had trust board attendance from the outset. Social services staff and managers who work alongside health care colleagues also attend the training. The training programme sets standards of behaviour, and promotes ownership of the development of culturally integrated services by requiring participants to take personal responsibility for change.

The commitment of the trust and its senior managers to tackling racial harassment is well publicised through the display of zero tolerance posters across all areas. In addition, the trust has sought to sustain this commitment by maximising the involvement of staff at all levels, and service users, in the work to tackle racial harassment and deliver culturally integrated services.

Many staff have commented on over-reliance on formal complaints procedures on the part of their employers. The formal and often adversarial nature of formal complaints procedures can often discourage those who experience racial harassment from raising justified concerns in the first place. Formal resolution can sometimes be too heavy-handed. Informal resolution can be more sensitive to the needs of the individual experiencing the harassment, as well as giving the harasser more of an opportunity to correct his or her unacceptable behaviour. It is important to realise that there will be some occasions when there is no intent on the part of the harasser, or a lack of appreciation of the impact of the unacceptable behaviour.[22]

The general failure of employers to have effective arrangements in place for recording and monitoring incidences of harassment was commented on in most focus groups. This shortcoming was confirmed in the review of trust harassment policies, which showed that very few employers had arrangements in place to ensure boards received formal feedback on the level and nature of harassment within their organisation – the absence of such information making it difficult to properly monitor the success of stated policy objectives to tackle harassment, including racial harassment. The result is that few NHS boards will have an understanding of the real extent and nature of racial and other forms of harassment. From April 2000, NHS employers were required to set targets to reduce harassment at work.[23] *The vital connection* required that employers should:

1. Be able to demonstrate a year-on-year increase in the level of confidence that staff have in their ability to tackle harassment at work, as measured through the annual staff attitude survey
2. Agree a target reduction in the level of harassment at work, and to have arrangements in place to be able to demonstrate this progress year-on-year.[23]

Guidance developed by the local networks of NHS employers – on the principles that should underpin effective policies to tackle racial and other forms of harassment – makes clear the importance of employers providing a range of options for resolving issues and complaints speedily, and in a way that does not discourage those experiencing harassment from taking action to ensure the unacceptable behaviour ceases. A summary of this guidance is given in Box 8.4.

BOX 8.4 CONTENT OF HARASSMENT POLICIES

The purpose of a harassment policy is to set the standards of behaviour required in order to maintain organisational values, to describe the arrangements that have been made to eradicate harassment at work, and to tackle it effectively when it occurs.

The content and style of harassment policies will differ between NHS employers, reflecting, for example, local organisational factors and 'house style'. However, one thing they should have in common is a firm commitment from senior managers to bring about changes in organisational and individual behaviours, and that policy is translated into actions to bring about change.

The key elements of an effective harassment policy should be as follows:

A clear statement of commitment from the board to ensure a working environment free from harassment and that harassment will not be tolerated at any level.
A clear description of the objectives that the policy sets out to achieve.   *cont'd.*

Box 8.4 Content of harassment policies (*CONT.*)

Reference to the legal obligations and duties.

Definitions of harassment, including racial harassment, together with examples of the behaviours involved.

A definition of bullying, recognising this involves abuse of power or authority.

A clear statement that it is for the recipient to define whether any behaviour is unacceptable.

A recognition of the extent and causes of harassment, including organisational factors.

An outline of the action that will be taken to address the organisational factors that lead to harassment.

A recognition of the effects of harassment on the individual and organisation.

An outline of the responsibilities that the board, managers, trades unions and individuals have to ensure harassment does not occur, and that the policy is fully implemented.

A clear statement on the rights and responsibilities of patients, clients and members of the public, and the actions that will be taken if harassment occurs.

A clear statement encouraging staff who believe they have been harassed to ask the person responsible to stop, recognising that individuals are sometimes not aware of the impact of their behaviour.

A clear summary of the range of options and procedures for resolving issues and complaints.

The informal system (including details of advice and support).

The formal system (including details of the formal complaints procedure, investigations, disciplinary and appeals procedures).

A message that complaints will be taken seriously and will be dealt with without delay.

A clear statement that confidentiality will be maintained, but setting out the circumstances under which confidentiality cannot be guaranteed.

A clear statement that victimisation will not be tolerated as a result of raising an issue or making a complaint.

Details of the skills and behaviour training that will be provided to support the policy.

An outline of the arrangements for recording and monitoring incidents of harassment.

Details of how the policy will be publicised and communicated to all staff and to the public, and how awareness will be maintained.

Race equality training

Effective training of both managers and staff is critical if NHS employers are to ensure that behaviours change, and this is increasingly recognised by NHS employers. A number of those employers who collaborated in the running of focus groups also provided cultural awareness training for staff. However, the experience of black and minority ethnic staff would indicate that the training being provided is failing to eliminate discrimination and harassment in the workplace. These experiences reflect an often-voiced criticism of diversity, equality or cultural awareness training, in that it frequently fails to translate better awareness and understanding into changed behaviours.

Hemphill and Haines describe the failure of diversity training that does not focus on changing workplace behaviours. They suggest that whilst 'it is useful to recognise and acknowledge our unique differences, it is far more essential to address effective and appropriate workplace behaviours'.[24] The fact that many black and minority ethnic staff and service users in the NHS continue to experience racial harassment, despite the investment in diversity and multicultural awareness training, indicates that the design and planned outcomes of this training needs to be reviewed.

The failure of many NHS employers to provide adequate training in this area has also been highlighted by the Mental Health Act Commission. In its study of 104 mental health and learning disability units, the Commission found that two-thirds had no policy on training in race equality and anti-discriminatory practice for staff, and a similar number did not provide training on this for their staff.[25]

NHS employers also need to do more to ensure that managers have the necessary interpersonal management skills, including those dealing with personal conflict, and difficult and sensitive issues, so that they have the competence to deal effectively with racial harassment issues. Managers need to understand the nature, extent and causes of racial harassment, so that they are better equipped to deal with individual cases of harassment, as well as come to more informed decisions on the local policies and practices that need to be in place.

Ethnicity monitoring

The failures of many NHS employers to conduct effective ethnicity monitoring of their workforce has been highlighted by the Commission for Racial Equality. The Commission found that only 65 per cent of NHS trusts surveyed in 2000 actually used the data generated to evaluate and develop policy and practice, and that very few conducted ethnicity monitoring of performance reviews, grievances or disciplinary cases.[20]

The only way in which NHS employers will know whether policies and practices to tackle racial discrimination and harassment are working is to maintain data on the ethnic profile of the workforce, and to analyse ethnicity of staff in those processes and events that will provide evidence of discrimination and harassment.

Reporting and recording of incidents

Given the often ineffectual responses of NHS employers towards the problem of racial harassment, it is perhaps not surprising that most incidents go unreported. This under-reporting is not confined to the workplace. Notwithstanding an increase in the number of racially motivated incidents that have been reported to the police in the 1990s, partly explained by changes in the way police record incidents, the British Crime Survey shows that the level of racially motivated incidents far exceeds that reported to the police.[26]

Virdee concludes that there are three main reasons for this under-reporting:

1. Having to live and work alongside the perpetrators, with the fear of victimisation and further racial harassment.
2. Lack of confidence in the ability of the police to effectively deal with incidents reported, and a concern that many issues may be trivialised.
3. The police being regarded by some as part of the problem, instead of part of the resolution.

Parallels can be drawn between the reasons for under-reporting of racial harassment in the workplace and the reasons for under-reporting in the wider community. NHS employers need to be mindful of this, and of the wider experiences of staff racial harassment and discrimination, when seeking to encourage black and minority ethnic staff to report incidences of racial harassment at work. Certainly, many black and minority ethnic staff in the NHS fear being victimised for reporting racial harassment, and have little confidence in the ability of managers to effectively deal with incidents.

There must be effective arrangements in place for recording and monitoring incidents of racial harassment, whether or not these result in formal complaints, and that the data collected is regularly analysed and reported on to senior management and shared with both trades unions and BME staff. Arrangements for dealing with cases of racial harassment should centre on meeting the needs of the individual experiencing the harassment, in terms of ensuring the unacceptable behaviour ceases, in providing a range of options for support and resolution, and in dealing firmly with the perpetrators.

It is important that procedures do not in themselves present obstacles to staff in raising concerns or complaints about racial harassment. The approach to tackling harassment at work in general, and racial harassment in particular, needs to be publicised and communicated to all staff and the public, and awareness maintained. Certain key messages need to be communicated, and reinforced at regular intervals by senior management in particular, to encourage staff to challenge and report racially harassing behaviours. These include a recognition of the extent and nature of harassment, that complaints will be taken seriously and will be dealt with without delay, that victimisation will not be tolerated, and that confidentiality will be maintained.

Box 8.5 North Mersey Community Trust

North Mersey Community Trust is another trust where the commitment to tackle racial harassment is well publicised, ensuring that the message 'racial harassment will not be tolerated' is widely disseminated and is visibly evident through its 'Stamp it Out' posters and explanatory leaflets. As well as encouraging staff who experience racial harassment to report incidents, the publicity materials encourage them to reflect on their own behaviour towards colleagues and service users. Action to tackle racial harassment is part of an integrated and well-publicised action plan to manage diversity in both employment and service delivery.

Conclusion

The widespread existence of racial harassment within the NHS has to be a cause of great concern. NHS employers have policies in place to tackle racial harassment at work, and a number have been reviewed and revised to improve their effectiveness. But more needs to be done to bring about the necessary changes in organisational and individual behaviours, and to ensure that policy really is translated into actions to bring about change.

There is no quick fix to tackling racial harassment in the workplace. To successfully tackle racial harassment, senior managers and boards need to move from good intentions to demonstrating firm commitment to ensure action is taken and sustained. The case for action is clear, and the costs to NHS employers of failing to tackle racial harassment are equally clear.

The importance of securing and developing a workforce that reflects and understands the diversity of the population cannot be overstated. The NHS has to respond to the needs of this distinctive workforce, ensuring that it achieves employment standards that match those of the best. The importance of ensuring equality of opportunity in employment, with fair access and outcomes for all, welcoming in and building on the great diversity among the people who work in the NHS, was recognised in *The vital connection*, the equalities framework for the NHS published in April 2000:

> *The NHS has to show that there is no place for discrimination, harassment and stereotyped or prejudiced treatment – whether on an individual or institutional basis – on grounds of age, gender, sexual orientation, disability, race or ethnicity, religion, class, nationality, income or employment status. It has to create an environment in*

which individuals feel valued and in which differences are recognised and fully utilised in delivering service goals.[23]

In practice, however, the efforts of many black and minority ethnic staff have been rewarded with harassment and discrimination over a number of years, a situation that should not be tolerated in a service that rightly prides itself on its intrinsic fairness.

We are now beginning to see a cultural shift in the NHS on tackling racism within the service, and there are an increasing number of examples of good practice in terms of actions being taken by NHS employers to tackle racial harassment. One common feature of those employers that are taking positive action to tackle racial harassment is clear leadership and commitment from senior management, and an understanding of the extent and nature of racism and harassment at work.

The challenge for all NHS employers is to build on the commitment being demonstrated by the large number of individual managers, staff and trades union representatives, at all levels and in all parts of the country, who want to make a difference, and want to see equality of opportunity for all black and minority ethnic staff become a reality.

Central to any successful plan of action to tackle racial harassment is the need for NHS employers to set acceptable standards of behaviour for both staff and service users, to ensure these are known and understood, that they become an integral part of organisational culture, and are reinforced in all aspects of training and development.

Actions to tackle racial harassment and achieve race equality need to be part of broader integrated diversity and equality programmes of action, and these in turn should be mainstreamed into the human resource and business planning process. Responsibilities for tackling all forms of harassment should be part of all managers' job plans, and their performance should be measured against their ability to provide a positive and supportive working environment.

We are all different, but it is these differences that invariably generate harassing behaviours on the part of others. Effective actions to tackle racial harassment, therefore, need to be underpinned by an organisational culture that accepts and embraces the fact that the workforce consists of a diverse population of people, and that differences should be embraced and harnessed to create a productive environment in which everybody feels valued, and where everyone's talents are being fully utilised.

At the same time, it is important to acknowledge that whilst we are all different, we are not all equal. Black and minority ethnic staff in the NHS are particularly disadvantaged, commonly experiencing racial discrimination and harassment. NHS employers must, therefore, ensure that their approach to diversity includes positive actions to address discrimination against the most vulnerable groups, a responsibility now emphasised by the positive duties placed on employers by the Race Relations (Amendment) Act 2000. Employers need to work in partnership with staff, trades unions and local communities to ensure a fair and just working environment that values diversity and gives everyone an equal chance to work, learn and develop, free from discrimination, prejudice and racism.

References

1.   Chahal K, Julienne L. *We can't all be white*. York: Joseph Rowntree Foundation, 1999.
2.   University of Central England. *Recruitment and retention in nursing and professions allied to medicine of individuals from black and minority ethnic communities*. Birmingham: University of Central England, 1999.
3.   Department of Health. *Positively diverse: report 2000*. London: Department of Health, 2000.
4.   Department of Health. *Tackling racial harassment in the NHS: a plan for action*. London: Department of Health, 1998.
5.   Commission for Racial Equality. *Racial harassment at work*. London: Commission for Racial Equality, 1995.
6.   Rayner C. *Bullying and harassment at work: a review of current research*. Paper presented at national conference on tackling racial harassment in the NHS, 18 February 2000.
7.   Hoel H, Copper C L. *Destructive conflict and bullying at work. (Summary report)*. Manchester: Manchester School of Management, UMIST: 2000.
8.   Royal College of Nursing. *Challenging harassment and bullying: guidance for RCN representatives, stewards and officers*. London: Royal College of Nursing, 2001.
9.   Newham Community Health Services. *Valuing diversity: action plan, 1999–2000*. London: Newham Community Health Service NHS Trust, 1999.
10. Beishon S, Hagell A, Virdee S. *Nursing in a multi-ethnic NHS*. London: Policy Studies Institute, 1995.
11. Department of Health. *Tackling racial harassment in the NHS: a plan for action*. London: Department of Health, 1998.
12. The NHS Confederation. *Good practice in tackling racial harassment in the NHS*. Update: Issue No 14. London: The NHS Confederation, 2000.
13. Department of Health. *Equal opportunities and monitoring in NHS trusts*. London: Department of Health, 1998.
14. Mahood T, Berthoud R, Lakey J, Nazroo J, Smith P, Virdee S, Beishon S. *Ethnic minorities in Britain: diversity and disadvantage*. London: Policy Studies Institute, 1999.
15. UNISON. *Harassment: a UNISON guide to policy and representation*. London: UNISON, 1997.
16. Gerrish K, Husband C, Mackenzie, J. *Nursing for a multi-ethnic society*. Milton Keynes: Open University Press, 1996.
17. Shields M, Price S. *Racial harassment, job satisfaction and intentions to quit: evidence from the British nursing profession*. Bonn: Institute for the Study of Labour, 1999.
18. Darr A. *Improving the recruitment and retention of Asian students on nursing, midwifery, radiography and physiotherapy courses*. Bradford: University of Bradford, 1998.
19. Camden and Islington Community Health Services NHS Trust. *Beech House inquiry*. London: Beech House Trust, 1999.
20. Department of Health. *Ethnic minority staff in the NHS: a programme of action*. London: Department of Health, 1993.
21. Commission for Racial Equality. *Racial equality and NHS trusts*. London: Commission for Racial Equality, 2000.

22. Ishmael A. *Harassment, bullying and violence at work.* London: The Industrial Society, 1999.

23. Department of Health. *The vital connection: an equalities framework for the NHS.* London: Department of Health, 2000.

24. Hemphill H, Haines R. *Discrimination, harassment, and the failure of diversity training.* Westport, Connecticut: Quorum Books, 1997.

25. Mental Health Act Commission. *Improving care for detained patients from black and minority ethnic communities: preliminary report.* London: The Sainsbury Centre for Mental Health, 1999.

26. Virdee S. *Racial violence and harassment.* London: Policy Studies Institute, 1995.

Chapter 9

Intercultural communication in a therapeutic setting

Lena Robinson

If we enquire wherein lies precisely the greatest good of all, which ought to be the goal of every system of law, we shall find that it comes down to two main objects: freedom and equality.

Jean-Jacques Rousseau

Introduction

Most accounts of racism in health service delivery focus either upon instances of direct discrimination[1,2] or more general discussions which argue that racism is a pervasive feature of British society and institutions, not least the National Health Service.[3,4] In a study of Aberdeen managers, workers and service users from mental health services in the voluntary sector, Lai[5] found that institutional racism and 'colour-blind' attitudes exist in some aspects of service provision. She argues that colour-blind attitudes 'can lead to denial that cultural differences exist and a lack of understanding of the implications of these differences for service users … [and] … services will continue to be provided in a purely ethnocentric way if there is no acknowledgement that this might cause problems of access for [black] people'.

Smaje[6] argues that 'although direct racism is present in the delivery of health care to minority ethnic populations, more complex problems also arise through difficulties of communication and ethnocentrism, which may also result in less satisfactory service provision.' The intercultural interaction involves users of health services who bring their specific values, beliefs and expectations about health, illness and appropriate health care to the health system. It also involves the 'culture' of the health system and the individual professionals who work within it. This culture may be alien to most black patients. Inadequate attention and superficial processing of information from intercultural clinical encounters contribute to racial bias in the clinical decisions made by white professionals. Health practitioners have to learn how to attend selectively to relevant cultural information and screen out irrelevant information.[7] Communication breakdown can occur when health professionals are not aware that cultural differences can affect the rules of communication competence, i.e. rules that determine *what* is said, *how* it is said, and *who* says it in particular situations. This chapter aims to address how intercultural communication in a therapeutic setting can be improved. It is written from a psychological perspective and provides an overview of some of the variables that are central to the topic of intercultural communication.

Intercultural communication

Little of the current health care literature in Britain has addressed the issue of intercultural communication. Articles and books written for health professionals on communication are basically Eurocentric in nature, and as a result require considerable adaptation before they can be responsive to some of the needs of black groups. Understanding minority communication styles and patterns is indispensable for health care workers working with ethnic minority groups. Euro-American cultural values have dominated the social sciences and have been accepted as universal. In turn, these values have been imposed on non-Western cultures. Most studies of intercultural communication are binary, invoking comparisons between European Americans and one other group, with the European-American group as the assumed norm or point of comparison. Most of the research is Eurocentric in theory, method and focus. Eurocentric theories are derived from European-American theories, conducted by whites about whites, and the results are assumed to be culture-general rather than culture-specific. Fairchild and Edwards-Evans[8] argue that 'Because of the omnipresence of white racism ... much of the social sciences ... has revealed clear white racial biases concerning studies of African Americans [and other black groups].' One of the major problems confronting the analysis of communicative behaviours among people is the Eurocentric manner in which all behaviour is assessed. We need to recognise that the Eurocentric view is only one way of looking at the world.

This chapter, therefore, attempts to articulate, from a black perspective, a precise framework in which to view and define the diverse factors at work during intercultural communication. Whilst acknowledging cultural diversity and ethnic differences, a number of practice principles of general applicability to most black people are described. These principles focus on some of the key communication attributes that affect the success or failure of intercultural contacts, such as the communicator's stereotypes, non-verbal and verbal language, self-disclosure and racial identity states.

Some definitions

Black

The term 'black' has direct relevance to the discussion throughout this article, and has been used to describe people from South Asian, African and Caribbean backgrounds. While it is necessary to emphasise the heterogeneity of black people, of equal importance is the consideration of how black people in Britain differ from the white group. In Britain, Asian groups claim they are not 'black' as part of their struggle to assert their own identity in historical, cultural, ethical and linguistic terms. This chapter does not, however, use the term 'black' to deny the uniqueness of different ethnic groups. It is used 'as an inclusive political term to counter the divisive aspects of racism'.[9]

Culture

The word 'culture' denotes a way of life (family life, patterns of behaviour and belief, languages, etc.) but it is important to note that cultures are not static, especially in a community where there are people from several cultures living side by side.[10] Culture refers to 'child rearing habits, family systems, and ethical values or attitudes common to a group'.[11]

According to Fernando, culture is characterised by behaviour and attitudes; it is determined by upbringing and choice, and perceived as changeable (assimilation and acculturation). Acculturation is a variable that must be considered in discussions of intercultural communication.[12] In general, acculturation may be defined in terms of the degree of integration of new cultural patterns into the original cultural patterns.[13] The construct of levels of acculturation provides an important way to begin to think about intracultural differences. It is important for white health care workers to determine the potential impact of different levels of acculturation upon intercultural communication.

In contrast to the usual perception of relatively fixed 'cultures', Fernando argues that 'culture' needs to be considered as something that is subject to a fluidity of movement. Indeed, over the last decade or more, the concept of culture has become a subject of critical debate in anthropology; and the idea of a stable, bounded and territorially specific culture has been transformed into a conception of culture as fluid, complex and trans-national.[14,15]

Although it is essential for health care workers to have a basic understanding of black people's cultural values, there is the ever-present danger of over-generalising and stereotyping. Information about Asian and African Caribbean cultural values should act as guidelines rather than absolutes. Belonging to a particular group may mean sharing common values and experiences, but individual members of a culture may vary greatly from the pattern that is typical within that culture.

Cultural racism

Cultural racism is a relatively new form of racism and has been called 'modern racism',[16] 'aversive racism'[17] and 'symbolic racism'.[18] The root of 'modern racism' is in a continuing Eurocentric philosophy that values mainstream (dominant culture) beliefs and attitudes more highly than culturally diverse belief systems.

According to Fernando,[11] 'racism affects our perceptions of culture and these assumptions are incorporated into the training of professionals.' In British society, Ahmed notes that 'there is a hierarchy of cultures and those of "racial" minority groups are ranked very low indeed.'[19] White Western European religion, music, philosophy, law, politics, economics, morality, science and medicine are all considered to be the best in the world. Thus, 'references to black clients' cultures frequently reflect negative valuations rather than sensitivity.'[19] Gushue[20] also notes that certain cultures (for example Northern European) are judged as more acceptable by the dominant culture than are others (e.g. African and Asian). Cultural racism includes the individual and institutional expression of the superiority of the cultural heritage (and concomitant value system) of one race over that of other races. Therefore, the white majority value system, summarised by Katz[21] and elaborated upon in more recent texts,[22,23] serves as a foundation for cultural racism when it is perceived as the 'model' system, and when those individuals who possess alternative value systems are thought of by the white majority as being deficient in some way. Moreover, white communication styles and patterns (verbal and non-verbal) are considered to be superior to black communication styles.

Black perspective

The framework for developing a black perspective is based on the notion of common experiences that black people in Britain share. A black perspective in the study of cultural differences is concerned with combating racist and stereotypical, weakness-dominated and inferiority-oriented conclusions about black people. This perspective is interested in the psychological well-being of black people and is critical of oppressive research paradigms and theoretical formulations that have a potentially oppressive effect on black people. Much of the work and research involved in developing a black perspective in psychology was initiated in the US by black psychologists.[24,25] The black perspective in Britain has referred to the knowledge base of black research in the US and adapted it to fit in with the British experience. An understanding of the black frame of reference will enable health care workers to come up with more accurate and comprehensive explanations of black behaviour, including black communication patterns.

The training health workers usually receive is primarily in white middle-class institutions, culturally Eurocentric and American (i.e. US) in origin. Therefore, 'many white people are quite unable to cope with radical black perspectives and black people's pain and anger, specifically in relation to racism.'[26]

Intercultural communication

According to Porter and Samovar,[27] intercultural communication 'occurs whenever a message produced in one culture must be processed in another culture'. Intercultural communication, therefore, 'entails the investigation of those elements of culture that most influence interaction when members of two different cultures come together in an interpersonal setting'.[27] My usage of the term 'intercultural communication' parallels that of Portar and Samovar's definition. Intercultural communication does not take place in a vacuum, isolated from larger socio-political influences. It mirrors the state of interrelationships in the wider society, that is, the differential power-influenced communication between whites and blacks in a white-dominated society, with black people occupying a marginal position in the society.

Stereotypes

The dynamics of stereotyping ascribe to a single individual the characteristics associated with a group of people, or extend to a group the characteristics attributed to a single individual.[28] The stereotype generally represents a negative judgement of both the group and the individual, and emphasises negative differences. For black people, negative stereotyping has revolved around skin colour, assumed low intelligence, pathological behaviour, etc. Stereotyping occurs in the context of racism as a means of explaining away black people as inferior.[7]

Stereotypes profoundly affect human behaviour, particularly intercultural communication, for they determine how we react to and interact with environmental stimuli. Many problems erupting in intercultural communication settings can be attributed to our tendency to perceive selectively and perpetuate stereotypes. Health care workers must note that the tendency to rely on stereotypes to ease the difficulty of interacting with the unfamiliar is very strong for all people, regardless of racial or ethnic identity. It is easier for us to draw on preconceptions, when in doubt, than it is to make the effort to seek out and know individuals.[29]

If a practitioner has stereotypical expectations and attitudes, he or she will tend to select information to confirm them. Several studies have examined bias in mental health professionals' judgements concerning the racial stereotype of black people as violent. Black psychiatric patients with case information identical to that of white patients are often given a more severe diagnosis because they are stereotyped as more dangerous.[30] If the persons under assessment perceive themselves to be the object of categorical or stereotypical assessment, they will tend to withdraw from the interaction and give as little information and collaboration as possible. This may well be interpreted by the more powerful in the interaction as unco-operative behaviour or having 'something to hide'. Practitioners in intercultural communication must address themselves to the problem of overcoming the effects of strong racial stereotyping if effective communication is to occur.

Health professionals are products of their culture, and their clinical training is unlikely to overcome the stereotypes and prejudice inherent in their socialisation. In order to improve the decision-making of white practitioners with respect to the health needs of black patients, awareness of the effects of racism on both providers and recipients of services need to become a part of the core curriculum of clinical training for health professionals. Until such material on societal racism is incorporated into professional training, black persons seeking health care will continue to be subjected to racially biased clinical practices.

Racial identity development

This section discusses briefly the relationship between black people's stages of racial identity development and interracial communication. A perspective that has largely been ignored by traditional Eurocentric psychology is the research on racial identity development.

Racial identity theories 'do not suppose that racial groups in the United States [and Britain] are biologically distinct, but rather suppose that they have endured different conditions of domination or oppression'.[31] Membership of these groups is determined by 'socially defined inclusion criteria (e.g. skin colour) that are commonly (mistakenly) considered to be "racial" in nature'.[31] Racial identities arise from the process of racialisation.[32] Racialisation occurs whenever 'race' is used to categorise individuals or explain behaviour. Since 'race' is not a biologically defensible phenomenon, racialisation always involves an ideological process in which 'race' is given status as an apparent truth.

Perhaps the best-known and most widely researched model of black racial identity development is Cross's[33,34] model of the conversion from 'Negro' to 'black'.

Cross suggests that the development of a black person's racial identity is often characterised by his or her movement through a five-stage process, the transformation from pre-encounter to internalisation-commitment. Briefly, the five stages are:

- *Pre-encounter*: In this stage, the individual's racial identity attitudes are primarily pro-white and anti-black. That is, the individual devalues his or her ascribed racial group in favour of Euro-American culture.
- *Encounter*: Encounter describes the awakening process experienced by black people. This awakening is often the result of a critical incident in one's life that leads the individual to reconceptualise issues of race in society and reorganise racial feelings in one's personal feelings. For example, a white individual with racist attitudes and practices may act as a catalyst to racial identity attitude change.
- *Immersion-Emersion*: This stage involves learning and experiencing the meaning and value of one's own racial group and unique culture. Immersion attitudes are pro-black.
- *Internalisation*: This is the stage of racial identity in which the individual achieves pride in his or her racial group and identity.
- *Internalisation-Commitment*: In this stage, the person finds activities and commitments to express his or her new identity.

There is an extensive empirical literature that confirms Cross's model of black identity development.[33,35] Parham[36] has an expansion of Cross's nigrescence model. Although Cross's identity development model has been developed with African American samples in the US, it is argued by various authors, such as Maximé,[37,38] and Sue and Sue,[39] that other minority groups share similar processes of development.

Parham and Helms[36] have found that the stage of racial identity does influence clients' responses to counsellors. Black people at the pre-encounter phase preferred a white counsellor while those in the other stages preferred a black counsellor. A person's stage of racial identity may have a stronger impact on the communication process than race *per se*. That is, cognitions arising from one's racial world-view may influence how participants perceive and interact with each other. Different combinations of stages should result in different styles of interactions. Health care workers need to recognise that black clients' responses to them will be largely determined by the particular stage of racial identity they are at. Some assessment of racial identity may be useful to a practitioner to allow him or her to hypothesise the types of conflict the client may be undergoing and the way the world is viewed. In Britain, little research has addressed the relationship between the racial identity attitudes of black clients and interracial communication.

Language

Black English

Some black groups define themselves in part through language, and members establish identity through language use. Black English is a distinctive language code for some black people. A Creole language or dialect, referred to as 'Black English', has been identified as a distinctive language characteristic of black (African American and African Caribbean) culture.[40] There is a tendency among some authors to describe Black English as a deviant or deficient form of mainstream or Standard English.[41] Viewing Black English as a dialect stems from a Eurocentric perspective that only describes what is 'missing' and what is grammatically 'incorrect'. Therefore, we need to use the term 'Black English' rather than 'Black Dialect' to indicate the language form. Black English is now recognised as a legitimate language form with a unique and logical syntax, semantic system and grammar[41,42] that varies in its forms depending upon which African language influenced it and in which region it was developed. There is strong evidence of the African influence in both the early and current forms of Black English. Baugh[43] has a detailed discussion of this.

Black (African Caribbean) people often feel the need to switch between their own cultural language code and that of the more dominant white society. Speech that marks the individual as a member of the group can be important for in-group acceptance. In Britain, Creole is used to establish in-group identity.[44] Teenagers seem to equate strength and assertiveness with Creole, and use it strategically with authority figures such as police and social workers. Where there is a power differential, Creole use takes on political and cultural significance because it denotes assertiveness and group identity.[44] Smithermann-Donaldson,[41] therefore, proposes 'a new approach to study and research on Black language, one that is conceptualised within the political context of the black experience and the black liberation struggle'.[41]

Health care workers in intercultural interaction should have an understanding of different language habits – different denotations, connotations, grammar, accents and concepts of the function of language. Sensitivity to such differences and a willingness to make the adjustments necessary for common understanding is a big step toward resolving the difficulties resulting from linguistic diversity.

White practitioners should resist judging and evaluating a black person's language, since ethnocentric judgements will interfere with effective communication. Practitioners who view Black English as a legitimate code spoken by many African

Caribbean people are likely to attain greater satisfaction from communication with speakers of Black English than are those who see the language as negative.

Bilingual issues and intercultural communication

People make a positive or negative evaluation about the language that others use. Generally speaking there is a pecking order among languages that is usually buttressed and supported by the prevailing political order. In Britain, 'there is a temptation to disparage others' language forms as deficient ... [But] as with the concept of culture, others' language forms are different, not deficient.'[45] Those who speak English often lack sympathy for and patience with those who do not. Since many Western societies place such a high premium on the use of English, it is a short step to conclude that minorities are inferior, lack awareness, or lack conceptual thinking powers. Ahmed and Watt[46] quote a Sikh woman who speaks three Indian languages but cannot speak English: 'You know, in this country if you don't know English they make you feel you are nothing, and that attitude makes you feel so small and insignificant.' In a study of the attitudes of midwives to their Asian patients, Bowler[47] found that the Asian women's generally poor grasp of the English language led to stereotypes of lack of intelligence and rudeness. On the other hand, those who speak English are evaluated according to their various accents and dialects.

There is evidence that doctors communicate differently with black patients. Doctors 'tend to provide more directive information to a patient who is not fluent in English than would be given to a patient who is fluent and can therefore articulate their fears and questions easily'.[48] In a study on the health and social care needs of black communities in Brighton, Hove and Lewes area, Yazdani and Anjum[49] reported that communication was a major problem for people who could not speak English, with implications for diagnosis/needs assessment and health promotion work. Communication problems created feelings of frustration and alienation in service users. For instance, one Bengali woman in the study stated:

> My main problem is communication. Because of the language problem, often I feel dumb and can't express my positive or negative feelings ... I stayed in hospital for two weeks. Two of the nurses neglected me. Of course, I didn't know whether it was because of my colour or because of the communication problem ... I am still not sure about the exact medical term of the operation.

Health care workers need to respond patiently to clients who have a limited knowledge of English. They need to be aware of the jargon in their speech and provide a clear definition of technical terms. They must withhold judgements and negative evaluations; instead, they must show respect for the difficulties associated with learning a new language. White health care interviewers tend to assume that black people are familiar with the dominant ways of conducting interviews. If a black client gives what is felt to be an irrelevant answer to a question, this is likely to be put down to the client's lack of co-operation, and so forth, and not to the possibility of miscommunication. Thus, black clients may be denied valuable services 'through misconceptions based upon cultural insensitivity and dominance'.[50] Health care workers may attribute the difficulty they experience in dealing with black patients to the clients' 'incompetence or unco-operativity or some other stereotyped trait, rather than to different dialect or discourse norms, perhaps low proficiency in a second language or stress in an unfamiliar environment'.[51] Similar problems may arise for white working-class clients.

Mares *et al.*,[52] working in the field of health care, have suggested some practical ways in which practitioners can communicate more effectively with people who speak little or no English, or who speak English as a second language. These are:

- to reduce stress – most, if not all, people seeking health care are under physical and/or mental stress. Even when patients from non-English-speaking backgrounds seem to have an adequate command of English, their proficiency may deteriorate when they are under pressure, or when they communicate with professionals who speak quickly, using colloquial language or professional jargon. Practitioners need to allow more time for interviewing the client than they would for an English-speaking client, and practitioners should also give plenty of non-verbal reassurance
- to simplify their own language – for example, practitioners should speak clearly in simple English, avoiding the use of slang or idioms
- to avoid raising their voice in order to get 'heard'
- to check back for understanding – for example, practitioners need to develop a regular pattern of checking that what they have said has been understood.

Participants in intercultural interaction must realise that members of different racial and ethnic groups have different language habits – different denotations, connotations, grammar, pronunciation, and concepts of the function of language. Sensitivity to such differences and a willingness to make the adjustments necessary for common understanding is a giant step toward resolving the difficulties resulting from linguistic diversity.

Racist language

The health practitioner's choice of language sends messages continuously to the client about his or her values. The language used by the practitioner will betray the practitioner if he or she does not genuinely respect his or her client's culture; for example, the use of blatant derogatives such as 'nigger' or 'Paki', or political evaluations such as 'underdeveloped', 'cultural deprivation', or the use of ethnocentric descriptions of 'huts' in Africa. Are the religions of other cultures treated with respect? Is black people's culture trivialised or ridiculed? Is an obvious distinction made between 'us' and 'them' in such a way that black people are referred to as not part of 'us' or Britain?

A health care worker who employs racist language may be unaware that his/her expressions are racist, or are likely to be perceived as racist by black clients. White people have been conditioned to accept certain forms of expression and see nothing wrong in the employment of clichéd language patterns. Terms that white people employ to 'put down' black people, to define a subjugated position for blacks, are also racist, even though they are frequently employed on an unconscious level. The use of such terms as 'you people' when referring to black people causes great anger in intercultural interaction. According to Lago,[53] the use of phrases such as, 'You're one of them' are 'inferred slants/strong reference to something other, you're not sure of what/but it has negative vibes'. It should be recognised that any language that, consciously or unconsciously, places a particular racial or ethnic group in an inferior position, is considered racist and is almost certain to produce angry responses that will be highly disruptive in a consultation.

Racist language, be it obvious or subtle, is an enormous deterrent to effective intercultural communication. Health practitioners who want to communicate on an intercultural level in a productive fashion must become sensitive to their offensive racist expressions. A way of developing sensitivity is to engage in open dialogue with black people, who will usually tell which expressions cause hostile responses.

Non-verbal communication

Another critical area is non-verbal communication. Much of the communication that takes place between members of racial groups is non-verbal. (See Hecht, Andersen and Ribeau for reviews of ethnicity and non-verbal behaviour.)[54] Some communication specialists believe that only 30–40 per cent of what is communicated conversationally is verbal; for example see Condon and Yousef.[55] Non-verbal communication includes facial expressions, gaze, distance between persons, touch, gestures and paralinguistic signals such as rate of speech, volume, pitch and tone of voice.

What is the basis of our evaluation of a client's appearance, walk, posture and eye contact? By what means do white health care workers judge black clients? If health care workers use the criteria of their 'race' or culture, their assessment of the client may be inappropriate since certain non-verbal expressions may mean one thing to the health worker but have a completely different meaning for the black client. Health care workers interviewing black clients may make judgements of them, unaware that they are misinterpreting behaviour that has a cultural basis. A good example is cultural differences in eye contact behaviour. If a client failed constantly to make eye contact, it may be interpreted as being disrespectful. However, such behaviour may communicate a great amount of respect for what he or she perceives as the status difference between him or herself and the health worker.

Other differences between cultures include factors such as people's use of personal space, i.e. how close it is considered appropriate to stand in conversation with another person or when and how often you touch another person. Touch, or the study of haptics, provides a rich insight into intercultural communication. Many white people feel uncomfortable when a person from a culture where touching is the norm greets the white person 'by touching the shoulders and arms for what seems like a long time'.[56] Conversely, many members of a 'haptically active' culture feel equally uncomfortable when the white person maintains a distance and avoids touching, since this behaviour is perceived as unfriendly and cold. Some cultures such as Asian, African, and Arabic are highly touch-oriented, while others such as German and English are considered to be non-touching cultures.[57] Differences in the overall amount of touching that cultural groups prefer can lead to difficulties in intercultural communication.

In general, white practitioners may be perceived as cold and aloof by black clients, who in turn may be regarded as aggressive, pushy and overly familiar by their white service providers. It is important to note that not every black person will exhibit the non-verbal behaviours described above. Although health care workers must be aware of cultural differences in non-verbal behaviour, they must be careful not to stereotype (non-verbally) people from different cultures into set cultural slots.

Non-verbal cues are often the best indicators of an individual's true attitudes or intentions, irrespective of what has been said. Unlike spoken language – which is used as often to conceal thought as it is to express thought, and which people largely control for their own purposes – much non-verbal behaviour seems impossible to control. Individuals are not aware of most of their own non-verbal behaviour, which is enacted mindlessly, spontaneously and unconsciously.[58,59,60] Majors[61] argues that the lack of trust among the races has caused interracial communicators to reject the values of verbal communication and to search for non-verbal cues as indicators of real meaning and response in interracial communication situations. Although much of the work in this area comes from the United States, the results have clear implications for practitioners in Britain. Health care workers must realise that, at least some of the time, there will be a mismatch between their non-verbal behaviour and their spoken words.

Argyle *et al.*[62] proposed a 'games' model for understanding interaction in social situations. Just as you need to know the rules of a game (tennis, for example), you need to know the rules, goals, roles and expectations of the client in the inter-ethnic communication situation. For instance, one needs to know which non-verbal behaviours reflect positive intimacy, affiliation, confidence; which ones are reinforcing; and which reflect non-verbal involvement of black clients. Literature that addresses non-verbal behaviours among Asian and African Caribbean cultures is limited at best. If we are to appreciate and understand Asian and African Caribbean communication styles, much more research on non-verbal behaviour is needed. At the very least, health care workers need to be aware of the possibility that differences in non-verbal behaviour, both in style and interpretation, may occur between white and black people.

Self-disclosure

'Self-disclosure' refers to the client's willingness to tell the practitioner what he or she feels, believes or thinks. Inter-ethnic comparisons of self-disclosure patterns show that European Americans are more disclosive than African Americans[62] and Asians. Segal[63] describes Indians as being 'reserved and reluctant to discuss their problems outside the family'. Most forms of counselling tend to value one's ability to self-disclose and talk about the most intimate aspects of one's life. Indeed, self-disclosure has often been discussed as a primary characteristic of the healthy personality. The converse of this is that people who do not self-disclose readily in counselling are seen as possessing negative traits such as being guarded, mistrustful and/or paranoid.

Intimate revelations of personal or social problems may not be acceptable to many Asians, since such difficulties reflect not only on the individual, but also on the whole family. According to Segal, for most Indians, 'family integrity is sacred, and any threat to it is viewed as a failure on the part of the parents'.[63] An individual's emotional problems bring shame and guilt to the Asian family, preventing any family member from reporting such problems to others outside the family. Health care workers unfamiliar with these cultural ramifications may perceive their clients in a very negative light. They may erroneously conclude that the client is repressed, inhibited, shy or passive. On the other hand, Asian clients may perceive the 'direct and confrontative techniques [of white practitioners] in communication as "lacking in respect for the client", and a reflection of insensitivity'.[64]

Black people may also be reluctant to disclose to white practitioners because of the hardships they have experienced through racism.[65] The impact of racism and discrimination on the 'way in which black people relate to each other and to the outside world must not be underestimated'. The process of discrimination is evident at all levels of society reinforced with theories about genetic inferiority and cultural pathology.[66] Few, if any, black individuals can live in Britain and the US and not be affected by racism and discrimination. According to Davis and Proctor, 'virtually all minorities in the United States [and Britain] have negative experiences with white people that contribute to their tendency toward concealment of true feelings.' The authors note that: 'While white practitioners tend to minimise the importance of racial or cultural factors, minorities wonder why whites cannot acknowledge the impact of colour in a racist society.'[67]

For black people, 'race is a significant part of history and personal identity'.[67] Thus, white health care workers need to recognise and allow for the effects of racism on black people's self-disclosure patterns.

Use of interpreters

The term 'interpretation' emphasises the exchange of connotative meaning between languages so that both effect and meaning are conveyed, whereas 'translation' refers to the exchange of the denotative meaning of a word, phrase or sentence in one language for the same meaning in another language. The 'translator should be someone with cultural knowledge and appropriate professional background'.[45] Most of the literature and studies on intercultural communication refer to 'interpreting' services.

Yazdani and Anjum's 1994 study,[49] cited above, illustrates the problems associated with communication difficulties. The participants in the study felt that they could not make themselves understood properly, which had implications in making a diagnosis. An interpreter is essential where precise and often intimate details of the patient's medical history are required, and when the situation requires medical terminology to be understood. There is often a temptation to use relatives, hospital staff or anyone nearby, who can speak both English and the language of the patient. This brings its own problems. For example, in the gynaecological department, taking your children to interpret would seem utterly shameful for most parents.

Rack[68] argues that 'under no circumstances should children be asked to interpret medical details for their parents'. It cannot be assumed that people would wish to ask friends or acquaintances to interpret for them in highly personal and confidential situations. The disadvantages of using family members as interpreters should be recognised by health professionals.[49,68,69]

It is also essential to use trained interpreters, as using untrained interpreters contravenes the professional ethics of interpreting and can seriously impair the confidentiality and objectivity of the intervention process.

In the intercultural setting, health practitioners should not assume that if the client and the interpreter speak the same language, there will be an instantaneous dialogue between them. Variables such as region of birth in a country, political and religious affiliation, age and sex, have been known to inhibit the interview. Other problems that may arise in using interpreters include:

- the possibility of bias, as communication is dependent on a third party; meanings can be changed in the process of translation
- the messages uttered by both the practitioner and client have the potential to be modified and indeed changed through the interpreter
- breach of confidentiality (some Asians reject interpreters who belong to the same community)
- incorrect interpretation of the patient's ideas, or imprecise abbreviated responses
- the practitioner's inability to assess intonation, pauses and emotionality in the client when using a translator[70]
- even with a correct translation, the lack of subtle non-verbal cues makes assessment difficult.[71]

Shackman[69] has provided a useful checklist of practical ways of using an interpreter. She recommends that interviewers should:

- check that both the interpreter and client speak the same language or dialect
- allow time for a pre-interview discussion with the interpreter to establish the content of the interview and the way in which they will work together
- include goals of the evaluation (areas of focus, sensitive topics, confidentiality and objectivity)
- use simple and straightforward language
- check throughout the interview that the client has understood what has been said
- have a post-interview discussion with the interpreter about the interview.

Working with skilled interpreters can provide an excellent opportunity for health professionals to improve their awareness of their client's background, behaviour and circumstances. Additionally, interpreters can assist health care workers by indicating where their form of questioning is inappropriate; where their manner, style and non-verbal language may be offensive; or where their interpretation or assessment may be culturally miscued.

Conclusion

In this chapter I have discussed some of the communication attributes that affect the outcome of intercultural contacts. In order to work effectively with minority ethnic groups, health care workers from the majority group need to have an understanding of the communication styles and patterns of these groups. From a black perspective, the most important factors are:

- the black person's development of their black identity
- the use and interpretation of language – the implied lower status accorded to 'Black English' and non-English languages
- the impatience or disdain for people who do not speak English well or at all
- the use of racist language, particularly the unconscious use of language that is 'heard' as racist
- non-verbal communication, especially the use of eye contact, touch and physical proximity to people.

Training programmes should include courses that help health professionals become more sensitive to racial issues in the provision of health services. White health practitioners must become aware that black people have different interpretations of what is said as opposed to what is intended. Practitioners must learn how their own cultural experiences affect their perceptions of black people and the circumstances that activate racial stereotypes.

In sum, health professionals in Britain must ensure that they have the awareness, knowledge and skills to communicate effectively in intercultural situations.

References

1. Kushnick L. Racism, the National Health Service, and the health of black people. *International Journal of Health Services* 1988; 18 (3): 457–70.
2. Pilgrim S, Fenton S, Hughes T, Hine C, Tibbs N. *The Bristol black and ethnic minorities health survey report.* Bristol: University of Bristol, 1993.
3. Ahmad W. 'Race', disadvantage and discourse: contextualising black people's health. In: Ahmad W, ed. *The politics of 'race' and health.* Bradford: Race Relations Research Unit, 1992.
4. Torkington P. *Black health: a political issue.* London: Catholic Association for Racial Justice, 1991.
5. Lai C. Reaching out to black ethnic minorities: a voluntary sector perspective on mental health. *Practice* 2000; 12 (1): 17–28.
6. Smaje C. *Health, 'race' and ethnicity.* London: King's Fund, 1995.
7. Ridley C. *Overcoming unintentional racism in counselling and therapy.* London: Sage, 1995.
8. Fairchild H, Edwards-Evans S. African American dialects and schooling: a review. In: Padilla A M, Fairchild H, Valadez C M, eds. *Bilingual education: issues and strategies.* Newbury Park, CA: Sage, 1990.
9. Dominelli L. *Anti-racist social work.* 2nd ed. London: Macmillan, 1997.
10. Fernando S, ed. *Mental health in a multi-ethnic society: a multidisciplinary handbook.* London: Routledge, 1995.
11. Fernando S. *Mental health, race and culture.* London: Macmillan, 1991.
12. Danna R H. *Multicultural assessment perspectives for professional psychology.* Boston, MA: Allyn and Bacon, 1993.
13. Moyerman D R, Forman B D. Acculturation and adjustment: a meta-analytic study. *Hispanic Journal of Behavioural Sciences* 1992; 14: 163–200.
14. Hannerz U. *Transnational connections.* London: Routledge, 1996.
15. Olwig K F, Hastrup K. *Siting culture.* London: Routledge, 1997.
16. McConahay J B. Modern racism, ambivalence, and the modern racism scale. In: Dovidio J F, Gaertner S L, eds. *Prejudice, discrimination, and racism.* New York: Academic Press, 1986.
17. Gaertner S L, Dovidio J F. The aversive form of racism. In: Dovidio J F, Gaertner S L, eds. *Prejudice, discrimination, and racism.* New York: Academic Press, 1986.
18. Sears D. Symbolic racism. In: Katz P A, Taylor D A, eds. *Eliminating racism: profiles in controversy.* New York: Plenum, 1988.
19. Ahmed S. Anti-racist social work: a black perspective. In: Hanvey C, Philpot T, eds. *Practising social work.* London: Routledge, 1996.
20. Gushue G V. Cultural identity development and family assessment: an interaction model. *The Counseling Psychologist* 1993; 21: 487–513.
21. Katz J H. The sociopolitical nature of counseling. *The Counseling Psychologist* 1985; 13: 615–24.
22. Pedersen P. *A handbook for developing multicultural awareness.* Alexandria, VA: American Counselling Association, 1988.

23. Ponterotto J G, Casas J M. *Handbook of racial/ethnic minority counseling research*. Springfield, IL: Charles C Thomas, 1991.

24. White J L. Toward a black psychology. In: Jones R L, ed. *Black psychology*. 2nd ed. New York: Harper and Row, 1980.

25. Akbar N. Africentric social sciences for human liberation. *Journal of Black Studies* 1984; 4 (4): 395–414.

26. Lago C, Thompson J. Counselling and race. In: Dryden W, Charles-Edwards D, Thompson J, eds. *Handbook of counselling Britain*. London: Routledge, 1994.

27. Porter L A, Samovar R E. *Intercultural communication*. Belmont, CA: Wadsworth, 1994.

28. Hinton P. *The psychology of interpersonal perception*. London: Routledge, 1993.

29. Atkinson D R, Morten G, Sue D W, eds. *Counseling American minorities: a cross-cultural perspective*. New York: McGraw-Hill, 1993.

30. Loring M, Powell B. Gender, race, and DSM III: a study of the objectivity of psychiatric behavior. *Journal of Health and Social Behaviour* 1988; 29: 1–22.

31. Helms, J. An update of Helms's white and people of color racial identity models. In: Ponterotto A J, Casas J M, Suzuki L S, Alexander C M, eds. *Handbook of multicultural counseling*. London: Sage, 1995.

32. Miles R. *Racism*. London: Routledge, 1989.

33. Cross W E. The negro to black conversion experience: towards the psychology of black liberation. *Black World* 1971; 20: 13–27.

34. Cross W E. Models of psychological nigrescence: a literature review. In: Jones R L, ed. *Black psychology*. 2nd ed. New York: Harper and Row, 1980.

35. Cross W E. *Shades of black: diversity in African-American identity*. Philadelphia: Temple University Press, 1991.

36. Parham T A, Helms J. The influence of black students' racial identity attitudes on preference for counselor's race. *Journal of Counselling Psychology* 1981; 28: 250–57.

37. Maxime J. Some psychological models of black self-concept. In: Ahmed S, Cheetham J, Small J, eds. *Social work with children and families*. London: Batsford, 1986.

38. Maxime J. The therapeutic importance of racial identity in working with black children who hate. In: Varma V, ed. *How and why children hate*. London: Jessica Kingsley, 1993.

39. Sue D W, Sue D. *Counseling the culturally different*. New York: John Wiley and Sons, 1990.

40. King N G, James M J. *The relevance of black English to intercultural communication*. Paper presented at the annual conference of the Western Speech Communication Association. Albuquerque, NM, 1983.

41. Smitherman-Donaldson G. Discriminatory discourse on Afro-American speech. In: Smitherman-Donaldson G, Dijk T A, eds. *Discourse and discrimination*. Detroit: Wayne State University Press, 1988.

42. Jenkins A H. *The psychology of the Afro-American: a humanistic approach*. Elmsford, NY: Pergamon, 1982.

43. Baugh J. *Black street speech: its history, structure and survival*. Austin: University of Texas Press, 1983.

44. Hewitt R. *White talk black talk: inter-racial friendship and communication amongst adolescents*. Cambridge: Cambridge University Press, 1986.

45. Lago C, Thompson J. *Race, culture and counselling*. Buckingham: Open University Press, 1996.

46. Ahmed G, Watt S. Understanding Asian women in pregnancy and confinement. *Midwives Chronicle and Nursing Notes* 1986; 99: 98–101.

47. Bowler I. They're not the same as us: midwives' stereotypes of South Asian descent maternity patients. *Sociology of Health and Illness* 1993; 15 (2): 157–78.

48. Eleftheriadou Z. Communicating with patients from different cultural backgrounds. In: Lloyd M, Bor R, eds. *Communication skills for medicine*. London: Churchill Livingstone, 1996.

49. Yazdani L, Anjum A. *Report of the Brighton, Hove and Lewes district ethnic minorities council health needs project*. Brighton: Council Voluntary Service, 1994.

50. Fairclough N. *Language and power*. London: Longman, 1989.

51. Giles H, Coupland N. *Language: contexts and consequences*. Buckingham: Open University Press, 1991.

52. Mares P, Henley A, Baxter C. *Health care in multiracial Britain*. Cambridge: Health Education Council/National Extension College, 1985.

53. Lago C, Thompson J. *Race, culture and counselling*. Buckingham: Open University Press, 1996.

54. Hecht M L, Andersen P A, Ribeau S A. The cultural dimensions of non-verbal communication. In: Asante M K, Gudykunst W B, eds. *Handbook of international and intercultural communication*. Newbury Park, CA: Sage, 1989.

55. Condon J C, Yousef F. *An introduction to intercultural communication*. New York: Bobbs-Merrill Co., 1975.

56. Dodd C H. *Dynamics of intercultural communication*. Dubuque, IA: William C. Brown, 1987.

57. Mehrabian A. *Silent messages*. Belmont, CA: Wadsworth, 1971.

58. Burgoon J K. Non-verbal signals. In: Knapp M L, Miller G R, eds. *Handbook of interpersonal communication*. Newbury Park, CA: Sage, 1985.

59. Samovar L A, Porter R E. Non-verbal interaction. In: Samovar L A, Porter R E, eds. *Intercultural communication: a reader*. Belmont, CA: Wadsworth, 1985.

60. Andersen P A. Consciousness, cognition and communication. *Western Journal of Speech and Communication* 1986; 50: 87–101.

61. Majors R. Non-verbal behaviours and communication styles among African Americans. In: Jones R, ed. *Black psychology*. 3rd edition. Berkeley, CA: Cobb and Henry, 1991.

62. Argyle M, Furnham A, Graham J. *Social situations*. Cambridge: Cambridge University Press, 1981; Argyle M. *Bodily communication*. London: Methuen, 1988.

63. Segal U A. Career choice correlates: an Indian perspective. *Indian Journal of Social Work* 1988; 69: 338–48.

64. Sue D W, Sue D. *Counselling the culturally different*. New York: John Wiley and Sons, 1990.

65. Vontress C. Racial and ethnic barriers in counseling. In: Pedersen P, Draguns J G, Lonner W J, Trimble J E, eds. *Counseling across cultures*. Honolulu: University of Hawaii Press, 1981.

66. Boyd-Franklin N. *Black families in therapy*. London: The Guildford Press, 1989.

67. Davis L E, Proctor E K. *Race, gender and class: guidelines for practice with individuals, families and groups.* Englewood Cliffs, NJ: Prentice-Hall, 1989.

68. Rack P. *Race, culture and mental disorder.* London: Tavistock, 1982.

69. Shackman J. *The right to be understood.* Cambridge: National Extension College, 1985.

70. Marcos L R. Effects of interpreters on the evaluation of psychopathology in non-English-speaking patients. *American Journal of Psychiatry* 1979; 136: 2–10.

71. Gomez E A, Ruiz P, Laval R. Psychotherapy and bilingualism: is acculturation important? *Journal of Operational Psychiatry* 1982; 13, 1: 13–16.

Chapter 10

Recruiting doctors: fair selection

John McClenahan, Anne Yardumian

With a little more training, you'll be ready for a consultant post in one/two/ ... five ... years.

Anonymous

Introduction

There is widespread inequity in the selection and appointment of doctors in the UK. It takes several forms: discrimination by gender, age and race among them. There is some good evidence of age and gender discrimination, but this is overshadowed by overwhelming evidence of widespread race discrimination, which is therefore of the greatest concern and is the main subject of this chapter. In essence, black and minority ethnic groups suffer an 'ethnic penalty', whereby their abilities to join and progress through the ranks of the medical profession are hindered on 'racial' grounds, creating an unacceptable barrier to personal and professional development.

The existence of racism in recruitment and promotion of doctors has been widely acknowledged for many years – initially, only informally. However, since the mid-1990s it has also been acknowledged publicly. For example, the BMA published guidelines aimed at tackling it (first published in 1994 and updated in 2000), and held a conference in 1997 on the subject. Furthermore, medical schools have begun to review the outcomes of their selection processes.

Discrimination by race and gender has been illegal for many years. Yet such inequality of opportunity continues to hinder the careers of doctors, in spite of the existence of legislation and of plentiful, readily available practical guidance on how selection can be undertaken fairly. We know what *should* be done, and *how to do it*, but it still isn't happening widely. There seems to have been a considerable lack of will, and a dearth of effective leadership to improve the process. So how might readers of this chapter work to improve the parts of the process they themselves could influence?

This chapter highlights the nature and extent of the problem, and aims to encourage doctors to reflect on how they may participate in promoting fairness and transparency in the recruitment and promotion process. This can be achieved by examining and improving recruitment practices at several levels: for example, in one's own organisation, through regional deaneries and educational consortia, or nationally through involvement in the royal colleges, the NHSE, or other influential bodies.

Successive sections of this chapter attempt to answer the following questions:

- How do we know there is inequity?
- Why does inequity matter?
- What would fair selection and appointments look like?
- How would we know if fair selection practices are happening?
- How might change be stimulated more widely in medical selection processes?

Evidence of inequity

There are plentiful examples of inequity in the selection and appointment processes for doctors (many of these have been included in different parts of this book). In the late '80s, one London medical school was found to be using a computer programme to shortlist applicants that downgraded those with 'non-English' names.[1] In 1991, a survey of 7000 applicants to five medical schools demonstrated that similarly qualified applicants from minority ethnic groups were 1.46 times more likely to be rejected than their white peers,[2] with a second study in 1992 reporting similar findings.[3]

Admission to medical school is just the first uneven hurdle. Asian students at Manchester University Medical School, most of whom were UK-born, were more likely than white students to fail final clinical examinations, despite good written examination results.[4] Two well-publicised studies provide evidence of discrimination on the basis of race against ethnic minority graduates of British universities during the 1980s and early '90s respectively. The first[5] reported that ethnic minority doctors find it more difficult to get house officer and registrar posts, and places on vocational training schemes in general practice, than their white counterparts. They are also more likely to have experienced spells of unemployment, and to have changed their original career choice because of difficulty in obtaining suitable training posts or unfavourable career prospects in their chosen specialty. Most of the discrimination appeared to occur at the stage of shortlisting for interviews. The second study[6] gained brief notoriety because its authors, a general practitioner and senior registrar in public health, were arrested by the fraud squad mid-way through it and were charged with making fraudulent job applications. Before this premature halt, however, they had submitted 46 'paired' applications to 23 advertised posts in a variety of specialties. In each pair, one of the supposed applicants had an Asian name, and the other an English name; the CVs and applications were otherwise identical in every respect. Of the 18 applications that resulted in shortlisting for interview, 12 were among the applications bearing English names and only half as many were from the applications carrying Asian names. In no case was only the 'Asian' applicant shortlisted. As well as being stark evidence of discrimination, this also implicated the 'shortlisting' stage as an obvious problem area.

A broad-based survey by the Commission for Racial Equality, published in 1996,[7] once again demonstrated that doctors from ethnic minority backgrounds were far less likely to be given consultant jobs or other senior positions in the health service than white doctors. Over 400 vacancies in 45 NHS trusts or health authorities arising in a six-month period in early 1992 were studied. Of more than 1000 applicants for 147 consultant posts, 53 per cent were from ethnic minority backgrounds, but only 27 per cent of the appointments went to these doctors. At senior registrar grade, 37 per cent of applications but only 17 per cent of successful ones were from ethnic minority doctors. The report concluded that there was great cause for concern in the way these posts were appointed, commenting that 'the disparities in success rates for different ethnic groups were so marked and consistent, and the omission of procedural safeguards so routine, that the possibility of discrimination cannot be ignored.'

Doctors from minority ethnic groups trained within or outside the UK, who succeed in getting senior appointments, are substantially more likely to end up in:

- unpopular parts of the country
- less prestigious institutions
- less popular and prestigious specialties
- associate specialist, staff grade or locum posts, rather than as substantive consultants or GP principals.

The non-consultant career grade of associate specialist is overwhelmingly composed of minority ethnic doctors who have repeatedly failed to obtain consultant posts despite, in a number of cases, having better qualifications and experience than the successful candidates. Such doctors also report repeatedly broken promises, along the lines of: 'with a little more training, you'll be ready for a consultant post in one/two/ … five … years.'

Discrimination against doctors by virtue of personal details other than ethnic origin, for example gender or age, is less clearly evidenced. The study that reported excessive difficulties in career progression for ethnic minority British graduates in the '80s,[5] yielded no evidence of discrimination against women in competition for posts. A recent report was not so reassuring, finding that although there was no evidence of a true 'glass ceiling' for women doctors, there was evidence of some disproportionate promotion that was best interpreted as direct or indirect discrimination.[9] There are reports of employment difficulties experienced by gay and lesbian doctors, resulting in the feeling among some that they cannot be open about their sexuality.[10] One should need no reminder that discrimination on the basis of sexuality, as well as race, colour, sex or age, contravenes the GMC's specific guidance.[11]

Failure of fair selection because of age is complex. It has been pointed out that four groups of doctors suffer particularly from age discrimination in career progression: those qualifying abroad and who have taken longer to reach each grade because of having had to 'start again' after moving from another country; those who enter medical school after the usual age of 18–19; those who have had prolonged illness; and women who have interrupted their careers to have and care for their children. Failure to select a suitable candidate because of age may often be a covert form of race or gender discrimination.[12]

Why does it matter?

Racism in medical appointments matters for two overarching reasons. It is wrong *in principle*, and it has deleterious effects *in practice*: on the profession of medicine itself, on the thousands of individual doctors affected by discrimination, and on patients who may thereby be denied the services of the best qualified and most suitable doctors.

In principle

Racism is morally unacceptable and it is illegal. Because it can be difficult to prove in individual cases, one has to look more broadly at its effects on groups of people, over time, to be convinced that it exists. Individuals' concerns about their own experiences may be suppressed because of fear for the consequences on their own future appointment prospects.

Employers and employees should both be aware, however, that 'victimisation' – an individual being treated less favourably because he or she tried to assert their rights under the Race Discrimination or Sex Discrimination Act – is also unlawful.

Equal opportunities legislation has made little impact so far on medical appointments, yet should have influence throughout doctors' careers, to ensure not only fair selection, but also fair opportunities for personal and professional development, access to specialist training and experience, appraisal, and promotion.

In practice

Racism in practice disillusions a very large number of ethnic minority doctors (perhaps up to 10,000 in the NHS) who cannot get consultant posts or good training that should lead to such posts. This reduces motivation and carries a higher risk of poor performance or burn-out.

It will discourage continuing entry into the profession from the important and growing pool of skilled and motivated young people from such backgrounds in the UK and abroad. And medicine needs more, not fewer, successful recruits. While medicine remains individually very competitive for prestigious posts, there is likely to be an increase in the number of jobs in the NHS for doctors at all levels, including consultants. To meet acknowledged needs for more doctors, every suitable applicant will need to be seriously and fairly considered.

What constitutes fair selection?

Fair selection requires:

- a willingness to acknowledge present unfairness and to do something about it
- adoption of the available codes of good practice with regard to the selection process from start to finish
- explicit and relevant selection criteria, fairly applied, at all stages of the application process
- those who draw up shortlists, and who interview, to have 'equal opportunities' and 'fair selection' training, and to apply it effectively
- systems of monitoring applications, shortlists, and interview outcomes to confirm that selection is taking place on the basis of applicants' ability to fulfil the pre-agreed criteria.

Advertisements

For medical appointments, it is unusual not to advertise formally. However, it is worth stressing that failure to advertise, but to recruit internally or by word of mouth, is a potent potential cause of racial or other discrimination. Advertisements should encourage applications from all suitable candidates of both sexes and all sections of the community, and should include a clear statement of equal opportunities. They should not make reference to UK residence status. It should be made clear that equivalent overseas qualifications are as acceptable as UK qualifications.

Explicit and relevant selection criteria

The job description and person specifications are crucial, and form the foundation for a fair selection process.[13] In the absence of explicitly stated specifications, decisions are often subjective and inconsistent, and discrimination can easily occur.

Job descriptions

Job descriptions generally provide a broad account of the purpose, scope and responsibilities of a particular job. They may also specify the nature of accountability and the limits of authority within a particular function. Some question the necessity of having a job description as they believe that in a dynamic organisation jobs need to change according to changing circumstances, and as such job descriptions soon become 'out of date'. Nevertheless, job descriptions are invaluable in clarifying to potential candidates what is expected from a particular post, and on what basis they will be assessed and selected. The descriptions also serve to assist the organisation in ensuring that selection decisions are made on an objective and factual basis. It is recommended that job descriptions should be developed for all posts, including trainee posts.

Person specifications

Criteria on person specifications are frequently grouped under one of two headings: 'essential' and 'desirable'. There is a school of thought which suggests that desirable criteria are sometimes misused to discriminate between candidates and that only the essential criteria should be utilised in order to avoid this. The person specification should reflect the competences required for the post, i.e. the essential personal and practical skills, qualifications, knowledge and abilities. These essential criteria should be based on the requirements as outlined in the specification, included in the advertisement, and referred to and scored against throughout the selection process. All criteria should be job related, and care should be taken not to overstate the requirements.

Whenever possible, criteria should be expressed in such a way as to relate to performance, not experience, and emphasise skills and abilities. Education or experience are often used as shorthand for skills and abilities, and can be misleading.[13] Selectors must be mindful about the extent to which training and work outside the UK can generate skills that are entirely transferable.

Indirect discrimination occurs:

- when a requirement or condition is laid down that cannot be shown to be justifiable for the needs of the job and,
- when it is applied equally to people of all groups, and only a considerably smaller proportion of a particular racial or gender group can comply with it.

There may, however, be a 'genuine occupational qualification' that would give preference to a member of a particular gender, ethnic or cultural group. This could be the case if the job involves providing personal services to a particular group, and where those services can be most effectively provided by a person of the same group. For example, a Turkish-speaking doctor may be recruited preferentially to work in a practice with a large number of non-English, Turkish-speaking patients.

Appropriate selection panels

Putting together a selection panel requires careful thought and consideration. Panellists must not only understand the practicalities of the job but they must also have the necessary skills and experience of interviewing. Moreover, members of the shortlisting and interview panels should receive 'equal opportunities' and 'fair selection' training. This will help to raise their awareness of both conscious and unconscious bias. They should also gain some insight from the trainer and from 'practice' (or real) candidates into the emotional and practical consequences of biased selection on both the candidate and the organisation.

Unless there are strong and documented reasons to the contrary, it should be expected that panels will reflect local population ethnicity and be balanced in terms of gender representation, at least for panel membership taken together over time, if not in every individual case. Finally, all panellists, from the outset, should have an agreed understanding of the criteria and qualities that the candidates require in specific areas.

Shortlisting

The process of deciding whom to call for interview must relate directly to the essential criteria identified in the advertisement, and applications should be scored quantitatively against these, rather than just 'by eyeball' or a quick overview. Candidates should be excluded if they fail to meet the essential criteria, not the desirable criteria. It is recommended that all members of the appointment panel should be involved in the short-listing process to allow cross-checking against conscious or unconscious bias.

The study referred to earlier (in which paired applications demonstrated that otherwise comparable applicants with English names were about twice as likely to be shortlisted as those with Asian names) concluded that discrimination at this stage might be countered by preventing those who undertake shortlisting from having access to name, age and sex of the candidates, for example by having these details on a detachable front sheet of the application, which is then held separately. This generated a lively exchange in the *BMJ* letters section. Some respondents felt that ethnic origin should not be concealed, on the basis that selectors would find ways to deduce or guess at it, and then have the defence of claiming ignorance,[14] or that doing so would only postpone the discrimination to the interview stage.[15] Those of the latter persuasion noted that a doctor is unlikely to obtain a career registrarship without having published anything, and that names would therefore be obvious (or traceable) from publication lists. One particular letter signs off forcefully: 'Anyway, what's wrong with our names that we need to hide them?' It is hard to argue with that.

Nevertheless, the recommendation that application forms should not show name, sex, marital status, age, religion, place of study or ethnicity is included in the BMA *Guidelines for good practice*. On balance, it is felt that equity is more likely to result from withholding than including these details, even if this carries the regrettable implication that selectors are potentially biased.

The pre-interview visit

Informal pre-interview visits are for the benefit of the candidates, who can learn more about the job and potential colleagues than can be gleaned from paperwork. All candidates must be given the same opportunity to visit and be accorded equal treatment.

It should be made clear to candidates and potential employers that such visits constitute no part of the formal selection process, as otherwise the formal procedures aimed at making the selection process fair can be circumvented. However, it has been acknowledged that the pre-interview visit has, on a number of occasions, formed part of a 'covert' selection process. This is a risk because the visits are informal, without records, and conversation is likely to be one-to-one. Potentially discriminatory or inappropriate questions, which should not be asked at interview, should of course not be asked at these visits either.

The interview

The evidence for discrimination at interview is less substantial, with differences in success rates between 'white' and ethnic minority graduates being much less clear-cut than those at shortlisting.[5]

The need for each candidate to be asked equivalent interview questions is now well known. Questions must be directly relevant to the job, questions about family commitments or plans should not be asked, candidates should not be asked if social customs or religious practices may affect their ability to undertake the duties of the post, and candidates who may reasonably be expected to have family ties outside the UK should not be asked questions about 'home visits'.

There are ways of making questioning at interview less biased. One such technique[13] is called 'funnelling', described as follows:

> It starts with an open question to get the applicant talking, and then 'funnels in' on more specific points.

> There are three stages to the technique:

> - Begin by asking an open question to help the candidate's self-expression. (An 'open' question is one that cannot be answered simply 'yes' or 'no' but needs a longer and more descriptive answer.) What we want at this stage is an overview of a particular aspect of the candidate's experience. Subsequent questions should be identified from this overview and/or from the person specification – not from the experience, interest or assumptions of the interviewer. On occasions you may need more than one question to get a satisfactory overview.
> - From the overview, select an area relevant to the person specification and seek more information on that area. Again, more than one question may be needed for the candidate to give a satisfactory description.
> - Having listened to the candidate's outline, the interviewer then asks probing questions to clarify, quantify and draw out detailed information, for example: 'Tell me about X? What did X involve? When did it happen? Why? Who else was involved? What happened then? How was it resolved?'

Subjective effects of stereotyping

It should be recognised that panellists will have their own opinions, prejudices, stereotypes and attitudes, all of which will inevitably lead to 'subjective' judgement. Stereotyping will distort the panellists' views of the candidates' abilities, and will leave them open to manipulation by an adept candidate. For example, if an interviewee answers a question that resonates with the interviewer's views, it is likely that the interviewer will judge answers to subsequent questions in a favourable light, and vice versa. In addition, some people have a way of conveying a confident air, but self-confidence does not always equate with ability to do a job. It should also be noted that stereotypes of the person, e.g. concerning sexual orientation or class, may also cloud an interviewer's judgement.

Recording

Interviewers cannot be expected to remember the answers given by all the candidates at an interview, and an agreed method for taking notes can be useful. A common practice is for all interviewers to complete a standardised assessment form that is completed after each candidate's interview. These assessments can help to ensure that the interview panel observes the principles of equal opportunity.

The notes taken during the interview are also useful for giving feedback to both successful and unsuccessful candidates. Many organisations handle this part of the recruitment process incompetently. Lack of appropriate and objective feedback to unsuccessful candidates has resulted in allegations of favouritism or discrimination. It is accepted practice for one member of the panel to provide feedback to all the candidates.

All records, including personal notes made by individual panel members, should be retained for at least one year. In accordance with current data protection regulations, applicants have the right to view all such paperwork.

References

It is recommended to use structured references relating directly to the person specification, asking for specific and relevant information about essential criteria only. In this way, all referees answer the same questions about all applicants. References should be overt and open, so the applicant should be shown a copy if requested. Unsolicited informal references can clearly lead to bias or prejudice and are to be avoided.

How can progress be assessed?

Monitoring outcomes

Local monitoring of successful and unsuccessful job applicants by ethnicity and other factors has been recommended as good practice for many years. From 1993, the NHSE began the central collection of data for ethnicity monitoring for appointments. Some of these monitoring systems have now started to 'get teeth'. Thus, in 1999 the Thames Postgraduate deans and other deaneries stressed that, as part of their educational contract, individual hospital trusts must be able to demonstrate and provide evidence of good equal opportunities practice in the recruitment of SHOs. A monitoring protocol is provided and it is required that this be completed and returned, within two weeks of recruitment, for every SHO appointment. Returns include breakdown by ethnic origin of applications received, candidates interviewed and successful applicants. As 50 per cent of the salary for these posts is provided by the deanery, this is a contractual obligation likely to be observed.

Targets for fair employment in the NHS are included in the National Plan, and the national human resource strategy, *Working together: securing a quality workforce for the NHS*, reflects these. Submissions, including ethnicity monitoring data, are required by the regional offices as part of the performance management process.

The recently implemented amendments to the Race Relations Act 1976 have important implications, making monitoring and the previously *recommended* aspects of equal opportunities employment practice *mandatory*. This will provide a base-line against which 'positive action' to promote employment of a workforce, which reflects the make-up of the local community, can take place. The positive duty of organisations, and the responsibility and liability of individuals within those organisations in promoting race equality, is also clarified.

It is self-evident that ethnicity monitoring is not a solution to unfair selection practices; it is merely a means of checking whether unfair discrimination is occurring, and whether proper equal opportunities policy is being implemented. It provides no guarantee in itself, but is a basis for triggering further investigation.

What makes change happen?

We know from previous studies that research evidence alone is never enough to change clinical practice and behaviour.[16] We should, therefore, not expect evidence to have significant impact upon the even more sensitive and emotive issue of racism. We also know that legislation alone is not enough. Employers, for example, often still ignore legal requirements for basic health and safety precautions, such as implementation of the Manual Handling Regulations in NHS trusts and commercial companies.[17] Consequently, it cannot be guaranteed that the recently introduced Race Relations (Amendment) Act will bring about appropriate improvements.

However, experience of successful evidence-driven change in clinical practice suggests that:[17]

- we should not expect quick results
- flexible, multiple channels of approach are needed
- consistent reiteration of the message from credible and respected sources makes action more likely
- progress is easier starting small, and expanding from there
- building on existing structures and processes saves time and effort, compared with trying to develop entirely new communication channels and influencing routes
- more response is obtained by targeting enthusiasts first and using the benefits they obtain to influence others
- we should engage in personal and interactive contact with credible stakeholders and other change agents, rather than impersonal, didactic or written communication to 'the world at large'.

Given the slow pace of change, even in the face of widespread evidence that there is a major problem, what can be done to make a real difference? The following are a number of suggestions to accelerate change:

1. engage the attention of the Equal Opportunities Commission
2. encourage the BMA and royal colleges to put their own appointment processes in order when they select for senior posts and committee membership
3. review the operation of the PLAB test
4. improve pay for associate specialists to reduce the economic incentive to employ them instead of consultants
5. link fair recruitment, selection, training and development to NHS modernisation agenda
6. follow up selected reported cases where 'careers advice' was followed, but promises were not kept.

Conclusion

There is abundant evidence of discrimination on the basis of race in the appointment of doctors and strong grounds to support the view that, in general, those from black and minority ethnic groups carry this burden throughout their careers – from the first step of applying to medical school through to attempts to secure senior posts within the profession. That equally well-qualified black and minority ethnic candidates find it more difficult to gain entry into medical school than their white counterparts is clearly unacceptable, as is the fact that individuals from black and minority ethnic groups who are apparently progressing up the career structure tend to be less favourably rewarded in terms of location, institution and specialty, and in reaching the highest and most prestigious positions. However, there are numerous easily available good practice guidelines and codes of conduct aimed at reducing – ideally eliminating – unfair selection, a number of which have been provided here. (See Table 10.1 at the end of this paper for a summary of the BMA's recommendations in this regard.) These include the areas of job advertising, job description and person specification; the make-up and duties of selection panels; shortlisting candidates; the pre-interview and interview stages; the collection of references; and feedback to applicants. In addition, there are legal and moral obligations on organisations and individuals to undertake selection without prejudice, and clear and detailed frameworks in place to monitor whether or not this is happening. There is clearly the means to address the problem, however it is not yet clear whether there is the will to do so.

It has been possible for unfair selection to continue in a semi-conscious sort of way, not necessarily through ill will but through casual selection processes and thoughtlessness. However, now that there are clear legal obligations on individuals, and mandatory monitoring and reporting is in place, it is reasonable to hope – indeed expect – the minds of selectors to be sharpened on the subject. It can only be hoped that a combination of guidelines, pressure, conscious will and indeed shame will bring about change. Only time will tell, but now it will tell publicly, and this gives the best chance of seeing an end to this long-standing problem.

Diversity embodies the principle of fair and equitable treatment for all. Promoting diversity will create a productive environment in which everyone feels valued. It will improve recruitment and retention, and employee relations. And as a *BMJ* editorial in 1995 commented: 'we are unlikely to produce an equitable NHS for patients if we do not have the will to produce it for doctors.'[18]

Table 10.1 BMA recommendations – summary

Recruitment and selection of doctors (First published June 1994, revised January 2000) Reproduced with permission. For full version see: http://web.bma.org.uk/members/mededdisc.nsf/miscdocsvw/

There are still some practices within the selection of medical staff which do not promote equal opportunities. Trusts, health authorities and health boards, and general practices need to improve recruitment and selection practices. This should ensure that they select the best available person for the job, they are being cost effective and they avoid legal proceedings.

Taking account of the current legislation and codes of practice, a working party of the BMA's Career Progress of Doctors Committee considered the different stages of the selection process. It produced the following guidelines for good practice in the recruitment and selection of doctors:

1. Each candidate should have an equal and fair opportunity to demonstrate his or her suitability for the job. A systematic approach should be applied to each step of the selection process – from the job description and person specification, to advertising, short-listing, interviewing and final selection.
2. The job description and person specification should form the basis of the selection process in advertising the post, in short-listing and in assessing applicants at interview.
3. Postgraduate deaneries, trusts and general practices should develop job descriptions and person specifications for all posts, including vocational training scheme and GP registrar applicants, and general practitioners. The person specification should reflect the competencies, i.e. the skills, knowledge and attributes, required for the post. Trusts and practices should send job descriptions and person specifications to all applicants so that they know on what criteria they are to be judged.
4. All posts should be advertised nationally, with the exception of those allocated to pre-registration house officers through matching schemes. This would ensure applications from a wide range of candidates and a fairer selection procedure. Applicants should continue to be warned by the BMJ important notice ('black box') against applying for non-standard career grade and training posts.
5. Medical royal colleges should publish lists of equivalent overseas qualifications which are as acceptable as UK qualifications.
6. Application forms should not show name, sex, marital status, age, religion, place of study or ethnicity. These should be shown on a detachable front sheet.
7. Candidates should apply for posts on application forms, not by curriculum vitae. The application form should support the overall selection process. It should be designed to formally assess specific aspects of the person specification.
8. Applicants should not have to provide multiple copies of application forms. They should be informed whether their application will be acknowledged. Application forms should be available by electronic means.
9. All members of appointment panels selecting candidates should be involved in short-listing applicants. Advice on relevant equal opportunities procedures, and UK and European legislation must be available to those involved in short-listing. All staff involved in the selection process should have training in fair recruitment and selection procedures, including training on race, disability and sex discrimination.

Table 10.1 BMA recommendations – summary (*cont.*)

10. For GP partnership vacancies and salaried doctor appointments in general practice, all partners should be involved in the short-listing and interview processes.

11. The short-listers' decision-making process should be standardised. They should use a scoring system based on agreed criteria drawn from the job description and person specification. Candidates should be assessed against the agreed criteria at all stages of the selection process.

12. Reasons for not short-listing candidates must be clear and well documented.

13. Only structured references should be used. They should ask only for relevant information about the applicants' suitability for the post. Unsolicited references must form no part of the selection process.

14. A pre-interview visit can be helpful for a candidate to find out about a future place of work and prospective colleagues. Information obtained at informal pre-interview visits for hospital and academic posts should not form part of the selection process. For GP vacancies, it must be made clear to the applicants whether the visit constitutes part of the selection process or not.

15. Appointment panels should be properly constituted for all posts. All interview panel chairs and members should have training in how to short-list and select applicants, and in skills in interview techniques.

16. Interviewers should plan the structure and content of the interview in advance. This will ensure that all necessary issues are covered in the interview.

17. All records, including personal notes made by individual panel members should be retained for at least one year.

18. Members of the interview panel should appraise their participation in the interview process. Feedback from the human resources department would be particularly valuable on interview technique, skills assessment and objective scoring. This feedback is essential to ensure that the panel observes equal opportunities practices.

19. There should be an independent skills assessment of candidates who have a disability or where there are doubts about candidates on health grounds. The purpose of providing a skills assessment is to ensure that doctors with disabilities are fit to perform effectively the tasks involved in their duties without risk to the health and safety of themselves or others.

20. Feedback to unsuccessful candidates is an essential part of the interview process and an appropriate member of the interview panel should be responsible for providing this feedback.

21. Each trust, medical school, and GP practice should monitor applicants and appointees by grade and specialty on the basis of sex, disability and ethnic origin, and of religion in Northern Ireland. They should take appropriate action to investigate any concerns about under-representation.

22. The NHS Executive should make sure that trusts and general practices are collecting and monitoring data, and that they are making any necessary changes. It should regularly monitor and publish the aggregated data on the implementation of equal opportunities policies within the NHS for all hospital and community health service staff.

References

1. Commission for Racial Equality. *Report of a formal investigation into St George's Hospital Medical School.* London: Commission for Racial Equality, 1988.

2. McManus I C, Richards P, Winder B C, Proston K A, Styles V. Medical school applicants from minority ethnic groups; identifying if and when they are disadvantaged. *BMJ* 1995; 310: 496–500.

3. Esmail A, Nelson P, Primarolo D, Toma T. Acceptance into medical school and racial discrimination. *BMJ* 1995; 310: 501–02.

4. Dillner L. Manchester tackles failure rate of Asian students. *BMJ* 1995; 310: 209.

5. McKeigue P, Richards J, Richards P. Effects of discrimination by sex and race on the early careers of British medical graduates during 1981–7. *BMJ* 1990; 301: 961–64.

6. Esmail A, Everington S. Racial discrimination against doctors from ethnic minorities. *BMJ* 1993; 306: 691–92.

7. Commission for Racial Equality. *Appointing NHS consultants and registrars: report of a formal investigation.* London: Central Books, 1996.

8. Career Progress of Doctors Committee. *Recruitment and selection of doctors: guidelines for good practice.* BMA, January 2000.

9. McManus I, Sproston K. Women in hospital medicine in the United Kingdom; glass ceiling, preference, prejudice or cohort effect? *J. Epidemiol. Community Health* 2000; 54 (1): 10–16.

10. Anonymous. Not coming out. *BMJ Classified* 1997; 13 December; 2

11. General Medical Council. *Duties of a doctor: good medical practice.* London: GMC, 1996.

12. Shore E. The fortysomething barrier. Letter. *BMJ* 1993; 306: 854.

13. Otitoju F. *Recruitment and selection skills.* Course notes. London: King's Fund, 2000.

14. Johnson M. Racial discrimination against doctors. Letter. *BMJ* 1993; 306: 853.

15. Chong N. Racial discrimination against doctors. Letter. *BMJ* 1993; 306: 853.

16. Wye L, McClenahan J W. *Getting better with evidence: experiences of putting evidence into practice.* London: King's Fund, 2000.
    (See also www.doh.gov.uk/ntrd/pdf/getbtr.pdf and www.doh.gov.uk/ntrd/pdf/allappxs.pdf)

17 Sang B, McClenahan J W. *Up the down escalator? Health at work implementation programmes in selected NHS trusts: an evaluation and frameworks for understanding.* London: Health Education Authority, 1999.

18 McKenzie K J. Racial discrimination in medicine. Editorial. *BMJ* 1995; 310: 478–79.

Chapter 11

Leading for inclusion, valuing diversity: challenge for leadership

Naaz Coker

To raise new questions, new possibilities, to regard old problems from a new angle, requires creative imagination and marks real advance in science.
Albert Einstein

Introduction

Britain is now a multicultural, multiethnic society, with many people speaking different languages, adhering to different beliefs and practices, eating different foods and seeing things within different cultural frameworks. This is not a new phenomenon as minority groups, predominantly of European origin, have lived in Britain for a long time. The post-war expansion policy led to the arrival of new Commonwealth citizens and more recently Britain has seen the arrival of refugees and asylum seekers from many parts of the world, including Eastern Europe. Many people from black and minority ethnic groups are now well settled in Britain, and arguably face less racism now than in the past. However, systematic inequalities continue to exist for black and minority ethnic groups in terms of their experiences of employment, health and health care, and racial disadvantage is still a fact of working life for many in the NHS.

Current government commitment to reduce inequalities in health, and the Macpherson Inquiry into the death of Stephen Lawrence, have provided added impetus for tackling ethnic inequalities in health. With a strong definition of institutional racism and a clear message that colour-blind policies and practices were insufficient to tackle it, the Macpherson Report has been a catalyst for action against all forms of racist behaviour. Numerous research reports confirm that people from many of Britain's black and minority ethnic communities have lower than average incomes, suffer more ill health, experience more problems getting work and are at greater risk of becoming victims of racist crime. In public services, including the NHS, there is a growing body of evidence which shows that discrimination blocks both access to appropriate services and opportunities for employment.

Of course, not everyone from a black or minority ethnic community experiences the same disadvantage. Ethnic groups in the UK are heterogeneous, and it is well known that particular groups have greater health needs than others. Responding to such heterogeneity means moving away from an approach that stereotypes all those from ethnic groups as passive victims, to one where health professionals and policy-makers are able to recognise and respond appropriately to social diversity in their communities. Arguably, the principles and processes required to address diversity will also benefit white majority populations.

Sadly, evidence for racial discrimination in the medical profession has been found at all levels: from entry into medical schools to career development, promotion and in complaint procedures. Voluntary compliance with the previous race relations legislation in the NHS has, at best, been sporadic. People from black communities are disadvantaged by a system that has tackled neither the underlying causes of ethnic inequality nor the impact of prejudice in decision-making and employment practice within their organisations. Doctors from minority ethnic groups believe that they cannot achieve their full potential because of the limitation in other people's minds. If the contribution of black doctors is defined in 'white norm terms', then their contribution will never be given equal merit. The medical world needs to embrace meritocracy, which recognises individuals for their achievements and not for what they have inherited, whether that is pigmentation, class or money. Career development and promotion can no longer rely on patronage and networking. The aspirations of young second- and third-generation graduates must be encouraged and their potential harnessed.

There is now a political and social will to confront and tackle racial prejudice and discrimination throughout the private and public sectors. Many employers are implementing race equality policies and strategies to bring more workers from minority ethnic communities into a wider range of jobs, particularly at the more senior levels in the organisations. There is growing recognition that apart from the unfairness of exclusion, there is a large pool of potential skill and talent that is being wasted as academic qualifications among minority ethnic people continue to rise.

Achieving systemic change is a responsibility for leaders. Leadership is re-emerging as a critical skill for initiating and sustaining cultural change in organisations.

Against a background of efficiency cuts, demanding expectations from the public and the politicians, growing interdependence of different agencies in delivering health, combined with a low professional morale, leaders have to develop new skills and practices. Some of these skills must include team working, networking, harnessing the skills of a diverse workforce and creating effective partnerships within a quality-driven practice base.

The challenge for medical leadership in delivering equality is to provide political will and strategic direction in taking this inclusion agenda forward. This will require action in six key areas:

- recognition and public acknowledgement of racism and discriminatory practices
- developing new strategic directions
- taking the lead for training and advocacy
- clarity about accountability
- embracing a whole systems approach
- tackling the difficult issues first.

In addressing these six areas, leaders will be assisted by a more positive policy environment. The Government certainly feels that it has fulfilled its role by setting a clear policy framework supported by relevant legislation (see below) for achieving race equality and for addressing all inequalities in health. Now it expects the health system to deliver more than mere exhortation of equality. Clear action and change in performance has to be demonstrated.

The legislative environment

The Race Relations Act 1976

The Race Relations Act 1976 was an important instrument for combating discrimination and in promoting equality of opportunity. The Act makes it illegal to discriminate on the grounds of colour, race, nationality, citizenship, ethnic or national origin in recruitment, selection, training, promotion, access to benefits, facilities and services. In November 2000, the Race Relations (Amendment) Act received royal assent; this new Act, which strengthens and extends the scope of the 1976 Act, is targeted specifically at the public sector – the NHS, schools, police, local councils and government ministers. Its two major implications are:

- it extends protection against racial discrimination by public authorities
- it places a new enforceable positive duty to promote race equality on public authorities.

Specific duties will be imposed on all public sector bodies to implement and audit race equality strategies. Every major proposal to change service provision will need to be assessed for its impact on black and minority ethnic users. The Act also applies to all private or voluntary agencies that carry out public functions, such as health services, prisons and local authority functions. Its main provisions are expected to have come into force by April 2001.

Furthermore, the incorporation of human rights legislation within UK law is likely to have an impact on the inequality debate. For the NHS, it means ensuring that racial equality mechanisms form an integral part of mainstream health services and employment practices.

Government initiatives

In December 1997, the Government set up the Social Exclusion Unit to co-ordinate and improve government action to reduce social exclusion. Race is a specific remit of the unit. Then, in June 1998, the Home Secretary established a Race Relations Forum, with a remit to advise government on issues affecting minority ethnic communities and to act as a voice for minority ethnic interests.

The recent Social Exclusion Unit report[1] put forward recommendations aimed specifically at tackling minority ethnic social exclusion. These focused on five types of action:

- tackling racial discrimination
- ensuring mainstream services are more relevant to the circumstances of people from minority ethnic communities
- implementing programmes specifically targeted at minority ethnic needs
- tackling racist crime and harassment
- improving the information available about minority ethnic communities to the public.

In addition, over the last three years, the NHS Executive has launched several initiatives to address both racial discrimination and racial harassment of employees, and to promote race equality in the service:

1. In 1998, the NHS Equal Opportunities Unit launched the 'Positively Diverse' programme[2] to address equality in employment; the focus of this programme is diversity management in NHS trusts.

2. *Tackling racial harassment within the NHS: a plan for action*[3] provides guidance for NHS organisations to tackle racial harassment within the health service.
3. *The vital connection: an equalities framework for the NHS;*[4] this framework for action is significant in that it focused on three strategic equality aims for the NHS:
   - to recruit, develop and retain a workforce that is able to deliver high-quality services that are accessible, responsive and appropriate to meet the diverse needs of different groups and individuals
   - to ensure that the NHS is a fair employer, achieving equality of opportunity and outcomes in the workplace
   - to ensure that the NHS uses its influence and resources as an employer to make a difference to the life opportunities and the health of its local community, especially those who are disadvantaged.

These initiatives suggest that the policy environment is ripe and supportive for tackling this difficult and complex agenda.

Why does leadership matter so much now?

There is burgeoning literature on the need to develop transformational leadership skills for the future. Leadership capability is being ranked as the number one skill for all organisational leaders in the public and the private sectors of the future. It is leaders in organisations who make change happen. The debate about the distinction between leaders and managers is on-going. What is evident in most contemporary writing on the subject is that the notion of leaders being born, leaders as 'heroes' and leadership being for the blessed few, are outdated. The emerging picture is of leadership that can manage the complexity of the inter-relationships between personal attributes and mind-set (the self), the needs, aspirations and behaviours of the people one leads (the followers), the political, economic and social environment in which one operates (the reality of the environment), and the characteristics, values and ethics of the organisation in which one works (the organisational culture). As Margaret Wheatley points out:

> Leadership is always dependent on the context, but the context is established by the relationships we value. We cannot hope to influence any situation without respect for the complex network of people who contribute to our organisations.[5]

'Leadership for health', 'Primary Care Group/Trust leadership', 'Clinical Governance leadership', 'Leading strategic partnerships' – these are some of the recent initiatives in the NHS that emphasise the need for effective leadership. Most studies in leadership skills highlight people-orientated skills as the most important skill for leaders of the future. A major survey[6] of over 2000 NHS staff, which included clinicians, revealed that the most important characteristic of leadership was 'a concern for others, which included showing a genuine interest in staff as individuals, seeing the world through their eyes, valuing their contributions, developing their strengths, coaching, mentoring and having positive expectations of what staff can achieve'. These were followed by the ability to communicate and inspire. An earlier study[7] of business leaders and directors in 375 City of London institutions highlighted a similar range of skills, and the importance of developing leaders with the apposite skills was an overriding feature of the study.

Yet many of the formal leaders in the NHS, especially in medicine, have acquired their positions through the 'specialist ticket'. Career progression in the clinical professions is dependent upon achieving success in one's craft and generally the teaching of leadership skills has not been a significant part of their training. This poses two options for the medical profession: either specialists acquire leadership skills and it becomes a pre-condition for recruitment to senior positions or generalist doctors make leadership their 'specialist craft'. This is clearly not an either-or option, and pragmatically there will have to be room for both. However, what is absolutely critical is that the profession needs enlightened leadership capability.

For leaders in the medical profession, re-inventing new images of the medical institutions as organisations that value diversity and difference, with principles and practices that promote genuine equality of opportunity, is an important leadership task. But it is not an easy task. If organisations were objective and rational entities, prejudice and discrimination would not be as integral to the decision-making processes as they seem to be. While most people today would uphold the values of equality and justice, the integration of those principles into organisational practice has not been achieved. New ways of thinking and organising are needed. Gareth Morgan[8] has coined the term 'imaginization' which, he describes, is a different way of thinking for organisational leaders that enables them to instil a spirit of imagination and creativity into difficult problems. His approach offers leadership ways of challenging existing assumptions and ideologies while opening innovative 'avenues for understanding and action'. Human dignity and social justice must surely be a fundamental moral requirement and the driving force of future images of the medical profession.

Acknowledgement of discrimination

Many doctors and professionals in the health service find it difficult to acknowledge the existence of discrimination in a profession that is underpinned by a strong ethic of humanitarianism, and yet there are numerous reports and stories of widespread racial discrimination within the profession and its institutions. Medical leaders must accept that racial discrimination exists within their institutions and that very specific actions will need to be taken to eradicate it. The Stephen Lawrence Inquiry report made abundantly clear that in cases where discrimination is suggested, it should be considered as the most likely scenario, until proven otherwise. It is unlikely to be any different in medicine.

The Royal College of General Practitioners' discussion document[9] issued in 1999 outlined the College's views of racial discrimination within general practice and how it intended to address prejudice as an institution. The subsequent press release, entitled 'Royal College produces programme to address racial discrimination', was a clear and significant signal to the profession and the public that the College was serious about tackling the race equality agenda. The success of their programme of action awaits assessment and scrutiny.

In 1995, the General Medical Council (GMC) invited the Policy Studies Institute (PSI) to investigate the allegation of racial bias in its handling of complaints against doctors. The PSI report,[10] which was published in 1996, concluded that it did not find explicit evidence of overt racial discrimination, however the authors were critical of the GMC's data recording and decision-making processes that made it difficult to say that racial bias did not exist. As Fiona Godlee, assistant editor of the *BMJ* said: 'The report does not find it guilty of racial bias, but neither does it find it not guilty.'[11] While the GMC has to be applauded for allowing its processes to be monitored, it is imperative that it now responds by making its decision-making processes transparent and its record keeping stringent to avoid any future allegations of racial bias.

New strategic directions

Today's rapidly changing environment requires a radical rethink of our ideas about organisations and functions. Strategic thinking is a process that requires an organisation or an institution to ensure that it is 'fit for purpose' within the environment in which it operates. The relationships within the organisation and between the organisation and its environment are therefore critical. It is about seeing the world in a new way, through a new lens, imagining new possibilities and destinies. A few people at the top cannot achieve it. Innovation in the creation of new strategies will only happen if many voices and new perspectives inform it. Doctors at all levels should have a say in their destiny. It is important that they are given a chance to shape the direction of their future enterprise. Doctors from different cultures should be invited to participate in designing options and contribute to a future that enables them to achieve their aspirations without giving up their identities. All doctors should be involved in articulating a clear vision of what a medical profession committed to equality and social justice would look like. How would such an institution operate? What would it do differently? What would be its core values and its ethical principles?

Linking ethical principles to business practice is not new. Many private sector organisations, notably The Body Shop and the Co-operative Bank, have incorporated ethical issues as key components of their corporate practice. Public concern about issues such as child labour, animal cruelty and environmental abuse has forced multinational corporations to examine their business policies and practices. Equality principles have to become part of this ethical agenda. Equality and ethical practice are sides of the same coin.

Training and advocacy

Health professionals in general, and doctors in particular, have always emphasised the need for effective communication, but the cultural context in which communication takes place is not always recognised. Health and illness are expressed in different ways, informed by cultural and religious beliefs; so, successful communication in a therapeutic setting will require more than negotiating around language barriers. Doctors need training in intercultural communication and this should become an integral component of undergraduate and postgraduate training. In fact, the whole of the medical education system must incorporate anti-racism and cultural awareness training throughout its education and examination processes.

Roberts et al.[12] highlighted the enormous difficulties candidates from non-English-speaking backgrounds may encounter in oral examinations. These difficulties were not ascribed to vocabulary or grammar; they were a consequence of differing styles of communication as well as interpretation of questions. The authors' analyses of the use of language in oral examinations showed how easily examiners and candidates could end up talking at cross-purposes and misinterpret each other's responses due to linguistic and cultural differences. They concluded that oral examinations had the potential to be indirectly discriminatory.

The Royal College of General Practitioners (RCGP) has to be commended in its determination to evaluate and change its examination procedures to remove discrimination and bias. Other medical examining bodies should follow this lead. Guidelines for all royal college examining boards should include:

- training of examiners in anti-racism and cultural sensitivity, especially the complex demands of intercultural communication – this should be mandatory
- regular monitoring of oral examinations, especially in an intercultural setting, to expose discrimination
- the requirement of all examination boards to publish examples of questions posed in oral examinations, with all the possible answers accompanied by comments from examiners. This will at least ensure that candidates taking oral examinations will start with a common understanding of the requirements.

The RCGP commissioned a training pack on diversity training[13] that was launched in 1999. The pack, which includes a video, offers guidelines for teaching about race, culture, individual attitudes and behaviours, working with interpreters, intercultural communication, etc. Although the training pack is targeted at GP registrars and medical students, it has the potential for much wider use.

'Advocacy' has been defined as 'helping people to say what they want, obtain their rights, represent their interests and gain the services they need'.[14] In the NHS, the use of health advocates for patients and users of services is widely accepted, but advocacy for marginalised groups of health professionals is not so common. Some positive action programmes for women and black and minority staffs are the exception. The RCGP has provided a lead in recognising its role in advocacy for black doctors.

'Positive action' refers to specific actions designed to remove obstacles and provide specific resources or development opportunities for disadvantaged or under-represented groups in organisations. In promoting equal opportunities policies, organisations frequently assume that there is a level playing field and all potential applicants will be judged on their merits. However, this is not always the case. The aim of positive action is to equip individuals and groups with particular skills so that they can be judged on merit. Examples of positive action include language training for refugee doctors, management development programmes for black health care professionals or shadowing opportunities to acquire specific competences. In the UK, positive action is within the law, whereas positive discrimination is not.

Other forms of positive action have focused on encouraging people from minority ethnic groups, especially those who are under-represented, into medical and nursing professions. Examples include providing alternative training pathways and sensitive careers advice for Bangladeshi women into accessing health care professions and targeting young people from the African Caribbean community to encourage them to consider medicine as a career.

In the current climate of acute shortage of doctors, the medical leadership will have to make a concerted effort to become innovative in their recruitment and training approaches and ensure that this is achieved in an environment of explicit equality and anti-racist principles.

Accountability

Questions around the nature of medical accountability always seem to begin with individual misdemeanour, error or an extreme performance problem, as in the case of Harold Shipman. After such cases, newspapers cry out for greater medical accountability, and the politicians and professional leaders get into reactive mode and begin to create more *structural* solutions such as 'assessment authorities' and other regulatory bodies that can never deliver what true accountability is meant to deliver, and that must be a quality service by committed, compassionate, well-trained professionals in partnership with a public who can trust them to do their best, individually and collectively.

Health care professionals have always worked with multiple accountability – to their professional bodies, to their employers, to their communities and to their patients. However, the nature of that accountability was previously pretty fuzzy, leading to a relative lack of accountability to anyone, except perhaps to his or her professional body. The trajectory of personal accountability can lead to bizarre outcomes for the individual. A case in point is provided by the experience of Professor Joe Collier,[15] who showed enormous courage and responsibility in challenging his organisation's discriminatory practice. His sense of accountability both to his community and his personal values led him to action, which resulted in him being punished and ostracised by leaders in his organisation. Though he claims that his organisation eventually learned from this experience and strives to be less racist, his story is a shameful episode in the history of medical leadership.

Some key questions that need to be addressed about the nature of accountability are:

- What counts?
- Who is accountable for what?
- Who gives an account to whom?
- What does one hold oneself accountable for?
- Who is responsible for ensuring that the accountability is met?
- What are the criteria for judging?
- What will the leadership hold itself accountable for?

These questions need to be debated by the whole medical body. The government push for quality in the NHS[16,17,18] aims to establish accountability for clinicians and managers to improve clinical performance and quality. Clinical governance is intended to drive this agenda and there has been significant investment in health services to achieve progress. Are there lessons from clinical governance that can be transferred to the implementation of the race equality agenda?

Richard Horton[19] concludes his commentary on 'the real lessons from Harold Fredrick Shipman':

> Health care is at its best when delivered by committed and well-resourced multi-professional teams. Their work must be founded not on hasty gestures towards accountability but on systems of training, analysis and consultation that invisibly embed the principles of quality and accountability into day-to-day practice.

The same parameters that will deliver accountability to the public will also deliver accountability within the profession. Decision-makers should become accountable to all those who are affected by their decisions. What counts is how the leaders rebuild trust both within the profession and with the public. Having a significant proportion of the profession – the ethnic minority doctors, for example – not trusting its leadership and their institutional processes, does not bode well for the future of that profession.

A whole systems approach

Racial equality and valuing diversity cannot be addressed in a piecemeal fashion. It requires a whole system change from grass roots to senior leadership, from medical education to employment, from primary care to acute care, from trades unions to registering bodies, from black doctors and white doctors. It will require doctors to work in partnership with managers and other health professionals to ensure equality for staff and patients.

Challenging racist and discriminatory behaviours, whoever commits them, is a responsibility for black doctors too. This includes any racist attitudes and behaviours of black doctors. To be integrated, the marginalised must interact with the mainstream. Remaining at the margin may be tempting, but it will paralyse the process of change. Black doctors have to grasp at all available opportunities to participate in this change. As mentioned earlier, victimhood can only result in further disabling of oneself. Anti-racism is a value all must fight for.

Institutional racism cannot be removed by individuals. It requires the collective intent and action by the whole system. Combating institutional racism and promoting anti-racism is about educating people for a new society that values and promotes social justice. It will demand involvement and commitment by many that have not previously either been included or wished to be included. This will be the key challenge. A significant proportion of doctors at all levels has been used to the old ideology and power bases; systemic power is generally fed by individuals who choose not to support change. There will be the inevitable resistance to change, which will take the form of anger, denial and sabotage. Yet, the participation of many will be necessary for the creation of a culture in which human values will be esteemed above self-interest.

Tackling the difficult issues first

A clearly articulated decision by the medical profession to begin the process of eliminating racism and the publishing of a race equality strategy would create a dynamic momentum for change. Guidelines for rank-and-file practitioners should clearly state that racism is unacceptable, irrespective of whether it is perpetrated by a colleague or a patient. The so-called 'canteen culture' of racist acts, jokes and statements must be challenged with rigour. The Academy of Medical Royal Colleges, perceived as the 'voice of British medicine', should lead the way in initiating this change in the culture of British medicine.

Acknowledging the contribution made by minority ethnic doctors to the NHS will also be an important starting point. Many minority ethnic doctors expressed surprise and disappointment that hardly anyone in the medical establishment has ever acknowledged the important contribution of minority ethnic doctors and other health workers in the health service. On the contrary, many felt that they bore the brunt of many of the ills of the NHS. Recent media comments concerning the language skills of overseas doctors are prime examples of this. As one of the doctors said: 'We don't recall in 1997, whilst the NHS was both being congratulated and congratulating itself on its 50th birthday, any mention of the contribution of minority ethnic doctors.' Public acknowledgement by the NHS as a whole, and by professional associations like the BMA and the royal colleges in particular, would go some way towards reassuring minority ethnic doctors in the health service that their contribution is recognised. Some of the bitterness may be eased.

Medical institutions also have a responsibility to create easily accessible channels for members to report racist incidents. These must be channels in which they can have the confidence that their concerns will be addressed without the members being ostracised or marginalised. Leaders in medicine have explicitly to challenge racist behaviours and actions, regardless of whether they are dealing with colleagues or patients.

The complexity of ethnicity monitoring has been discussed in Part 1. Within the medical profession, ethnicity monitoring must be implemented across the total employment process – from admission into medical schools to representation in the democratic decision-making processes – if allegations of racial bias are to be exposed or refuted. The concerns and needs of the second-generation doctors must not be overlooked.

Conclusion

Addressing discrimination goes beyond the equal opportunities agenda, which has been considered as a largely bureaucratic exercise by many professionals. For too long, race equality has been someone else's business. One can argue that this is a moral and ethical issue, as highlighted by the GMC's president, Sir Donald Irvine, at the BMA conference on racial discrimination in 1997. As reported in the *BMJ* editorial of 1 March 1997,[20] Sir Donald argued that 'as a profession we have sometimes concentrated our efforts on quality standards for professional care and services to patients at the expense of considering the ethical context in which we deliver and practice care.'

Glaring inequalities continue to exist alongside increasing evidence of progress in a number of areas, with many examples of individual success. Against this background of complexity and growing diversity in British society, equal opportunities has been perceived as a mechanism for dealing with the interconnections and the contradictions between individual success and collective disadvantage. However, equal opportunities without any underpinning values of human dignity and social justice has not and will not deliver success in managing diversity and inclusion.

In the *Observer* of 11 February 2001, the article 'Despite victories, the discrimination battle continues on all fronts' was critical of the slow progress on equality on all fronts: gender, ethnicity and disability. The CRE, commenting on the importance of the changes in the Race Relations (Amendment) Act was quoted as saying: 'instead of knocking on doors and saying "could you ever so kindly work on racial equality?" we will have a code of practice that the public sector must abide by.' It is evident that bodies such as the CRE are convinced that statutory clout will improve their powers of persuasion. The public sector has reached a turning point, moving from voluntary action to statutory enforcement. It is a great pity that even in today's climate of greater awareness of social exclusion and injustice, change in organisations is still prompted through interventions of bodies such as the CRE or through racial discrimination cases brought by individuals against their organisations. The legislative environment expects change and will be able to enforce it. The real challenge is how to win the hearts and minds of all doctors in achieving a sustainable cultural change within the profession, beyond mere compliance with the legal requirements. Although this chapter is largely addressed at doctors in leadership positions (the majority of whom are white), race equality is the responsibility of all doctors, both black and white. The GMC and the Royal College of General Practice have to be commended for developing programmes to tackle discrimination. The success of their initiatives has yet to be assessed and audited.

The medical profession, notwithstanding the Shipman and Bristol cases, is regarded highly by the general public, and is therefore an important leader in influencing public and societal values and actions. It must take a lead in eliminating racism from within its own profession and set an example to society at large. Embracing anti-racism explicitly could be the catalyst for social change. The ethical and moral case for fighting discrimination is clear. In the newly emerging environmental context of globalisation and predicted labour shortages in the West, the economic and business case cannot be ignored. Equality principles and values of social justice must be integrated into the medical profession's practice and culture.

> We need words to keep us human. Being human is an accomplishment like playing an instrument. It takes practice. The keys must be mastered. The best of us is historical; the best of us is fragile. Being human is a second nature which history taught us and which terror and deprivation can batter us into forgetting.

Michael Ignatieff [21]

References

1. Social Exclusion Unit. *Minority ethnic issues in social exclusion and neighbourhood renewal.* SEU Report: Cabinet Office, June 2000.
2. Burford B, Bullas S, Collier B. *Positively diverse.* London: Department of Health, Equal Opportunities Unit, 1998.
3. Lemos and Crane. *Tackling racial harassment in the NHS: a plan for action.* London: Department of Health, Equal Opportunities Unit, 1998.
4. NHS Executive. *The vital connection: an equalities framework for the NHS.* London: Department of Health, 1998.
5. Wheatley M J. *Leadership and the new science.* San Francisco, USA: Berret-Koehler Publishers Inc.; 1992: 144–45.
6. Alimo-Metcalfe B, Alban-Metcalfe R. Heaven can wait. *Health Service Journal* 2000; 110 (5726): 26–29.
7. Rajan A, Van Eupen P. *Leading people.* Tunbridge Wells: CREATE, 1996.
8. Morgan G. *Imaginization.* Newbury Park, California, USA: Sage Publications Inc., 1993.
9. Pringle M, Joshi H. *Tackling discrimination in general practice.* Discussion document. London: Royal College of General Practitioners, 1999.
10. Allen I, Perkins E, Witherspoon S. *The handling of complaints against doctors.* London: Policy Studies Institute, 1996.
11. Godlee F. The GMC, racism and complaints against doctors. *BMJ* 1996; 312: 1314–15.
12. Roberts C, Sarangi S, Southgate L, Wakeford R, Wass V. Oral examinations – equal opportunities, ethnicity and fairness in the MRCGP. *BMJ* 2000; 320: 370–74.
13. Kai J, ed. *Valuing diversity: a resource for effective health care of ethnically diverse communities.* London: RCGP, 1999.
14. Silvera M, Kapasi R. *Health advocacy for minority ethnic Londoners.* London: King's Fund, 2000.
15. Collier, J. Tackling institutional racism. *BMJ* 1999; 318: 679.
16. Department of Health. *The new NHS: modern, dependable.* Leeds: Department of Health, 1997.
17. Department of Health. *A first class service: quality in the new NHS.* Leeds: Department of Health, 1998.
18. Department of Health. *Clinical governance: quality in the new NHS.* HSC 1999/065. Leeds: Department of Health, 1999.
19. Horton R. The real lessons from Harold Frederick Shipman. *Lancet* 2001; 357: 82–83.
20. Esmail A, Carnall D. Tackling racism in the NHS. *BMJ* 1997; 314: 618.
21. Ignatieff M. *The needs of strangers.* London: Vintage, 1994.